LECTURES ON
MATTER AND EQUILIBRIUM

Terrell L. Hill
University of Oregon

LECTURES ON

MATTER

AND

EQUILIBRIUM

W. A. BENJAMIN, INC.   New York, Amsterdam   1966

LECTURES ON MATTER AND EQUILIBRIUM

Library of Congress Catalog Card Number 66-10909
Manufactured in the United States of America

*The manuscript was put into production on June 7, 1965;
this volume was published on March 31, 1966*

W. A. BENJAMIN, INC.
New York, New York 10016

To Mary and Otto Gano, for all they gave to me

PREFACE

THIS BOOK may be useful in several ways, but it is intended primarily as a supplement to part of a freshman honors course in chemistry. It might be read either during or after such a course.

The book could also serve as collateral reading in a physical chemistry course. The level is less advanced than in most modern physical chemistry texts but some students may find this an advantage.

Actually, the author has used this material at the University of Oregon as the basis of the second term (out of three) in a general chemistry class for freshmen and also in an honors class at the same level. In the former case all the calculus and about half of the subject matter was omitted (the thermodynamics was confined to a study of finite changes and constant T,p processes). In the latter case calculus was employed but about a third of the material was not used. In both cases the first term covered the elementary concepts of quantum theory, atomic and molecular structure, stoichiometry, chemical bonding, resonance, etc., while the third term included ionic equilibria, electrochemistry, chemical kinetics, and structural organic and biochemistry.

Other potential readers to whom the book is addressed are biologists and physicists who, for one reason or another, have not had a formal course in physical chemistry but who would like to study this part of the subject on their own.

The reader is assumed to have some background on the "first term" subjects referred to above. He is also assumed to have at his disposal a standard general chemistry textbook. To avoid repetition, and to save space, we intentionally omit here many common definitions, routine calculations and problems, etc.

A short introduction to or review of calculus is given in Appendix 2.

Vector analysis is not required. The few vectors and tensors are treated like scalars.

TERRELL L. HILL

Eugene, Oregon
December 1965

CONTENTS

CHAPTER 1

STATES OF MATTER

THE PRINCIPAL object of this book is to provide an introduction to
intermolecular forces, states of matter, and especially thermodynamics for honors students in general chemistry.

The first six chapters are devoted to intermolecular forces and
states of matter. A number of thermodynamic concepts and terms
will be included in these chapters without being labeled as such. In
Chapters 7 through 10 we then introduce thermodynamics in a more
formal way, and apply the subject to some of the topics covered in
the first six chapters as well as to chemical equilibrium and solutions. The whole book thus presents a unified body of material.
However, the treatment is simplified and many aspects of thermodynamics are not even mentioned.

1-1 THERMODYNAMICS

AT THIS point, we should at least tell the reader what thermodynamics is about. It is concerned with the equilibrium properties of matter in bulk, and especially with relations between these properties.

Typical equilibrium properties are pressure, temperature, volume, number of moles, energy, specific heat, etc.

Individual atoms and molecules have certain intrinsic properties (as studied, for example, in the science of spectroscopy) but here we are concerned with the behavior of bulk matter, that is, with samples of matter that contain billions and billions of molecules. Of course in general these molecules interact with each other, physically or chemically, so that the bulk properties cannot easily be predicted from the properties of the individual molecules. To be a little more specific, by "bulk" (or "macroscopic") is ordinarily meant a sample of matter (gas, liquid, or solid) weighing more than, say, 10^{-3} g and therefore containing something like 10^{19} molecules or more.

To save words, let us begin to use the term system to refer to the bulk sample of matter that is under discussion or study.

The word equilibrium was introduced above and requires some explanation. In general, the properties of a system may change with time. If this is the case, eventually—faster or slower, depending on the system—these properties will approach constant values which are independent of time. This eventual condition or state of the system is either an equilibrium state or a steady state. It is called an equilibrium state if there are no net processes taking place inside the system or between the system and its surroundings. At both the bulk and molecular levels, each process and its inverse occur at exactly the same rate so that the net rate for each such pair of processes is zero. A great deal is happening at the molecular level in an equilibrium state—it is a dynamic state. However, there are no changes to be seen at the macroscopic level.

In a steady state, there are net processes occurring. A simple example is a piece of metal (the system) which is in contact on one side with a large heat reservoir at temperature T_1, and is in contact on the opposite side with a large heat reservoir at a higher temperature T_2. At steady state, there will be a continual flow of heat through the system from the hot reservoir to the cold reservoir.

Thermodynamics deals with equilibrium states only. Another and more complicated discipline known as irreversible thermodynamics treats steady states and the approach of systems toward equilibrium. This subject is not included in the present book.

Pure thermodynamics has to do with the measurement of the various equilibrium properties of systems, and with correlations between these properties. The theoretical interpretation of the properties in terms of the behavior of the molecules forming the system is the task of statistical mechanics. We shall mix in as much statistical mechanics—i.e., explanation at the molecular level—as we can, for this adds considerable interest to the subject matter of thermodynamics. But for the most part, in doing so, we shall use words rather than equations. Appendix 3 is an exception.

1-2   PHASE DIAGRAMS

MATTER, at equilibrium, occurs in the form of gas, liquid, or solid. Under different conditions of pressure and temperature, a given pure substance may exist in one or another of the above states. Our purpose in this section is to show how the conditions of occurrence of the different states of matter may be summarized, for each substance, in a so-called phase diagram, which is something like a fingerprint for the substance.

In the remaining two sections of the chapter, we shall discuss the volume changes in a pure substance that accompany pressure or temperature changes.

Since this chapter is concerned with all the states of matter and the relations between them, it serves as an introduction to Chapters 2 through 6. These chapters treat the separate states in more detail.

Let us consider a hypothetical, typical pure substance. We take a sample of the substance and examine it, at equilibrium, at every possible combination of pressure and temperature to ascertain its state—gas, liquid, or solid. What we find (Fig. 1-1) is that ordinarily <u>all</u> of the sample (or system) will be in one of the three types of of state mentioned but for certain values of p (pressure) and T

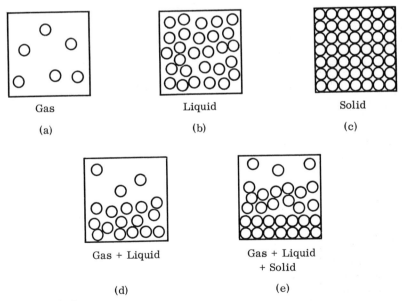

Gas	Liquid	Solid
(a)	(b)	(c)

Gas + Liquid   Gas + Liquid + Solid

(d)   (e)

Figure 1-1
Schematic representation of the states of matter.

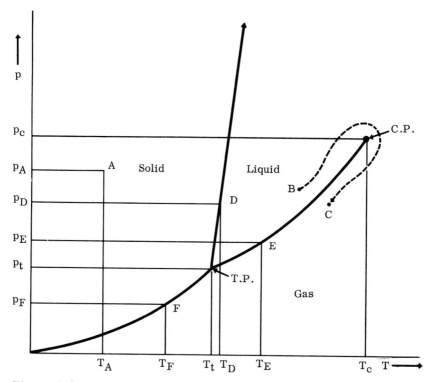

Figure 1-2
Schematic phase diagram for a typical substance.

(absolute temperature[1]), <u>two</u> different states will be present and in
equilibrium with each other. In fact, on rare occasions, <u>three</u> different states will be present simultaneously.

A homogeneous part of an equilibrium system — that is, a part
with uniform properties (such as density) — is called a <u>phase</u>. The
systems represented schematically in Figs. 1-1a, 1-1b, and 1-1c
are therefore one-phase systems; Fig. 1-1d shows a two-phase system; while Fig. 1-1e represents a three-phase system.

Figure 1-2 is a <u>phase diagram</u>. It indicates the conditions of occurrence of the different states of matter for our hypothetical, typical substance. There are three principal regions of the diagram,
separated by lines. At all points (values of p and T) in the "Solid"
region, the system is observed to be a solid; etc. Thus, when the
pressure is p_A and the temperature T_A (point A), the system is a

---

[1]The reader will be familiar with this term, but a definition is given in
Section 2-1.

solid. It is a liquid at point B and a gas at point C. These are all
one-phase points. Points D, E, and F, on the other hand, are two-
phase points. This means, for example, that at pressure p_E and
temperature T_E, the system is observed to contain both liquid and
gas, in equilibrium (as in Fig. 1-1d). In other words, p_E is the vapor
pressure of the liquid at temperature T_E. Similarly, at point F, solid
and gas are in equilibrium, and p_F is the vapor pressure of the solid
at temperature T_F. Point E is on the liquid-gas equilibrium line, F
is on the solid-gas equilibrium line, and D is on the solid-liquid
equilibrium line. These two-phase lines separate the one-phase regions.

A system containing one phase only is a homogeneous system;
a system with two or more phases is a heterogenous system.

The liquid-gas line is also a plot of the vapor pressure of the liquid as a function of temperature. Similarly, the solid-gas line gives
the vapor pressure of the solid as a function of temperature.

At the very special point (p_t, T_t) labeled T.P. ("triple point"),
all three phases are in equilibrium together (Fig. 1-1e).

If the properties (e.g., density) of liquid and gas phases (Fig. 1-1d)
are compared as one moves up the liquid-gas equilibrium line, it is
found that liquid-gas differences in properties decrease. In fact these
differences finally completely disappear at the critical point (C.P. in
Fig. 1-2; p_c = critical pressure, T_c = critical temperature). At
this point liquid and gas phases merge into a single fluid phase. The
liquid-gas equilibrium line stops at the critical point because beyond
this point there is no longer any distinction between liquid and gas.

The arrow on the solid-liquid line is meant to indicate that this
line goes on indefinitely (though it may branch — see Fig. 1-4 below,
for example). No case is known in which the solid-liquid line stops
at a critical point. This is intuitively reasonable because both gas
and liquid have disordered structures that can approach each other
continuously, but solid and liquid have structures of different types
(ordered and disordered, respectively) that cannot do this. The subject of order and disorder is considered further in Chapters 5 and
6, and also in Chapter 8.

The existence of the liquid-gas critical point has the following
interesting consequence. By simultaneously changing p and T,
a system starting at point B (Fig. 1-2) can be made to follow the
dotted path around the critical point, ending at point C. We start
with liquid and end with gas, but in going from one to the other
the system is always a one-phase system. The transition from
liquid to gas is gradual. On the other hand, the system can pass
from B to C by a path crossing the liquid-gas line. In this case
the transition from liquid to gas (called a phase transition or
phase change) occurs at the single point at which the line is crossed.
There are two phases present at this point (Fig. 1-1d), but the

proportion changes during the transition (start with all liquid; end with all gas).

At any T and p, the molecules of the system have the option, so to speak, of choosing the state of matter they prefer.[2] The thermo-dynamic and molecular factors that enter into this "decision" will be discussed in Chapter 8. We shall occasionally refer to the chosen state at each T and p (i.e., to the state shown in the phase diagram) as the <u>stable</u> state, or most stable state (of the three). At a two- or three-phase point, the phases involved are equally stable.

A familiar example of stability of similar type is the following. A macroscopic sample of matter of mass m at height zero in the earth's gravitational field is more stable than the same mass at height h, because the potential energy of the system is less at height zero by an amount mgh. If the system has the option, it will choose height zero rather than height h (i.e., it will fall from h to zero).

Phase diagram for water. As an illustration, Fig. 1-3 gives part of the phase diagram for water. Both scales are distorted for the sake of clarity. Some of the information on this diagram will be fa-miliar to the reader. For example, the <u>normal</u> <u>boiling</u> <u>point</u> of water is 100°C. This is defined, for any substance, as the temperature at which the vapor pressure of the liquid is 1 atm. Also, the <u>normal</u> <u>freezing</u> <u>point</u> is 0°C. This is the temperature at which a liquid freezes (or a solid melts) at 1 atm pressure. The diagram also tells us: that the vapor pressure of water at 25°C (about room tempera-ture) is 23.8 mm Hg; that the critical temperature is 374°C and the critical pressure is 218 atm; and that the triple point occurs at 0.0075°C and 4.58 mm Hg. We also see that the maximum possible vapor pressure for ice is 4.58 mm Hg.

A very unusual feature of the phase diagram for water is the fact that the solid-liquid line tilts to the left rather than to the right (as in Fig. 1-2). This will be discussed in the next section.

What becomes of the solid-liquid line for water at high pressures? This is a very difficult experimental question. But, because of the al-most unique importance of water (to us), a lot of effort has been ex-pended to answer it. Figure 1-4 summarizes the present state of our knowledge (the upper left part of the "map" is yet to be explored). Note that the pressure scale is very different from that in Fig. 1-3. The most striking feature shown by the diagram is that ordinary ice is only one of a number of different kinds of crystalline (solid) water. Under different conditions of pressure and temperature, different crystalline structures are stable.[2] There are six new triple points on this diagram, and many more phase transitions, or two-phase

---

[2]In fact, in the same sense, within the chosen type of state, the molecules "select" the favored detailed molecular structure (see Chapter 5 and Section 8-5).

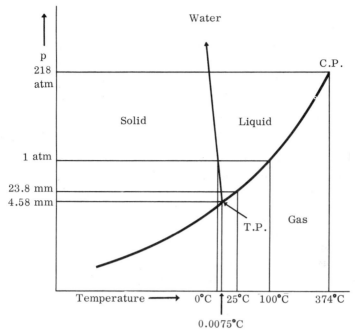

Figure 1-3
Phase diagram for water. The scales are distorted.

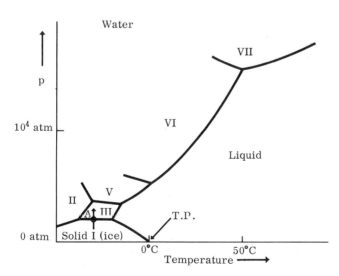

Figure 1-4
Phase diagram for water at very high pressures.

equilibria, become possible. For example, at point A, Solid I (ordinary ice) is in equilibrium with Solid III.

Incidentally, a phase transition from one type of solid to another, such as Solid I → Solid III, could well be a <u>very</u> slow process because it may be difficult for the molecules to initiate the required change in their crystalline arrangement. Thus if we start with Solid I and increase the pressure at constant temperature, as indicated by the arrow in Fig. 1-4, we might still have Solid I in the region marked Solid III. In this case, we say that Solid I is <u>metastable</u> relative to Solid III (the true stable state).

The analogue of this in the gravitational field example on p.6. would occur if the system were placed on a platform at height h. The system would then be "frozen" in a metastable state relative to the stable state at height zero, with no mechanism available to make the transition to the stable state.

Solid IV is omitted from Fig. 1-4 because its existence as a separate stable state has not been confirmed in recent work.

Phase diagram for carbon dioxide. The diagram for carbon dioxide has the typical appearance of Fig. 1-2. The only unusual

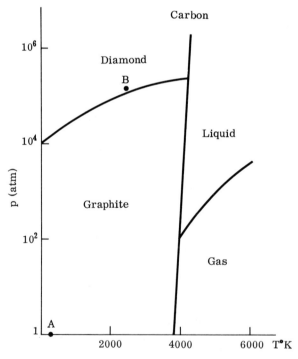

Figure 1-5
Phase diagram for carbon. The pressure scale is logarithmic.

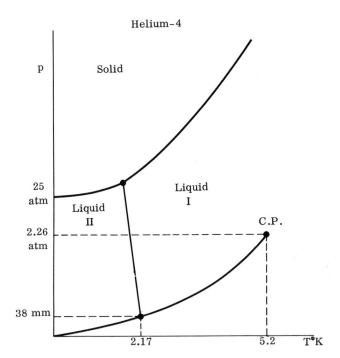

Figure 1-6
Schematic phase diagram for He⁴. The scales are distorted.

feature is that the triple point pressure p_t is above 1 atm, in fact p_t = 5.2 atm (the triple point temperature is −57°C). Therefore, if the solid ("dry ice") is heated at 1 atm pressure, it <u>sublimes</u> (at −78°C) rather than melts. That is, the solid goes directly into gas (as at point F, Fig. 1-2). The liquid phase can exist only if p ≥ 5.2 atm. The critical point occurs at 31°C and 73 atm.

Phase diagram for carbon. Figure 1-5 presents the phase diagram for carbon. Note that a logarithmic scale is used for the pressure. Diamond is metastable relative to graphite under ordinary conditions (point A). Fortunately, the transition from diamond to graphite is so slow that diamond has an indefinite lifetime. By use of a metal catalyst to initiate the change in crystal structure, synthetic diamonds have been made recently from graphite at about point B in Fig. 1-5.

Phase diagram for helium (He⁴). The condensed state of matter (solid and liquid) occur because of attractive forces between molecules. These forces are extremely weak in helium. Hence the condensed states of helium are observed only at very low temperatures. This in turn has interesting consequences. Because of the low temperature and the relatively small atomic mass of the helium atom, bulk helium exhibits unique quantum mechanical effects.[3] For example, the phase diagram is very odd (Fig. 1-6). There are two kinds of liquid helium. Furthermore, Liquid II does not freeze, even at 0°K, if the pressure is less than 25 atm. Liquid helium II is called a superfluid because its viscosity (resistance to flow) is practically zero. Thus, if some of this liquid is placed in a beaker, it will spontaneously escape by running up the inside wall (because of surface or capillary forces) and down the outside. Liquid helium I, on the other hand, is a normal sort of liquid.

1-3 VOLUME CHANGES

ALTHOUGH phase diagrams contain a lot of information, there is much they cannot tell us. For example, what is the density (or densities) of the substance at each point of the phase diagram? This particular kind of information can be presented most conveniently by means of curves called pressure-volume (or p-v) isotherms. This is the principal topic of the present section.

But first, a digression on notation is needed. If a system of volume V contains n moles of a pure substance of molecular weight M, then: (a) the molar volume (i.e., volume per mole) is denoted by $v = V/n$; (b) the concentration in moles per unit volume is $c = n/V = 1/v$; and (c) the density in grams per cubic centimeter is $\rho = nM/V = M/v$, where here V is in units cm^3 and v is in units $cm^3 \ mole^{-1}$. Thus the density is inversely proportional to the molar volume and easily calculated from it. We shall use v as our basic volume variable rather than ρ or c.

Now consider the following experiment. We place n moles of a pure substance in a container. The container is put in a large heat bath (Fig. 1-7) which is held at a constant temperature T_2. Thus, at equilibrium, the system will have the constant temperature T_2. Initially the pressure is set at p_1, a low enough pressure so that the system is a dilute gas (point 1, Fig. 1-8a). The volume is then measured and found to have the value V_1. Thus the initial molar volume is $v_1 = V_1/n$ (point 1, Fig. 1-8b). The piston is now pushed in steadily but very slowly (to maintain equilibrium inside the system, and between system and bath), keeping the temperature constant at T_2. For each position of the piston, p and V are measured and v calculated. As the piston is pushed in (volume decreases), the pressure rises or possibly stays constant, but it never decreases (this is a fundamental property of any sample of matter in equilibrium). Hence, as the experiment proceeds, we move up the long vertical arrow in Fig. 1-8a, starting from point 1.

------

[3]Under ordinary conditions, gases, liquids, and many solids behave "classically" (follow Newtonian mechanics).

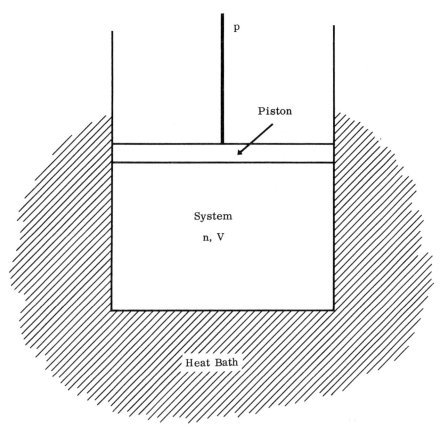

Figure 1-7
System in heat bath. Double lines represent thermal insulation.

Figure 1-8b is a plot of p against v in the above experiment, starting from point 1. Because the temperature is held constant, the curve
is called a p-v isotherm. At first the gas is simply compressed. But
just as the pressure reaches the value p_2 and the molar volume
reaches v_G, liquid droplets begin to appear on the walls of the container. As the piston is pushed in further, more gas condenses into
liquid, v decreases, but p stays constant at the value p_2. The system
is stationary at point 2 in Fig. 1-8a but it is moving from point 2 toward 2' in Fig. 1-8b. At point 2 (Fig. 1-8b) the system is essentially
all gas and at point 2' it is essentially all liquid. At intermediate
points gas and liquid are both present (Fig. 1-1d). Although gas is
being converted into liquid during the process 2 → 2', the properties
(except for amount) of each of the two phases remain constant.

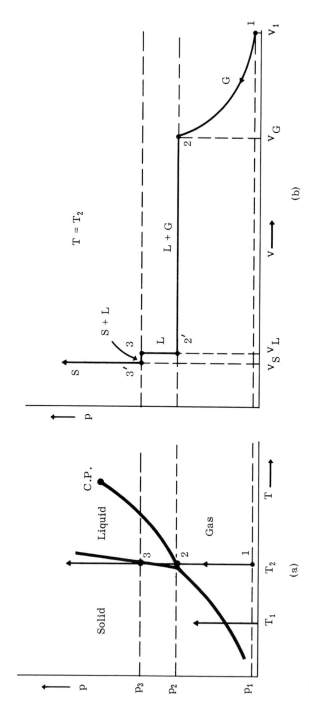

Figure 1-8

Schematic phase diagram (a) and p-v isotherm (b) for typical substance.

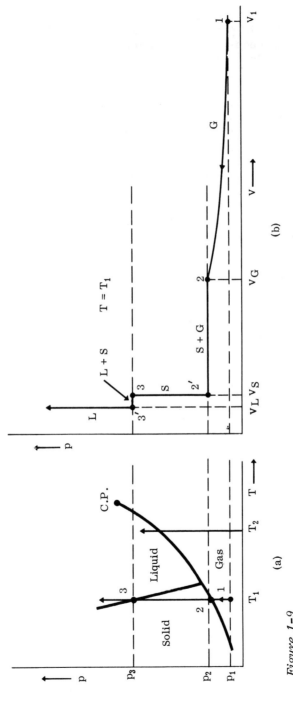

Figure 1-9
Schematic phase diagram (a) and p–v isotherm (b) for substance of water-type.

The pressure p_2 is the vapor pressure of the liquid at temperature T_2. In the process $2 \rightarrow 2'$ (or $G \rightarrow L$), the pressure remains constant because the vapor pressure of a liquid depends only on temperature and not on the relative amounts of the two phases present.

When all the gas has been condensed into liquid, the pressure will rise ($2' \rightarrow 3$) almost vertically. This is because the liquid state is ordinarily[4] very incompressible compared to the gas state. When the pressure p_3 is reached, the liquid will start to freeze into solid. This phase transition ($L \rightarrow S$) occurs in the interval $3 \rightarrow 3'$ in Fig. 1-8b. The volume change is relatively small. In fact, far below the critical temperature, v_G/v_L is typically 1000 or more (Fig. 1-8b shows $v_G/v_L = 5$), while v_L/v_S is often around 1.2.

After point $3'$, the pressure again rises steeply, owing to the relative incompressibility of the solid.

The short vertical arrow at temperature T_1 in Fig. 1-8a would have associated with it a simpler p-v isotherm. In this case there would be only one phase transition ($G \rightarrow S$), as the arrow crosses the solid-gas equilibrium line.

The complete volume behavior of a substance could obviously be presented if we had a series of vertical arrows covering the whole phase diagram, with each arrow accompanied by the corresponding p-v isotherm.

Figures 1-9a (left arrow) and 1-9b represent a similar experiment done on water at a temperature T_1 below the triple point temperature. The phase sequence is now different: $G \rightarrow S \rightarrow L$. At a temperature $T_2 > T_t$ (right arrow), for example at room temperature, only one transition occurs ($G \rightarrow L$) unless the pressure is pushed to extremely high values (Fig. 1-4).

We have seen in Figs. 1-8 and 1-9 that, as we move up the vertical arrows in diagram (a), the volume always decreases in diagram (b). At phase transitions in particular, the molar volume always decreases (e.g., $v_L > v_S$ in Fig. 1-8b). Therefore, we can deduce that when the solid-liquid line tilts to the right (Fig. 1-8; the usual case), $v_L > v_S$; and when this line tilts to the left (Fig. 1-9; water), $v_S > v_L$. In the former case, the solid is more dense than the liquid; in the latter, the opposite is true (ice floats on liquid water). Other examples: from Figs. 1-5 and 1-6 we can conclude that diamond is more dense than graphite and that liquid helium I is more dense than liquid helium II.

Constant pressure experiment. The volume behavior of a substance can be studied at constant pressure as well as at constant temperature. This corresponds to horizontal arrows on the phase diagram, rather than vertical arrows. Figure 1-10 illustrates this. We start at point 1 (solid) and heat the system at constant pressure

---

[4]Near the critical point is the exception. See Fig. 1-12.

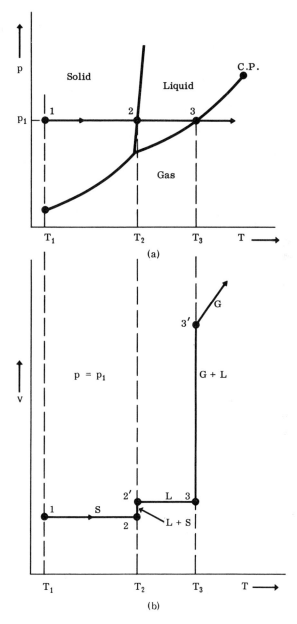

Figure 1-10
Schematic phase diagram (a) and v–T curve (b) for
typical substance.

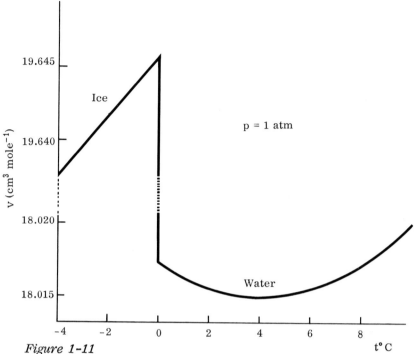

Figure 1-11
Molar volume of water as a function of temperature near the normal melting point.

$(p = p_1)$. The solid melts at T_2 and the liquid vaporizes at T_3. Figure 1-10b shows the hypothetical volume changes.

The sequence of phases will obviously be $S \rightarrow L \rightarrow G$ regardless of the direction of tilt of the solid-liquid line. But the volume will increase at a phase transition if the tilt is to the right (as in Fig. 1-10), and decrease if the tilt is to the left. Therefore a v-T (p const) curve does not always move upward and to the right, as might be expected intuitively. Sometimes it moves downward and to the right. This is in contrast to the invariable behavior of p-v isotherms.[5] Thus Fig. 1-11 shows v against T (p const) for water in the neighborhood of the normal freezing point. At 1 atm pressure, liquid water has a maximum density (minimum v) at 4°C. The interpretation of this at the molecular level is given in Section 6-4.

———————————

[5]It will be seen in Chapter 8 that the true analogue of p-v (T const) is T-S (p const), where S = entropy.

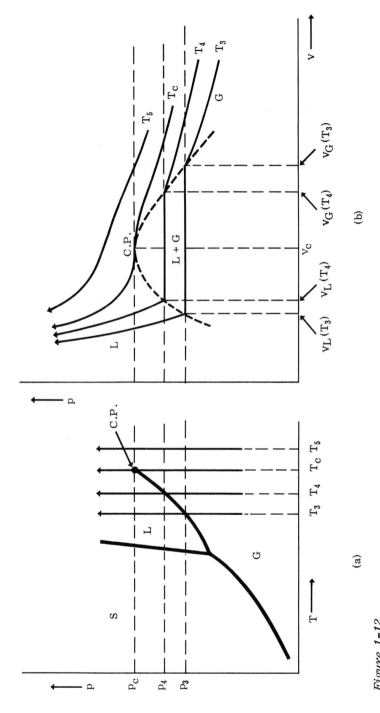

Figure 1-12
Schematic phase diagram (a) and p-v isotherms (b) in neighborhood of critical point, for a typical substance.

1-4   CRITICAL REGION

VOLUME changes in the neighborhood of the critical point require special discussion. Figure 1-12 is an extension of Fig. 1-8 to higher temperatures. The system is compressed isothermally at four different temperatures (arrows in Fig. 1-12a), including T_C. The p-v isotherm for each temperature is given in Fig. 1-12b. The most noteworthy aspect of these isotherms is that the horizontal part becomes smaller as T increases and disappears at $T = T_C$ (i.e., $v_G - v_L \rightarrow 0$ as $T \rightarrow T_C$). The dashed curve connects the ends of the horizontal sections of the isotherms and is called the <u>coexistence curve</u>, because any point inside this curve corresponds to a system with gas and liquid coexisting (in a two-phase equilibrium). At any point on or outside the coexistence curve, only one phase is present in the system.

The critical point is indicated by C. P. in Fig. 1-12b. Mathematically, this is an inflection point in the critical (T_C) isotherm (i.e., both dp/dv and $d^2 p/dv^2$ are zero at C. P.). The critical state is characterized not only by p_C and T_C but also by a critical volume, v_C. Each pure substance has its own characteristic set of critical constants: p_C, T_C, and v_C. Thus, for water, p_C = 218 atm, T_C = 647°K, and v_C = 54 cm³ mole⁻¹ (i.e., ρ_C = 0.33 g cm⁻³). Water in the critical state is one-third as dense as in the ordinary liquid.

A gas can be condensed into liquid when $T < T_C$, but not when $T \geq T_C$ (e.g., not at T_5 in Fig. 1-12b).

We have already mentioned that in a liquid-gas equilibrium system, $v_G - v_L \rightarrow 0$ as $T \rightarrow T_C$. A number of other quantities similarly approach the value zero as $T \rightarrow T_C$. Among these are the heat required to vaporize a given amount of liquid, and the surface tension of the liquid in equilibrium with vapor. Also, the meniscus between liquid and vapor phases can be seen to disappear at $T = T_C$.

A fluid at the critical point has a milky or opalescent appearance. This is due to unusually large fluctuations (variations) in density which cause extensive scattering of light.

PROBLEMS

1-1. Draw a family of schematic p-v curves for a set of temperatures in the neighborhood of the triple point temperature (see Fig. 1-2).

1-2. Draw a schematic p-v curve for He⁴ at 2°K.

1-3. Draw a schematic v-T curve (see Fig. 1-10b) for He⁴ at 28 atm.

CHAPTER 2

IDEAL GASES

IN CHAPTER 1, we considered interrelations between the different states of matter. Beginning with the present chapter, we discuss the states separately and in more detail.

There are attractive and repulsive forces between all molecules. The condensed states of matter (solids and liquids) owe their very existence to attractive intermolecular forces. That is, these forces are what hold the molecules of the condensed states together. Therefore, to understand the properties of the solid and liquid states, and indeed also the properties of dense gases, one must first study the nature of intermolecular forces. We do this in Chapter 3, and then turn, in succession, to dense gases (Chapter 4), solids (Chapter 5), and liquids (Chapter 6).

However, there are two situations (or a combination of them) in which intermolecular forces may be ignored. The first is the more important. (1) If a gas is very dilute, the amount of time that a given molecule spends near (i.e., within the range of intermolecular forces) any of the other molecules of the gas is very small compared to the time it spends essentially isolated from the other molecules. Of course equilibrium in such a gas is maintained by collisions between molecules and collisions of molecules with the walls, but these are relatively infrequent events if the gas is dilute enough. (2) At extremely high temperatures, the molecules move so fast on the average that intermolecular forces have a relatively small effect on the behavior of the molecules. In general one can think of there being a competition between intermolecular forces, which tend to pull the molecules together and organize them, and the kinetic energy (Appendix 4) which tends to randomize the motion of the molecules, as in a very dilute gas. The latter effect dominates at very high temperatures.

Under the conditions described above, the gas behaves (to within experimental error — see Section 4-1) as if there were no intermolecular forces. Consequently its properties are relatively simple. Such a gas is often called ideal. The term is also used to refer to a hypothetical gas in which there are no forces between the molecules. No such gas really exists.[1] In such a gas there would be no collisions between molecules, but equilibrium could be maintained by collisions with the walls. When we refer to an ideal gas we shall usually have in mind a real gas under the conditions described in the preceding paragraph.

Figure 2-1 shows schematically the region of the phase diagram in which a real gas behaves ideally. The boundary of the ideal gas region is somewhat arbitrary because it depends on the accuracy of the experiments; that is, it depends on our ability to measure deviations from ideal properties.

2-1   SOME OBSERVED PROPERTIES OF IDEAL GASES

THE OBJECT of this section is to outline the observed p-V-T properties of an ideal gas. Then, in the next section, we consider the theoretical interpretation of these properties.

The experimental facts to be presented can be summarized in four points:

(1) If a fixed amount of any gas is placed in a container held at constant temperature (as in Fig. 1-7), and the pressure of the gas is measured for each of a number of different choices of the volume, it is found that p is inversely proportional to V: $p \propto 1/V$ (the symbol $\propto$ means "proportional to"). This is known as Boyle's law. For example, if p = 0.100 atm when V = 1.00 liter, then p = 0.050 atm when V = 2.00 liters. The relation $p \propto 1/V$ can also be written as $V \propto 1/p$ or pV = const. The gas in Fig. 1-9b obeys Boyle's law.

---

[1]There are no intermolecular forces in a photon gas ("blackbody radiation"), but photons differ from molecules in other respects as well and are not included in the present discussion.

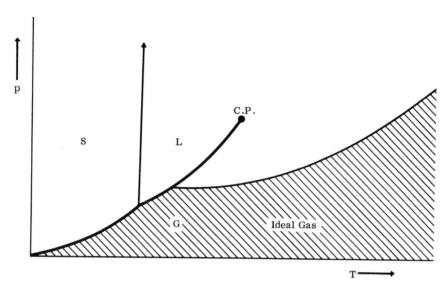

Figure 2-1
Schematic indication of the ideal gas region of a typical phase diagram.

(2) A fixed amount of any gas is placed in a container and the pressure is held constant (say by placing a fixed weight on the piston). The heat bath contains ice and water to begin with, and the volume of the gas is, say, V_0 liters. We next put boiling water in the heat bath and the volume of the gas is observed to have increased to 1.366 V_0 liters. This same expansion factor is found for all ideal gases. We can now use these points (Fig. 2-2) to fix an absolute temperature scale based on the ideal gas as our "thermometer." That is, the volume of any ideal gas rather than the volume of a liquid such as mercury is the basis of the thermometer. The scale is "absolute" in the sense that it locates a true zero in the temperature scale (in contrast to the arbitrary zero in the Centigrade scale — see below) and is independent of which gas is used as the thermometer.

We define the absolute temperature T by two statements: (a) T is proportional to the volume of an ideal gas ($T \propto V$; p and n constant); and (b) there are 100 units of temperature (i.e., "degrees") between the freezing point and boiling point of water (at 1 atm pressure). The degrees on this scale are denoted by °K (Kelvin).

What is the lowest possible absolute temperature? Of course a real gas will not remain ideal if it is cooled too much (in fact it will condense into liquid or solid). But we can extrapolate into the low temperature region (Fig. 2-2) or we can imagine the use of a hypothetical ideal gas with no intermolecular forces. Such a gas will

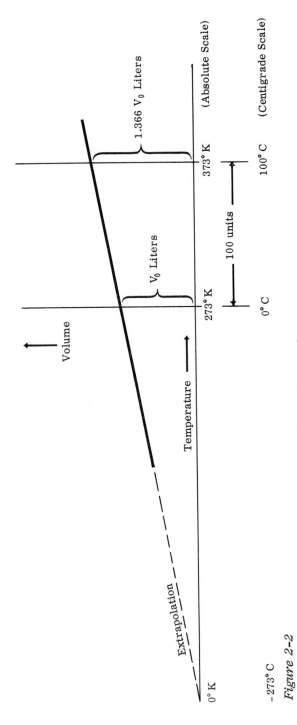

Figure 2-2
Use of dilute (ideal) gas to establish an absolute temperature scale.

remain ideal at any temperature. Now we have defined $T \propto V$. But the smallest possible volume of the hypothetical gas is $V = 0$. The temperature at which this would occur is therefore the lowest possible temperature, with numerical value $0°K$. The absolute zero of temperature is involved, incidently, in the third law of thermodynamics (Chapter 8).

To complete the argument, we should find the proportionality constant between T and V. Let us write $V = aT$, where a is to be determined. Let x be the freezing point of water in $°K$; then $x + 100$ is the boiling point of water in $°K$ [because of part (b) of our definition of T]. We have the experimental fact that

$$1.366V_0 = a(x + 100)$$

and also that

$$1.000V_0 = ax$$

Subtraction gives $0.366V_0 = 100a$, or $a = 0.00366V_0$. Then $x = 1.000/.00366 = 273°K$ and $x + 100 = 373°K$. If we had used more accurate data, we would have found $x = 273.15°K$ (freezing point of water at 1 atm pressure).

The Centigrade scale differs only in that the origin is shifted (Fig. 2-2). The size of unit (degree) is the same.

In summary, we have, as a consequence of the definition of T, that

$$V = 0.00366V_0\,T \qquad \text{(n, p const)} \qquad \qquad (2\text{-}1)$$

for <u>any</u> ideal gas, where V_0 is the volume of the gas at $273°K$.

Incidentally, the gas in Fig. 1-10b follows Eq. 2-1.

(3) If pressure and temperature are held constant, and the volumes occupied by different amounts of a gas are measured, it is found that V is directly proportional to the amount of gas: $V \propto n$ (p and T const).

Let us now assemble the facts available so far. We have seen that $V \propto 1/p$, $V \propto T$, and $V \propto n$. Putting these together, $V = RTn/p$, where R is a proportionality constant. If we compare this with Eq. 2-1, we note that

$$0.00366V_0 = Rn/p$$

or

$$R = 0.00366V_0\,p/n \qquad \qquad (2\text{-}2)$$

In this equation, the number 0.00366 is a "universal" expansion factor (i.e., it is the same for all gases). But is R a universal proportionality constant and, if so, what is its value? To settle this requires further experimental information.

(4) Suppose we take 0.0100 mole (i.e., the same number of molecules) of each of a number of gases at the ice point (273°K or 0°C) and measure the volumes at a low pressure (so the gases will be ideal), say 0.0100 atm. What we find is that V_0 = 22.4 liters for <u>all</u> gases. Thus R is indeed a universal constant. The numerical value of R is found from Eq. 2-2:

$$R = 0.00366 \times 22.4 \times 0.0100/0.0100$$

$$= 0.0821 \text{ liter atm deg}^{-1} \text{ mole}^{-1}$$

A volume of 22.4 liters is also the volume occupied by 1 mole of a gas at 0°C and 1 atm pressure (usually called <u>standard</u> <u>temperature</u> <u>and</u> <u>pressure</u>, or STP), if it behaves ideally under these conditions.

All of the experiments discussed above can now be summarized in one equation:

$$pV = nRT \qquad \text{or} \qquad pv = RT \qquad\qquad (2\text{-}3)$$

where $v = V/n$ and R is a universal constant, known as the <u>gas</u> <u>constant</u>. This is the <u>equation</u> <u>of</u> <u>state</u> (i.e., the relation between p, V, n, and T) for <u>any</u> ideal gas. It is often called the <u>ideal</u> <u>gas</u> law. The remarkable fact about Eq. 2-3 is that the nature of the molecules of the gas (e.g., the number of atoms per molecule, the mass of a molecule, etc.) does not enter into the equation; all that matters is the <u>number</u> of gas molecules (or, what is essentially the same thing, the number of moles of gas).

The numerical value of R depends on the units chosen for p and V. Accurate values are

$$R = 0.08206 \text{ liter atm deg}^{-1} \text{ mole}^{-1}$$

$$= 82.06 \text{ cm}^3 \text{ atm deg}^{-1} \text{ mole}^{-1}$$

$$= 1.9872 \text{ cal deg}^{-1} \text{ mole}^{-1}$$

To the same accuracy, V_0 = 22.414 liters is the volume occupied by 1 mole of an ideal gas at STP.

Equation 2-3 can be used to find the molecular weight M of an unknown gas. For if W grams of a gas produce a pressure p in a volume V at temperature T, then

$$pV = (W/M)RT \qquad \text{or} \qquad M = WRT/pV \qquad\qquad (2\text{-}4)$$

We are making use here of the fact that, in effect, the pressure "counts" the number of molecules. This number, together with W, gives the desired weight per molecule (or per mole).

It is often useful, especially in theoretical work, to rewrite the ideal gas law in terms of the number of molecules in the gas, N, rather than the number of moles, n. Since $N = nN_0$, where N_0 is Avogadro's number (6.023×10^{23} molecules per mole), Eq. 2-3 becomes

$$pV = NkT \tag{2-5}$$

where k is the gas constant per molecule (called the Boltzmann constant). It is related to R by $k = R/N_0$.

2-2   KINETIC THEORY OF GASES

IN THIS SECTION we give a very brief summary of the theoretical interpretation of ideal gas behavior. For a proof of many of the statements made here, the reader must turn to Appendix 4 which is a supplement to the present section.

Energy. In a very dilute gas, each molecule moves in a straight line path except for the relatively short periods of time in which it is involved in collisions with other molecules[2] or with the walls. At each such collision, a molecule not only changes direction but ordinarily also changes its velocity. This is because energy is transferred at a collision; the total energy of the two molecules (or one molecule plus wall) remains constant but usually one molecule gains some energy and the other loses some. For simplicity, we shall speak in terms of monatomic molecules for which the relation between the energy and velocity of a molecule is just $\epsilon = mv^2/2$, where m is the mass of the molecule. This expression also holds for polyatomic molecules if by ϵ we mean the translational kinetic energy and do not include rotational and internal vibrational energy.[3]

Thus each molecule of the gas has an energy which changes frequently owing to collisions. And if we consider all of the many molecules of a gas at some one instant of time, some will be going fast at that instant, some slow, etc. In other words, at any instant, there will be a distribution of energy among the molecules. That is, a certain fraction or percent of the molecules will have a certain energy ϵ within a range dϵ (an infinitesimal), another fraction will have another energy, etc. There will of course be a closely related distribution

---

[2]For example, the average distance an argon atom travels between collisions in argon gas at STP is about 600 Å. The diameter of an argon atom is about 4 Å.

[3]If some of these terms are new to the reader, see p. 107.

in molecular velocities. Furthermore, if the gas is at equilibrium, the energy (or velocity) distribution will not change with time (in fact, all properties of the bulk gas are independent of time at equilibrium), although there will be a lot of reshuffling of energy among the different molecules as time passes. Thus, as usual, the equilibrium state is dynamic, not static.

If the temperature of the heat bath (and walls) is increased, the molecules of the gas will experience a net gain of energy during their collisions with the walls until the temperature of the gas comes up to the temperature of the walls. There will then be new equilibrium energy and velocity distributions among the gas molecules at the higher temperature. Relative to the old distributions, the new ones will be shifted to higher energies and velocities.

It is shown in Appendix 4 (Eq. A4-7) that the fraction of gas molecules with energy between ϵ and $\epsilon + d\epsilon$ is proportional to

$$\epsilon^{1/2} e^{-\epsilon/kT} d\epsilon \tag{2-6}$$

and that the fraction of molecules with velocity between v and $v + dv$ is proportional to (Eq. A4-4)

$$v^2 e^{-mv^2/2kT} dv \tag{2-7}$$

Figure 2-3 shows the velocity distribution at two different temperatures, as calculated from 2-7, but with the additional feature of

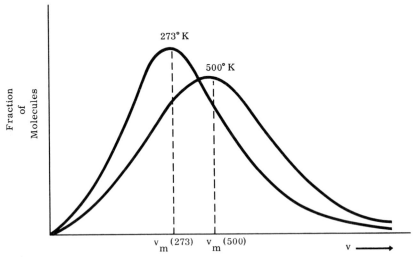

Figure 2-3
Velocity distribution in a gas at two different temperatures (see Eq. A4-4).

"normalization": that is, the area under the two curves is adjusted to be the same (this area is equal to unity because it is the total fraction of gas molecules). Note that the high temperature curve is shifted to higher velocities, as expected. The two energy distributions are quite similar to the velocity distributions.

Incidentally, the fraction of all molecules with velocity between v and v + dv (or energy between ϵ and ϵ + dϵ) at any instant is exactly equal to the fraction of time that any one molecule has a velocity between v and v + dv (or energy between ϵ and ϵ + dϵ).

The distributions 2-6 and 2-7 may be used to calculate some important average properties of the gas molecules (see Appendix 4 for details). From 2-6 we find that

$$\bar{\epsilon} = \tfrac{3}{2}kT \qquad \text{or} \qquad E = N\bar{\epsilon} = \tfrac{3}{2}NkT = \tfrac{3}{2}nRT \qquad (2\text{-}8)$$

where $\bar{\epsilon}$ is the average energy per molecule and E is the total energy of the gas. The average energy per molecule and the total energy of the gas both increase in proportion to the absolute temperature T. According to Eq. 2-8, the average energy per molecule depends only on T and not on the molecule. Thus a light molecule and a heavy molecule, both at T, have the same average energy.

The average velocity of the molecules follows from 2-7:

$$\bar{v} = \sqrt{\frac{8kT}{\pi m}} \qquad (2\text{-}9)$$

The most probable velocity v_m (i.e., the velocity corresponding to the top of the curve in Fig. 2-3) is

$$v_m = \sqrt{\frac{2kT}{m}} \qquad (2\text{-}10)$$

Note that $\bar{v}$ is slightly larger than v_m (the distribution in Fig. 2-3 is unsymmetrical). These velocities are both proportional to $T^{1/2}$ and inversely proportional to $m^{1/2}$.

If we have two different gases at the same temperature T, with masses m_1 and m_2, then

$$\bar{v_1} = \sqrt{\frac{8kT}{\pi m_1}} \qquad \text{and} \qquad \bar{v_2} = \sqrt{\frac{8kT}{\pi m_2}}$$

On combining these equations, we find

$$\frac{\bar{v_1}}{\bar{v_2}} = \sqrt{\frac{m_2}{m_1}} \qquad (2\text{-}11)$$

This shows how the ratio of the average velocities of two kinds of gas molecules at the same temperature depends on the ratio of the masses. Light molecules move faster, on the average, than heavy molecules at the same temperature. It is easy to see that this is also a consequence of the fact, mentioned above, that light and heavy molecules, both at T, have the same average energy.

In order to use Eq. 2-9 to calculate $\bar{v}$ numerically, we need k in cgs units:

$$k = 1.380 \times 10^{-16} \text{ erg deg}^{-1}$$

The mass m of one molecule (in grams) is given by $m = M/N_0$. We then obtain $\bar{v}$ in cm sec^{-1}. For example, at 273.1°K (i.e., at 0°C):

$$\bar{v}(H_2) = 1.69 \times 10^5 \text{ cm sec}^{-1} = 3780 \text{ miles hr}^{-1}$$

$$\bar{v}(O_2) = 0.425 \times 10^5 \text{ cm sec}^{-1} = 950 \text{ miles hr}^{-1}$$

Note that hydrogen molecules move about four times as fast as oxygen molecules, on the average, because oxygen is about 16 times heavier (see Eq. 2-11).

Pressure. The pressure, or force per unit area, exerted by the gas on the inside walls of the container arises from a very large number of individual collisions of the molecules with the walls. Of course the molecules hit the walls with different velocities (according to the velocity distribution already discussed) and at different angles. The average contribution to the pressure, per wall collision, is proportional to the average momentum of the molecules, $m\bar{v}$. The number of collisions made on a wall, in any unit of time, is proportional to the concentration of gas molecules, N/V, and also proportional to the average velocity of the molecules, $\bar{v}$. Putting these statements together, we have that

$$p \propto m\bar{v} \cdot \frac{N}{V} \cdot \bar{v} \qquad \text{or} \qquad p \propto \frac{N}{V} m\bar{v}^2$$

According to Eq. 2-9, $\bar{v}^2 \propto kT/m$. Therefore

$$p \propto \frac{NkT}{V} \tag{2-12}$$

The proportionality constant in Eq. 2-12 is the same for all gases because the only special property of any given gas which enters into the above argument is the mass m, and we have just seen that mass cancels out of the final result. Actually, we know (Eq. 2-5) that the proportionality constant is just unity, but to prove it theoretically requires a more detailed analysis than that which we have given here (see Appendix 4).

2-3 NUMERICAL ILLUSTRATIONS

Ideal gas at STP and at high vacuum. At $0°C$ and 1 atm pressure, 1 mole of an ideal gas occupies 22.4 liters (the reader should verify this number by calculating V from $V = nRT/p$). What is the volume per molecule, and how many molecules are there per cubic centimeter?

There are 6.02×10^{23} molecules (i.e., 1 mole) in $22,400$ cm^3. Therefore the number of molecules in 1 cubic centimeter is $6.02 \times 10^{23}/2.24 \times 10^4$, or 2.69×10^{19} molecules per cm^3. The volume per molecule is just the reciprocal of this: $1/(2.69 \times 10^{19})$ cm^3 molecule^{-1}. The volume per molecule in $Å^3$ is perhaps easier to comprehend. This number is $10^{24}/(2.69 \times 10^{19})$, or $3.72 \times 10^4 Å^3$ molecule^{-1}.

At any instant the molecules of a gas are scattered at random through the volume V, but we can get a rough idea of the average distance between any molecule and its nearest neighbors in the gas by taking the cube root of the volume occupied per molecule. Since $(3.72 \times 10^4 Å^3)^{1/3} = 33Å$, this is a typical distance between neighboring gas molecules at STP. By comparison, the diameter of an ordinary molecule is 3-$5Å$.

Now let us answer the same questions as above for a gas at $0°C$ and 1.00×10^{-5} mm Hg pressure. This is a high vacuum, but not extreme. For variety, we shall work directly with the ideal gas law. The number of molecules per cubic centimeter is

$$\frac{N}{V} = \frac{N_0\,p}{RT} = \frac{6.02 \times 10^{23} \times (1.00 \times 10^{-5}/760)}{82.1 \times 273}$$

$$= 3.53 \times 10^{11} \text{ molecules per } cm^3$$

Thus, even at this very low pressure, 1 cubic centimeter contains a huge number of molecules. The volume per molecule in $Å^3$ is $10^{24}/(3.53 \times 10^{11})$, or $2.83 \times 10^{12} Å^3$ molecule^{-1}. The average distance between neighboring gas molecules is then roughly $(2.83 \times 10^{12} Å^3)^{1/3} = 1.41 \times 10^4 Å$.

Expansion of water on boiling. The normal boiling point of water is $100°C$ ($p = 1$ atm). The question is: What is the expansion factor v_G/v_L at the normal boiling point? This subject is also mentioned briefly on p. 14 (see also Fig. 1-8b). We make the excellent assumption that water vapor at $100°C$ and 1 atm is an ideal gas. Then the molar volume of the vapor is

$$v_G = \frac{RT}{p} = \frac{82.1 \times 373}{1} = 30,600 \text{ cm}^3 \text{ mole}^{-1}$$

The observed value of the density of the liquid, ρ_L, at $100°C$ and

1 atm is 0.958 g per cm³. The volume of the liquid per gram is $1/\rho_L$, and the molar volume is

$$v_L = M \cdot \frac{1}{\rho_L} = \frac{18.02}{0.958} = 18.8 \text{ cm}^3 \text{ mole}^{-1}$$

The ratio v_G/v_L is then 30,600/18.8, or 1620. Thus there is a very considerable expansion of water when it boils.

The expansion factor at 25°C is even larger because the gas is more dilute. The vapor pressure is 23.8 mm Hg and the density of the liquid is 0.997 g per cm³. Therefore

$$v_G = \frac{82.1 \times 298}{(23.8/760)} = 7.81 \times 10^5 \text{ cm}^3 \text{ mole}^{-1}$$

$$v_L = \frac{18.02}{0.997} = 18.1 \text{ cm}^3 \text{ mole}^{-1}, \quad v_G/v_L = 43,200$$

2-4   IDEAL GAS MIXTURES

THE MOLECULES of an ideal gas are essentially independent of each other (the collisions between molecules merely serve to keep the system in equilibrium). Thus the pressure and energy are made up of independent contributions from the individual molecules. According to Eq. 2-5, the average contribution of any one molecule to the pressure is kT/V, and the total pressure is NkT/V. Similarly, in Eq. 2-8, the average energy per molecule is $3kT/2$, and the total energy is $3NkT/2$.

Because of the independence of molecules in an ideal gas, if the gas contains molecules of several different types, the contributions of the different kinds of molecule to p and E are simply additive:

$$p = p_1 + p_2 + \cdots = \frac{N_1 kT}{V} + \frac{N_2 kT}{V} + \cdots$$

$$= \frac{n_1 RT}{V} + \frac{n_2 RT}{V} + \cdots \tag{2-13}$$

and

$$E = \tfrac{3}{2} N_1 kT + \tfrac{3}{2} N_2 kT + \cdots$$

$$= \tfrac{3}{2} n_1 RT + \tfrac{3}{2} n_2 RT + \cdots \tag{2-14}$$

where there is one term on the right-hand side of each of these equations for each type of molecule. Equation 2-13 is known as Dalton's law of partial pressures.

PROBLEMS

2-1. Calculate the numerical values of $\overline{v}(H_2)$ and $\overline{v}(O_2)$ given on p. 28.

2-2. Derive Eq. 2-10 for v_m from Eq. 2-7.

2-3. Calculate the density of O_2 gas in g per cm^3 at STP.

2-4. 10 g of a gas occupy 2.80 liters at STP. What is the molecular weight of the gas?

2-5. The vapor pressure of a liquid is 0.100 atm at 0°C. What is the molar volume of the vapor in equilibrium with the liquid at this temperature?

CHAPTER 3

INTERMOLECULAR
FORCES

AS A CONSEQUENCE of chemical bond forces, atoms aggregate to form molecules. These are intramolecular forces. But there also exist generally weaker forces between molecules, or between atoms which do not join in a chemical bond. These are called intermolecular forces; such forces are responsible for the aggregation or condensation of molecules to form the liquid and solid states of matter. Intermolecular forces also cause the deviation from ideal behavior often observed in real gases.

Thus, in the next three chapters, on imperfect gases, solids, and liquids, we shall have frequent occasion to consider these forces. As a preliminary, however, we give a summary in this chapter of the more important types of intermolecular forces.

3-1 INTRODUCTION

AS WILL BE evident from the next section, all intermolecular forces have an electrostatic origin. The same is true of intramolecular forces. The basic electrostatic law is Coulomb's law which states that the force between two charges q_1 and q_2, a distance r apart in a vacuum (Fig. 3-1a), is

$$f(r) = \frac{q_1 q_2}{r^2} \qquad (3\text{-}1)$$

If q_1 and q_2 have the same sign, the force is positive (repulsion). If they have opposite signs, f is negative (attraction). This is the basic law of force whether one uses classical mechanics or quantum mechanics.

Force, work, and potential energy. If the charges q_1 and q_2 are a distance r apart and we then allow r to increase by an infinitesimal amount dr, the work done by the charges against an outside resisting force is <u>force</u> × <u>distance</u>, f(r) dr (this work is positive if q_1 and q_2 have the same sign). If we start at $r = r_0$ and increase r, in the above manner, by infinitesimal steps until finally $r = \infty$, the total work done by the charges is

$$\text{work } (r_0) = \int_{r_0}^{\infty} f(r) \, dr \qquad (3\text{-}2)$$

This work obviously depends on the starting point r_0. If we choose, as is conventional (but arbitrary), the value zero for the potential energy of the two charges when $r = \infty$, then the potential

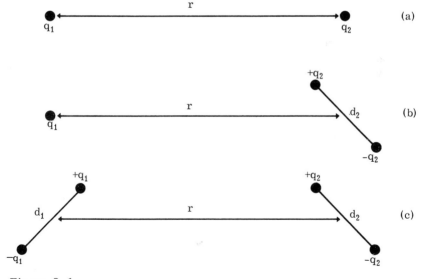

Figure 3-1
Coulombic interaction between: (a) two charges; (b) a charge and a dipole; and (c) two dipoles.

energy $u(r_0)$ at $r = r_0$ is <u>defined</u> as being equal to the total work referred to above. That is,

$$u(r_0) = \text{work } (r_0) = \int_{r_0}^{\infty} f(r) \, dr \qquad (3\text{-}3)$$

If the charges have the same sign, $f(r)$ is positive for all r and hence $u(r_0)$ is positive.

The definition of potential energy as work done <u>by</u> the charges against an outside resisting force is easier to visualize when the force between the charges is repulsive (positive) than when it is attractive. When the force between the charges is attractive, one can use an alternative but equivalent definition, if desired: the potential energy at r_0 is defined as the negative of the work that has to be done <u>on</u> the charges in order to pull them apart from $r = r_0$ to $r = \infty$. Mathematically,

$$u(r_0) = - \int_{r_0}^{\infty} [-f(r)] \, dr$$

which is the same relation between u and f as in Eq. 3-3.

Actually, Eq. 3-3 is the general relation connecting potential energy, work and force for <u>any</u> kind of r-dependent force between two molecules, providing $f = 0$ at $r = \infty$. In the special case of the coulombic force, Eq. 3-1,

$$u(r_0) = \int_{r_0}^{\infty} \frac{q_1 q_2}{r^2} \, dr = - \left. \frac{q_1 q_2}{r} \right|_{r_0}^{\infty} = \frac{q_1 q_2}{r_0}$$

Using the notation in Eq. 3-1, we can rewrite this as

$$u(r) = \frac{q_1 q_2}{r} \qquad (3\text{-}4)$$

This is Coulomb's law expressed in terms of potential energy rather than force. For most purposes (Section 3-4, for example), $u(r)$ is more useful than $f(r)$ though of course it is always easy to convert from one function to the other.

If q_1 and q_2 have opposite signs (attraction), the potential energy at a separation r is negative (recall that we have chosen $u = 0$ at $r = \infty$). This is similar to the gravitational example mentioned on p. 6, where an attractive force is also involved. The potential energy of the charges is less at r than it is at $r = \infty$. Hence charges of opposite sign are in a more stable configuration at r than at $r = \infty$. The reverse is of course true for charges of the same sign.

Equation 3-3 exhibits the integral relation between the functions u and f. The corresponding differential relation is

$$f(r) = -\frac{du(r)}{dr} \tag{3-5}$$

As a check, let us apply this to Eq. 3-4:

$$f(r) = -\frac{d}{dr}\left(\frac{q_1 q_2}{r}\right) = \frac{q_1 q_2}{r^2}$$

which is just Eq. 3-1. According to Eq. 3-5, if the potential energy u is plotted against r, f can be found at any point on this curve as the negative of the slope du/dr.

Dipole moment. As we shall see in the next section, there is not only an electrostatic force between two charges (Fig. 3-1a), but there is also a force between a charge and a neutral group of other charges (Fig. 3-1b), or between two neutral groups of charges (Fig. 3-1c). The simplest neutral group, and the only one we consider, is a pair of charges of equal magnitude but opposite sign, known as a dipole.

If a dipole consists of a positive charge +q separated from a negative charge −q by a distance d (as, for example, in Fig. 3-1c), then the dipole moment is defined as $\mu = qd$. That is, the dipole moment is simply the product charge × separation.

The electrons of an isolated atom have, on the average, a spherically symmetrical distribution centered on the nucleus (charge +q in Fig. 3-2a). Thus the average center of negative charge (electrons, −q) coincides exactly with the center of positive charge. But if, say, a positive charge is placed to the right of the atom (Fig. 3-2b), the electrons (being very light) will be pulled or shifted toward the positive charge. The atom is said to be polarized by the charge. The centers of positive and negative charge in the atom no longer coincide. The atom now has a dipole induced by the positive charge, and an induced dipole moment qd (Fig. 3-2b).

Molecules as well as atoms can have induced dipoles, but many molecules (called polar) have permanent dipoles in addition. These are dipoles that exist in the absence of other charges. For example, in unsymmetrical diatomic molecules (HCl, CO, etc.), the centers of negative charge (electrons) and positive charge (the two nuclei) do not coincide in general, and there is a permanent dipole moment.

If an electron and a proton are separated by a distance of 1.0Å, the dipole moment is

$$\mu = (4.80 \times 10^{-10} \text{ esu}) \times (1.0 \times 10^{-8} \text{ cm})$$

$$= 4.80 \times 10^{-18} \text{ esu} \cdot \text{cm}$$

where esu = electrostatic unit of charge $[1(\text{esu})^2 \text{cm}^{-1} = 1$ erg; see Eq. 3-4]. It is customary to write this as $\mu = 4.80D$ (Debye units of

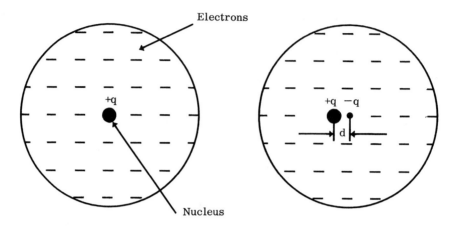

(a) Unpolarized Atom   (b) Polarized Atom

Figure 3-2
Schematic representation of an atom, polarized and unpolarized by an
electric field. The electric field shifts the electrons to one side of the
nucleus.

dipole moment). Table 3-1 gives experimental values of a few permanent molecular dipole moments in Debye units. Large dipole moments are correlated with large differences in so-called electro-
negativities of the chemically bonded atoms of a molecule. The
electronegativity of an atom is a measure of its power to attract the
electrons of a covalent bond in which it is taking part.

Polarizability. We have already mentioned that a dipole can be induced in an atom or molecule by other charges. Let us now be a little
more precise about this.

Table 3-1
Permanent Dipole Moments

Molecule	μ (in D)	Molecule	μ (in D)
Ar	0.00	HBr	0.78
H_2	0.00	HI	0.38
CH_4	0.00	H_2O	1.86
CO_2	0.00	H_2S	0.95
CO	0.12	NH_3	1.49
HF	1.98	LiH	5.88
HCl	1.03	LiF	6.7

First, we define the electric field strength $\mathcal{E}$. A set of one or more fixed charges $q_1, q_2, \ldots$ in a vacuum will exert a force f on a small test charge q placed at any point P. This force could be calculated by application of Coulomb's law to each of the pairs qq_1, $qq_2, \ldots$, or it could be measured experimentally. In either case, the field strength $\mathcal{E}$ at P is defined by the equation $\mathcal{E} = f/q$; that is, $\mathcal{E}$ is the force per unit of test charge exerted on the test charge by the fixed charges $q_1, q_2, \ldots$.

Now if, instead of the test charge, an atom or molecule is placed at P, where the field strength is $\mathcal{E}$, a dipole will be induced in the atom or molecule. Let the induced dipole moment be μ_{ind}. This dipole moment is observed to be directly proportional to $\mathcal{E}$ (unless $\mathcal{E}$ is very large). The proportionality constant between μ_{ind} and $\mathcal{E}$ is an intrinsic property of the particular atom or molecule being used in the experiment. It is called the polarizability, α:

$$\mu_{ind} = \alpha \mathcal{E} \tag{3-6}$$

Polarizability has dimensions of $(\text{length})^3$. This can be seen from the following dimensional equations:

$$f = \mathcal{E}q; \quad \mathcal{E} = \text{force/charge}$$

$$\mu_{ind} = \alpha \mathcal{E}; \quad \text{charge} \times \text{length} = \alpha \times \text{force/charge}$$

$$\alpha = \frac{(\text{charge})^2 \times \text{length}}{\text{force}} = \frac{(\text{charge})^2 \times \text{length}}{(\text{charge})^2/(\text{length})^2} = (\text{length})^3$$

where Eq. 3-1 has been used for the force. Common units for α are Å^3 per molecule or cm^3 per mole.

Table 3-2 contains a few experimental values of α in Å^3 molecule^{-1}. An approximate electrostatic argument can be given which

Table 3-2
Polarizability

Molecule	α (in Å^3 molecule^{-1})	Molecule	α (in Å^3 molecule^{-1})
He	0.20	CCl_4	10.5
Ne	0.39	H_2	0.79
Ar	1.62	HCl	2.63
Kr	2.46	HI	5.44
CH_4	2.60	NH_3	2.26
CO	1.99	H_2O	1.48

shows that $\alpha \cong R_0^3$, where R_0 is the approximate radius of the sphere, or effective sphere, occupied by the electrons of the atom or molecule. This rough correlation between size and polarizability is evident from the table.

3-2   TYPES OF INTERMOLECULAR FORCES

IN SOLIDS, liquids, and dense gases, a given molecule is generally near to and interacts simultaneously with (i.e., exerts a force on) several other molecules. As a very simple example of this, consider the system of four molecules in Fig. 3-3. The potential energy U of the four molecules in the configuration shown is the negative of the work necessary, starting with this configuration, to pull the molecules

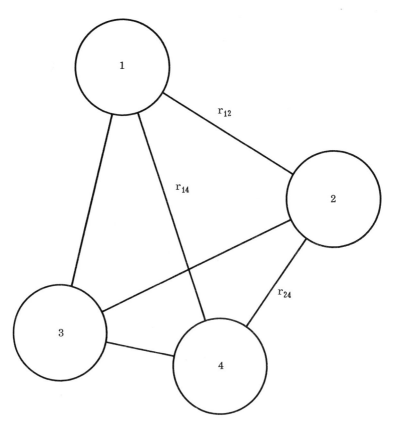

Figure 3-3
Pair interactions between four molecules.

apart until they are infinitely separated from each other. Except at extremely high pressures, when the molecules are abnormally closely packed, experimental and theoretical work both show that the total potential energy of a group of molecules is very nearly[1] equal to the sum of the pair potential energies. This is a very helpful simplification. Thus, in Fig. 3-3, if the molecules are of the same kind,

$$U \cong u(r_{12}) + u(r_{13}) + u(r_{14}) + u(r_{23}) + u(r_{24}) + u(r_{34}) \quad (3\text{-}7)$$

where $u(r)$ is the potential energy of just two of these molecules at a distance r apart in a vacuum.

In analyzing the origin of the total potential energy of dense systems of molecules it therefore suffices, for our purposes, to consider the different types of <u>pair</u> interactions in a vacuum. The rest of this section is devoted to a brief analysis of eight different and important kinds of intermolecular pair interactions. In each case we also ·mention illustrative experimental systems in which the given interaction occurs. These types are not mutually exclusive, and the list is by no means exhaustive. In fact, a pair of real atoms, or ions, or molecules would interact in not less than two of these ways, and often in more than two (see Section 3-3, for example).

Type 1. Charge-charge interaction. This case has already been considered in the preceding section. Equation 3-4 gives the potential energy between a pair of charges. Examples of occurrence are the interactions between Na^+ and Na^+, Na^+ and Cl^-, and Cl^- and Cl^- in a sodium chloride crystal (Chapter 5), or similar interactions in any ionic crystal.

Another example: at high temperatures sodium vapor ionizes to form gaseous Na^+ and e^- (electron); there are then coulombic interactions between Na^+ and Na^+, Na^+ and e^-, and e^- and e^-. Such an ionized gas is called a plasma, incidentally (see p. 240). The situation in sodium metal is very similar, except that the density is much higher and the sodium ions are arranged in a regular lattice (Chapter 5).

Type 2. Charge-dipole interaction. A charge interacts with a dipole, as shown in Fig. 3-1b. The exact expression for $u(r)$ can be deduced from Coulomb's law applied to each of the two interactions (q_1, $+q_2$ and q_1, $-q_2$ in Fig. 3-1b). The potential energy clearly depends not only on r but also on the orientation of the axis of the dipole. But, because real molecules rotate, what we really want for most purposes is $u(r)$ averaged over all possible orientations of the dipolar axis. In the averaging, the weight given to each orientation is

---

[1]This is exactly true for point charges and Coulomb's law, but not exactly true for real molecules and atoms because of quantum mechanical effects. Orientational averaging, as in Eq. 3-8, also introduces error.

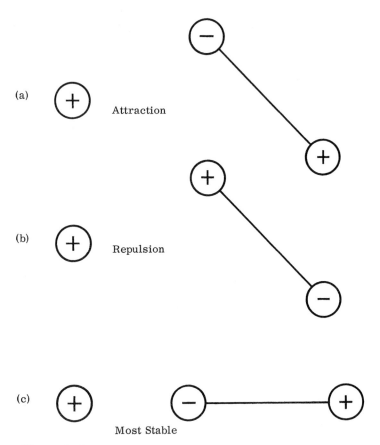

Figure 3-4
Interactions between a charge and a dipole (in different
orientations).

proportional to $e^{-u/kT}$ (Boltzmann distribution, Appendix 3), where
u is the potential energy in the orientation. The result[2] is

$$u(r) = -\frac{1}{3kT}\frac{q^2\mu^2}{r^4} \qquad (3\text{-}8)$$

where q is the charge and μ the dipole moment.

---

[2]This is not a completely general calculation. The length of the dipole is
assumed small compared to r, and the temperature is assumed high enough
that kT is large compared to u in the Boltzmann factor. Incidentally, an alternative quantity of perhaps more physical interest is the potential associated
with the average force rather than the average potential itself. The potential
of average force, in this case, turns out to be one half of the average potential.

The reason u(r) in Eq. 3-8 is always negative is the following: Orientations with an attraction between q and μ (e.g., Fig. 3-4a) have a negative potential energy and therefore receive a larger weight $e^{-u/kT}$ in the averaging than do orientations with a repulsion (Fig. 3-4b) and a positive potential energy. Hence the over-all average of u(r) is negative.

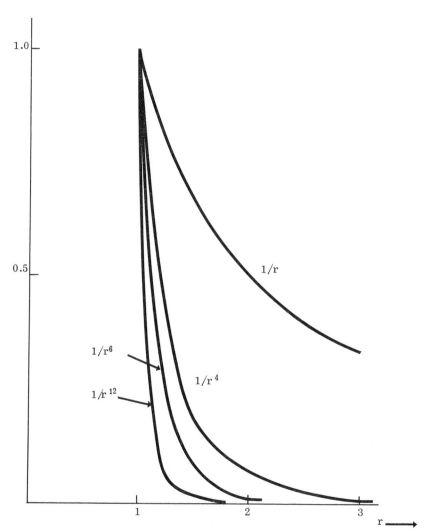

Figure 3-5
Plot of the functions $1/r$, $1/r^4$, $1/r^6$, and $1/r^{12}$.

Note that u(r) in Eq. 3-8 varies as r^{-4}, compared with r^{-1} in Eq. 3-4. Hence this is an interaction of much shorter range than the coulombic interaction. This is illustrated in Fig. 3-5.

The average pair potential (3-8) depends on temperature (because of the use of the Boltzmann factor in the averaging). At very high temperatures, u(r) → 0. Through the Boltzmann factor, the potential energy tends to orient the dipoles in such a way as to favor the most stable orientation (with lowest potential energy), shown in Fig. 3-4c. But random thermal motion (rotation, in this case) works against this ordering effect. When the temperature is very high, ordering is negligible, the rotation of the dipole is essentially random, and the average potential energy goes to zero (because orientations with negative and positive potential energies occur with equal frequency).

An example of a charge-dipole interaction is that between Na^+ or Cl^- and a water molecule (dipole) in an aqueous solution of NaCl.

Type 3. Dipole-dipole interaction. This is rather similar to (2) but the details are more complicated to work out. The dipole-dipole interaction shown in Fig. 3-1c depends on the orientation of both dipoles. For given orientations, u(r) can be calculated from Coulomb's law (there are four charge-charge interactions to add together). But again this u(r) must be averaged over all orientations (of both dipoles), with $e^{-u/kT}$ as the weighting factor. One finds for the average potential energy (see the footnote on p. 40).

$$u(r) = -\frac{2}{3kT} \frac{\mu_1^2 \mu_2^2}{r^6} \tag{3-9}$$

where μ_1 and μ_2 are the two dipole moments. This is an interaction of even shorter range than that in Eq. 3-8 (see Fig. 3-5). The average potential energy is always negative, and depends on temperature, just as in (2).

The interaction between two molecules of HCl in gaseous, liquid, or solid HCl is an example.

Type 4. Charge-induced dipole interaction. A charge q induces a dipole in a neutral atom or molecule (see Fig. 3-2b and Eq. 3-6). There is then an attraction between the charge and the induced dipole and consequently a negative potential energy of interaction. We can calculate, from Coulomb's law, that this potential energy is given by

$$u(r) = -\frac{q^2 \alpha}{2r^4} \tag{3-10}$$

where α is the polarizability of the neutral atom or molecule.

An example would be the interaction between Na^+ and Na, or between e^- and Na in partially ionized sodium vapor [see (1), above]. Another would be the interaction between Na^+ or Cl^- and a water molecule in aqueous NaCl. We have already mentioned this as an example of a charge-dipole interaction [see (2), above], because H_2O has a permanent dipole moment. But a charge induces an <u>additional</u> moment so that both of Eqs. 3-8 and 3-10 would apply. That is, the two expressions should be added together.

Type 5. Dipole-induced dipole interaction. A permanent dipole induces a dipole in a neutral atom or molecule. The potential energy (which is always negative) depends on the orientation of the permanent moment. On averaging over all orientations, in the usual way, it is found that

$$u(r) = -\frac{\mu^2 \alpha}{r^6} \tag{3-11}$$

A liquid solution of $CHCl_3$ (chloroform) in CCl_4 (carbon tetrachloride) provides examples. In the $CHCl_3 - CCl_4$ interaction, $CHCl_3$ induces a dipole moment in CCl_4, which has no permanent moment. In the $CHCl_3 - CHCl_3$ interaction, the permanent moment in each molecule induces an additional moment in the other. Hence, in this latter case we get a double effect and we have to multiply the right-hand side of Eq. 3-11 by two.

Type 6. Dispersion interaction. This is also often called an induced dipole-induced dipole interaction, or an attractive van der Waals interaction (see Section 4-2). This interaction exists between <u>any</u> two ions or molecules, polar or nonpolar (e.g., $Na^+ - Cl^-$, $Na^+ - H_2O$, $Na^+ - Ne$, $HCl - A$, $He - He$, $He - A$, $CCl_4 - CCl_4$, etc.). For this reason, it is especially important. For simplicity, let us discuss it in terms of two neutral, nonpolar molecules, 1 and 2. But the argument is very similar in more complicated cases.

The electrons of molecule 1 are not located in fixed positions relative to the nuclei but move about. Since we are assuming $\mu_1 = 0$, the <u>average</u> distribution of the electrons (as would be shown in a time exposure — if this were possible to obtain) is such that the center of negative charge (on the electrons) exactly coincides with the center of positive charge (on the nucleus or nuclei), as in Fig. 3-2a. That is, μ_1 is really an <u>average</u> dipole moment, with value zero. But at any instant the electrons will in general not be distributed in such a way that the centers of negative and positive charge coincide: there will be an instantaneous dipole moment which is <u>not</u> zero. This instantaneous dipole in molecule 1 induces a dipole in molecule 2, leading to an attraction between the instantaneous and induced dipoles which must then be averaged. This is of course only half of the effect because there is also an attraction between an instantaneous dipole in 2 and an induced dipole in 1. The whole phenomenon is quantum mechanical in nature. The theory was first worked out in 1930 by F. London. His approximate equation for the potential energy reads

$$u(r) = -\frac{3}{2}\left(\frac{I_1 I_2}{I_1 + I_2}\right)\frac{\alpha_1 \alpha_2}{r^6} \tag{3-12}$$

where α_1 and α_2 are polarizabilities and I_1 and I_2 are ionization potentials (the energy necessary to pull one electron away from an atom or molecule).

The magnitude of this interaction will be discussed at some length in the next two sections. But we emphasize here that $u(r)$ is proportional to $\alpha_1 \alpha_2$ and that the polarizabilities in turn are roughly correlated with the sizes of the molecules (see p. 38). Hence large molecules tend to have large dispersion interactions.

Type 7. Overlap or van der Waals repulsive interaction. When two nonbonding atoms, ions, or molecules gradually approach each other, there are at first interactions of the types already discussed. But a new effect comes into play when r is small enough so that the electron clouds of the two molecules begin to overlap. This effect is a repulsion (requiring quantum mechanics to calculate) which increases as the overlap increases (that is, as r decreases). When the overlap is so great that nuclei from the two molecules are very near each other, there is a large contribution to the repulsion of simple coulombic origin (from the positive charges on the nuclei).

In effect, the existence of the overlap repulsion means that atoms and molecules have a space-filling quality (roughly that space filled by the electron clouds around the nucleus or nuclei). For this strong overlap or van der Waals (as it is often called) repulsion prevents two atoms or molecules from occupying the same space at the same time.

We have mentioned that intermolecular attractive forces are responsible for the condensation of molecules to form the liquid and solid states. One might have wondered what limits the extent of condensation. Since the attractive forces increase in strength as r decreases, why should not a liquid or solid condense to zero volume? The answer is that the overlap repulsive force enters the picture after the condensation reaches a certain point and this force overpowers the attractive forces. Hence the volume of a liquid or solid is largely determined by the amount of space occupied by the electron clouds associated with the atoms or molecules involved. We shall return to this subject in Section 3-4.

The mathematical form of the potential energy associated with the overlap repulsion is found to be approximately

$$u(r) = c_1 e^{-c_2 r} \tag{3-13}$$

where c_1 and c_2 are positive constants characteristic of each type of molecule. An alternative but somewhat more approximate expression for the potential energy is

$$u(r) = c_3/r^{12} \tag{3-14}$$

where c_3 is another positive constant. This latter form for $u(r)$ is used in the next section. The power 12 corresponds to a force of extremely short range (Fig. 3-5).

Type 8. The hydrogen bond. This is an electrostatic interaction between two strong and specifically oriented dipoles at least one of which contains a hydrogen atom. This interaction is not included in the dipole-dipole interaction (3), already discussed, for two reasons: Eq. 3-9 assumes (a) that the dipoles rotate and (b) that the length of the dipole is small compared to r. Neither condition is satisfied here.

When a hydrogen atom is chemically bonded to one of the highly electronegative atoms F, O, or N, the bond is very polar (i.e., it has a relatively large bond dipole moment). Given the opportunity, the hydrogen atom (with partial positive charge) will be strongly attracted, electrostatically, to another F, O, or N atom (with partial negative charge). This latter interaction is called a <u>hydrogen bond</u> (it is not a second chemical bond). The special role of hydrogen, in this connection, is due to its extremely small size which allows a very close

H—F---H—F   (HF vapor)

(formic acid vapor)

(ice)

C=O---H—N   (proteins and nucleic acids)

N---H—N   (nucleic acids)

(3-I)

electrostatic interaction. The small size also has as a consequence the fact that a chemically bonded hydrogen atom can participate in only one hydrogen bond at a time. Otherwise the electronegative atoms would get in each others way.

Examples are indicated schematically in 3-I (dashed line = hydrogen bond). Hydrogen bonds are especially important in biological macromolecules.

The strength of hydrogen bonds is generally intermediate between ordinary intermolecular interactions and chemical bonds (see Section 3-4).

3-3   LENNARD-JONES POTENTIAL

IN THIS SECTION we discuss the intermolecular potential energy for some relatively simple real molecules. The information available comes from a mixture of theory (e.g., Section 3-2) and experiment (primarily imperfect gas p-v-T and viscosity data). The most accurate data pertain to spherically symmetrical nonpolar molecules (i.e., monatomic gases). But, because of rotation, symmetrical diatomic molecules such as H_2, N_2, O_2, etc., are effectively spherically symmetrical, as are also molecules like CH_4 and CCl_4. For all of these molecules, the total pair potential energy has just two contributions out of the eight listed in Section 3-2: the dispersion interaction, (6), and the overlap interaction, (7).

The representation of the total pair potential energy by a combination of Eqs. 3-12 and 3-14 is much used and is known as the Lennard-Jones potential. There is a negative (attractive) term in r^{-6} and a positive (repulsive) term in r^{-12}. These r dependences determine the shape of the curve. As $r \to 0$, $u(r) \to +\infty$ because the repulsive term dominates ($12 > 6$). As $r \to \infty$, the r^{-12} term goes to zero first (the repulsive force has a much shorter range), followed later by the $-r^{-6}$ term. It is seen in Fig. 3-6a that this behavior leads to a minimum in $u(r)$. The constants ϵ and r^* that characterize the minimum (Fig. 3-6a) are convenient to use as parameters in the equation for $u(r)$:

$$u(r) = -2\epsilon \left(\frac{r^*}{r}\right)^6 + \epsilon \left(\frac{r^*}{r}\right)^{12} \qquad (3-15)$$

It can easily be checked that $u(r)$ in this equation has a minimum ($du/dr = 0$; $d^2u/dr^2 > 0$) at $r = r^*$, $u = -\epsilon$.

Of course, each type of molecule has its own values of ϵ and r^* for interactions between two such molecules; for example, $He - He$, $N_2 - N_2$, etc. For the interaction between unlike molecules (call them 1 and 2), a good approximation, with theoretical justification, is

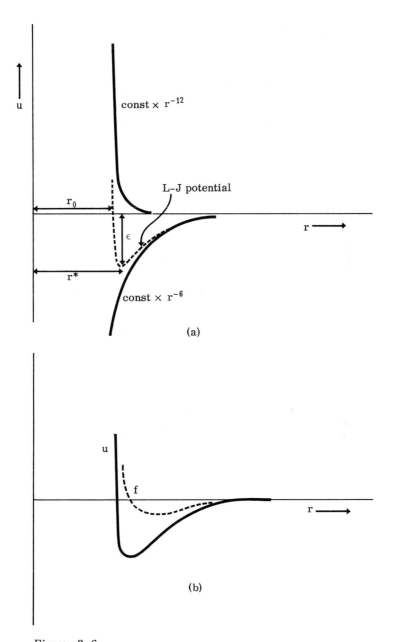

Figure 3-6
(a) Lennard-Jones potential (schematic) as a sum of two contributions. (b) Relation between potential energy and force (schematic): $f = -du/dr$.

$$r^* = \tfrac{1}{2}(r_1^* + r_2^*)$$

$$\epsilon = (\epsilon_1 \epsilon_2)^{1/2}$$

(3-16)

where ϵ_1, r_1^* and ϵ_2, r_2^* are the parameters for interactions of types 1-1 and 2-2, respectively. In the remainder of this chapter, we shall be referring primarily to interactions between like molecules.

The physical significance of r* is that this is the most stable intermolecular distance for a pair of molecules, as far as potential energy is concerned. To a first approximation (see the next section), one would expect this to be the distance between nearest neighbor molecules in a crystal at 0°K, because almost all of the energy of a crystal at 0°K is potential energy.

The quantity ϵ is the work or energy required to separate two molecules from the optimal distance r* to r = ∞. For a series of crystals of similar structure, ϵ should be nearly proportional to the heat of sublimation at 0°K (see the next section) since sublimation involves pulling apart the molecules in a crystal.

The potential energy is zero at $r = r_0$ (Fig. 3-6a) and rises almost vertically when $r < r_0$. Thus $r = r_0$ is essentially the distance of closest approach of two molecules; for $r < r_0$ the electron clouds overlap significantly and there is very strong repulsion. The quantity $r_0/2$ is the so-called van der Waals radius of a molecule (Fig. 3-7a), which determines the amount of space filled by the molecule and serves as the basis for the construction of molecular models. It is physically obvious that van der Waals radii of unlike molecules (Fig. 3-7b) can be added together to give the distance of closest approach. This is consistent with Eq. 3-16a because the relation between r_0 and r* is simply $r_0 = r^*/2^{1/6}$, as can be seen from Eq. 3-15. Incidentally, the connection between r_0 and R_0 (p. 38) is $R_0 = r_0/2$.

The force associated with the Lennard-Jones potential is

$$f(r) = -\frac{du}{dr} = -12\epsilon \frac{r^{*6}}{r^7} + 12\epsilon \frac{r^{*12}}{r^{13}}$$

(3-17)

Of course the force is zero where u is a minimum (r = r*). Figure 3-6b shows the force as a function of r.

Finally, we examine the actual values of ϵ, r*, and r_0 for a few simple molecules. These are presented in Table 3-3. The values of ϵ are given in calories per mole of pair interactions. The Lennard-Jones potential functions for He, Ne, Ar, and N_2 are shown in Fig. 3-8. We note from the table and the figure that the values of r* are around 3-6Å and that the range of the interaction is only 10-20Å [i.e., u(r) ≅ 0 for r > 10-20Å]. Both r* and ϵ tend to be larger for molecules with more electrons, as expected. But the most striking thing about the magnitude 20-650 cal mole^{-1} for the energy ϵ of typical van der

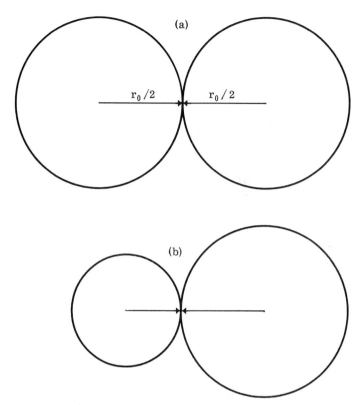

Figure 3-7
Molecules "in contact."

Table 3-3
Lennard-Jones Parameters

Molecule	ϵ (cal mole^{-1})	r*(in Å)	r_0 (in Å)
He	20.3	2.87	2.56
H_2	73.5	3.29	2.93
Ne	69.4	3.12	2.78
Ar	238.	3.82	3.40
Kr	340.	4.04	3.60
Xe	439.	4.60	4.10
N_2	189.	4.15	3.70
O_2	235.	3.88	3.46
CH_4	295.	4.28	3.82
CCl_4	650.	6.61	5.88

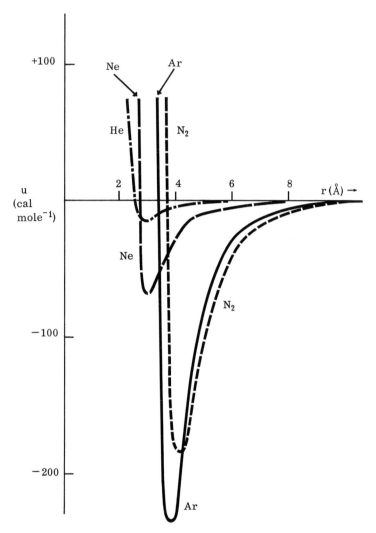

Figure 3-8
Lennard-Jones potentials for He, Ne, N_2, and Ar.

Waals interactions is that it is <u>much</u> smaller than chemical bond energies, which are ordinarily in the range[3] 30,000-200,000 cal mole^{-1}.
This difference is of course reflected in the experimental fact that it

[3]As will be seen in the next section, hydrogen bond energies are intermediate in strength; typical values are 2,000 to 8,000 cal mole^{-1}

Table 3-4
Lennard-Jones Potential for Polar Molecules

Mole-cule	ϵ (cal mole^{-1})	r* (Å)	μ (D)	α (Å^3 mole-cule^{-1})	(3) % dip-dip	(5) % dip-ind dip	(6) % disper-sion
CO	199.	4.23	0.12	1.99	0.005	0.08	99.92
HI	644.	4.64	0.38	5.44	0.09	0.44	99.47
HCl	716.	3.72	1.03	2.63	14.4	4.2	81.4
H$_2$O	—	—	1.86	1.48	77.0	4.0	19.0

takes much less energy to sublimate a molecular crystal or to vaporize a liquid than it does to dissociate chemically a like number of
molecules into atoms.

Polar molecules. The Lennard-Jones potential is sometimes extended to polar molecules as a useful approximation. The attractive
part of the potential has three contributions (all varying as r^{-6}):
dipole-dipole, (3); dipole-induced dipole, (5); and dispersion, (6). The
first of these depends on temperature. In addition there is of course
the repulsive overlap potential, (7). Table 3-4 gives ϵ and r* (experimental) for three polar molecules, and also the percentage contributions (theoretical) of (3), (5), and (6) to the total attractive (r^{-6})
potential at 293°K. The Lennard-Jones potential is not applicable to
H_2O for most values of r. But it is reasonable to compare the r^{-6}
attractive terms at large r. Table 3-4 shows that the dispersion interaction is always important. The dipole-dipole interaction is proportional to μ^4 and hence increases rapidly with μ.

3-4 ESTIMATES OF INTERMOLECULAR FORCES

TABLES 3-3 AND 3-4 in the preceding section illustrate the results
of a very careful approach to the subject of intermolecular forces.
But for many purposes a quick, rough estimate is all that is required.
In this section we point out useful approximate correlations between
intermolecular force parameters on the one hand and crystal properties and critical constants on the other.

As was seen in Section 3-3, the whole Lennard-Jones curve u(r) is
determined by two parameters: the depth ϵ of the potential energy
"well"; and the intermolecular distance r* that corresponds to this
maximum attractive potential (Fig. 3-6a). These are the two quantities, then, that we want to estimate.

Crystal properties. The structures of crystals are determined almost entirely by intermolecular forces, so this is the most natural
place to turn for information. In liquids and gases, on the other hand,
the situation is complicated by the fact that intermolecular forces
and random thermal motion are both very much involved and are difficult to disentangle.

To a good approximation, the molecules of a molecular crystal ar-
range themselves in such a way as to give the crystal the minimum
possible potential energy. Because u(r) goes rapidly toward zero for
r > r* (Fig. 3-8), the potential energy of the crystal is due largely to
interactions between molecules in the crystal which are nearest
neighbors to each other (if the meaning of the term "nearest neighbor" is not self-evident, see Chapter 5). Since u(r) has a minimum
at r = r*, we expect the nearest neighbor distance (let us call it a_1)
to be rather close to r*. In other words, we can use experimental

Table 3-5
Molecular Size (r*)

Molecule	a_1 (Å)	$r*$ (Å)	$r*/a_1$
Ne	3.20	3.12	0.98
Ar	3.83	3.82	1.00
Kr	3.94	4.04	1.02
Xe	4.41	4.60	1.04
N_2	3.96	4.15	1.05
CO	3.96	4.23	1.07

values of a_1 to give us an estimate of $r*$ (i.e., of molecular size). It would be best to use values of a_1 at 0°K to eliminate thermal motion as much as possible, but fortunately thermal expansion in crystals is very small (because of the dominance of the potential energy) so we can ignore this refinement.

Table 3-5 presents values of a_1 and $r*$ for some simple molecules for which both are known. The expected approximate equality is apparent. Generally $r*$ is a little larger than a_1 because second neighbor interactions are not completely negligible and are increased when $a_1 < r*$. Neon is expected to be a little odd because of quantum mechanical effects (which occur with low mass and temperature). Helium and hydrogen are distinctly odd for the same reason and so are omitted from Tables 3-5 through 3-7.

As indicated above, the potential energy of a crystal is due primarily to nearest neighbor interactions, each with energy $-\epsilon$. But we should expect a small additional contribution from second neighbor interactions. The heat of sublimation at 0°K is the energy

Table 3-6
Potential Energy (ϵ)

Molecule	Heat/6 (cal mole^{-1})	ϵ (cal mole^{-1})	Heat/6ϵ
Ne	83.3	69.4	1.20
Ar	304	238	1.28
Kr	415	340	1.22
Xe	577	439	1.31
N_2	250	189	1.32
CH_4	407	295	1.38
CO	272	199	1.37

Table 3-7
Lennard-Jones Parameters and Critical Constants

Molecule	T_c° K	RT_c/ϵ	v_c/r^{*3}
Ne	44.8	1.25	2.35
Ar	151	1.26	2.23
Xe	290	1.31	2.05
N_2	126	1.33	2.09
O_2	154	1.31	1.90
CH_4	190	1.29	2.09

required to pull all of the molecules of the crystal apart. If the crystal structure is such that each molecule has n_1 nearest neighbors, this heat per mole should be approximately equal to $n_1 \epsilon/2$, if ϵ is given per mole. The factor $\frac{1}{2}$ arises because each interaction involves two molecules: a crystal with N molecules has $Nn_1/2$ nearest neighbor (pair) interactions, not Nn_1.

The heat of sublimation at $0°K$ is not readily available for many substances. In its place, as a convenient approximation, we use the heat of fusion at the normal melting point plus the heat of vaporization at the normal boiling point. In Table 3-6 we compare ϵ with this approximate "heat of sublimation," divided by six, for a number of molecules having crystal structures with $n_1 = 12$ (Chapter 5). We see that the "heat of sublimation," divided by $n_1/2$, is certainly of the same magnitude as ϵ; in fact, it is about 30% larger. The main contribution to this excess is undoubtedly second neighbor interactions. A rough rule for estimating ϵ is therefore:

$$\epsilon = \frac{\text{"Heat of Sublimation"}}{1.30 \times (n_1/2)} \tag{3-18}$$

Critical constants. Because of intermolecular attractions, there is a tendency for gas molecules to condense into a liquid. This is countered by random molecular motion which increases in violence as the temperature increases. Above the critical temperature, intermolecular forces lose this competition and the liquid state does not occur. Thus the critical temperature can be used[4] as a measure of the strength of intermolecular attractive forces: the larger these forces, the higher the temperature required to abolish the liquid state. For example, consider the sequence of molecules He, Ar, HCl, H_2O, with increasing intermolecular attractions. The respective values of T_c are $5.2°K$, $151°K$, $324°K$, and $647°K$.

---

[4]One can also use T_b, the normal boiling point, but this is less accurate.

For spherical, nonpolar molecules there is in fact a quite accurate direct proportionality between ϵ and T_c, which can be deduced from statistical mechanics, the molecular theory of thermodynamic properties. A simple, special case of this theory will be encountered in Section 4-2. Table 3-7 gives values of RT_c (cal mole^{-1}) divided by ϵ (cal mole^{-1}) for several molecules. Although the values of ϵ and T_c represented in Table 3-7 vary by a factor of six, RT_c/ϵ is practically constant (average = 1.29). Hence an excellent estimate of ϵ for spherical, nonpolar molecules may be obtained from

$$\epsilon = \frac{RT_c}{1.29} \tag{3-19}$$

The proportionality constant would be different for other classes of molecules.

There is a similar but less intuitively obvious (see Chapter 4) connection between the critical volume v_c (cm^3 mole^{-1}) and r^{*3} (cm^3 mole^{-1}). Values of v_c/r^{*3} are included in Table 3-7. The approximate formula for r^* in terms of v_c is

$$r^* = \left(\frac{v_c}{2.12}\right)^{1/3} \tag{3-20}$$

Hydrogen bonds. We can get a rough idea of the strength of hydrogen bonds, relative to van der Waals forces, by an inspection of suitable "heats of sublimation" and critical temperatures. This is done in Table 3-8, where argon is chosen as a typical van der Waals (dispersion plus overlap) case, and HCl is also included as an intermediate type of molecule. It is quite clear from both the "heats of sublimation" and the critical temperatures that the hydrogen bonds in H_2O and NH_3 are relatively strong.

Hydrogen bonds are especially effective only when specifically oriented. This would not be the case at the critical point, where the densities are rather low and the molecules are not closely packed.

Table 3-8
Hydrogen Bond Energies

Molecule	Heat (cal mole^{-1})	$T_c\,°K$	ϵ (cal mole^{-1})
H_2O	11,160	647	—
NH_3	6,930	405	—
HCl	4,340	324	716
Ar	1,820	151	238

The values of T_c therefore reflect the interactions between <u>rotating</u> molecules. In this case, the $H_2O - H_2O$ interaction is only about $647/151 = 4.3$ times as strong as the $Ar - Ar$ interaction.

The "heat of sublimation" is much more useful for quantitative estimation of hydrogen bond energies. Let us choose H_2O as a specific example. It would appear off hand that the hydrogen bond in ice is $11,160/1,820 = 6.13$ times as strong as the argon van der Waals interaction. But this overlooks the fact that $n_1 = 12$ in crystalline argon while $n_1 = 4$ in ice (see p. 100). Hence a more accurate factor is $3 \times 6.13 = 18.4$. If we multiply 18.4 times the value of ϵ for argon we get 4400 cal mole^{-1} for the approximate hydrogen bond energy in ice.

PROBLEMS

3-1. Consider a proton at a distance 0.530Å from an electron, as in the Bohr theory for hydrogen. Calculate the work in calories necessary to pull apart to infinity a mole of these pairs of charges, using Coulomb's law (not quantum theory).

3-2. Verify that the right-hand sides of Eqs. 3-8, 3-9, 3-10, 3-11 and 3-12 all have dimensions of energy.

3-3. Calculate the value of $u(r)$ in cal mole^{-1} for argon (using Eq. 3-15 and Table 3-3) at 3.82Å, $2 \times 3.82\text{Å}$, $3 \times 3.82\text{Å}$, and $\frac{1}{2} \times 3.82\text{Å}$.

3-4. Calculate the work necessary in cal per mole (of NaF) to pull apart to infinity a sodium ion Na$^+$ from a fluoride ion F$^-$, starting from an interionic distance of 3.12Å. Take two contributions into account: the coulombic interaction, and the van der Waals attraction and repulsion. For the latter, use the Lennard-Jones potential between two neon atoms (because Na$^+$ and F$^-$ have the same number of electrons as Ne).

CHAPTER 4

IMPERFECT GASES AND VAN DER WAALS EQUATION

THIS CHAPTER is concerned primarily with the observed equation of state of real gases under conditions such that there are gas imperfections (i.e., departures from ideal behavior). These imperfections are caused by intermolecular forces. We also include a discussion of van der Waals equation. This is a very approximate, theoretical equation of state which is useful because it provides a simple picture of the gas-liquid phase transition, and of the critical region.

4-1 IMPERFECT GASES

WE SAW IN CHAPTER 2 that $pv = RT$ for a very dilute gas. We can express this mathematically by

$$\lim_{p \to 0} \frac{pv}{RT} = 1$$

But what is the value of pv/RT under nonideal conditions? The answer is rather complicated because pv/RT depends on p, T, and the

gas being studied. This is illustrated in Figs. 4-1 and 4-2. Figure
4-1 gives pv/RT as a function of p, at several temperatures, for N_2
gas, while Fig. 4-2 shows pv/RT as a function of p at $0°C$ for several different gases. The ideal gas limit, $pv/RT = 1$ at $p = 0$, is apparent in all curves. But significant departures occur at high pressures.

It should be noted that on these pressure scales $p = 1$ atm amounts
practically to zero pressure so that $pv = RT$ is an excellent approximation at 1 atm, for these gases. For example, the observed molar
volume of N_2 at STP is 22.403 liter mole^{-1} instead of the ideal value
22.414 liter mole^{-1}. Therefore, since $v_{ideal} = RT/p$,

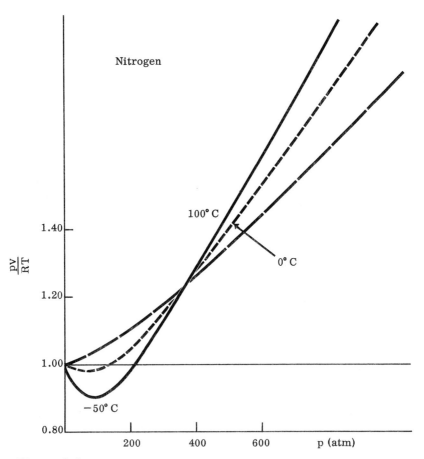

Figure 4-1
pv/RT as a function of p for nitrogen.

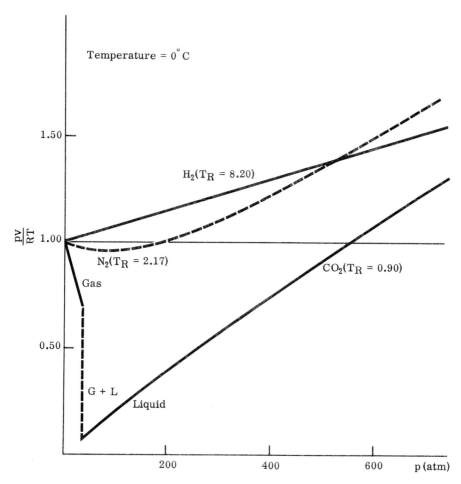

Figure 4-2
pv/RT as a function of p for three gases at 0°C. The vapor pressure of CO_2 at 0°C is 34.4 atm.

$$\frac{pv}{RT} = \frac{v}{v_{ideal}} = \frac{22.403}{22.414} = 0.99951 \qquad (N_2, \ 0°C, \ 1 \ atm) \qquad (4\text{-}1)$$

On the other hand, for NH_3, which has stronger intermolecular forces than H_2, N_2, or CO_2, it is found that v = 22.09 liter mole^{-1} at STP so that

$$\frac{pv}{RT} = \frac{22.09}{22.414} = 0.986 \qquad (NH_3, \ 0°C, \ 1 \ atm) \qquad (4\text{-}2)$$

Thus one makes an error of 1.4% if NH_3 gas is assumed ideal at STP.

Attractive forces tend to make $pv/RT < 1$ while repulsive forces have the opposite effect. The reason for this is the following. If a gas is at a pressure and temperature such that attractive forces dominate, the molar volume will be less than $v_{ideal} = RT/p$ $(pv/RT < 1)$ because the attractive forces tend to pull the molecules together and thus shrink the system. This is a sort of self-compression often attributed to an effective "internal pressure" (more about this later). Conversely, repulsive forces make $v > v_{ideal}$ $(pv/RT > 1)$.

Attractive forces are most important at low temperatures because of the dominating tendency at low temperatures for any system to minimize its potential energy. At high temperatures, the (attractive) potential well in $u(r)$ (Fig. 4-3) loses its influence because $kT \gg u(r)$ in the Boltzmann factor. But this is not true of the repulsive (r^{-12}) part of the potential because it rises so steeply; the temperature hardly affects u/kT for $r < r_0$ (Fig. 4-3). The conclusion we draw from all this is that pv/RT tends to be smaller at low temperatures (Fig. 4-1), and for molecules with large attractive forces (Fig. 4-2).

We turn next to the pressure dependence of pv/RT seen in Figs. 4-1 and 4-2. If the temperature is low enough, pv/RT begins by decreasing with increasing pressure because the system is more compressed at higher pressure, hence the molecules are closer together, hence attractive forces have more of an effect. Eventually $(p \rightarrow \infty)$, though, the system will be so compressed that the overlap repulsion goes into action and pv/RT rises. If the temperature is high enough that attractive forces are ineffectual, pv/RT will increase from the beginning (low p).

The temperature $273.1°K$ in Fig. 4-2 means different things, so to speak, to molecules of H_2, N_2, and CO_2. It is a high temperature to H_2 $(T_c = 33.2°K$, $\epsilon = 73.5$ cal mole^{-1}), a moderate temperature to N_2 $(T_c = 126°K$, $\epsilon = 189$ cal mole^{-1}), and a low temperature to CO_2 $(T_c = 304°K$, $\epsilon = 205$ cal mole^{-1}). In fact, since $273.1°K < T_c$ for CO_2, there is condensation of gas into liquid in this case, as is indicated in the figure (the vapor pressure of liquid CO_2 at $0°C$ is 34.4 atm).

The above comments about temperature suggest the definition of a reduced or relative temperature which, for any substance, compares the temperature T with the critical temperature T_c. Therefore, we define the reduced temperature by $T_R \equiv T/T_c$. In Fig. 4-2, $0°C$ corresponds to $T_R = 8.20$ for H_2, $T_R = 2.17$ for N_2, and $T_R = 0.90$ for CO_2. In a similar way, one can also define a reduced volume and a reduced pressure: $v_R \equiv v/v_c$; $p_R \equiv p/p_c$.

The usefulness of reduced quantities is very apparent in Fig. 4-4. One finds, to a good approximation, that the pv/RT curves for a number of different gases become superimposed if p_R and T_R are used

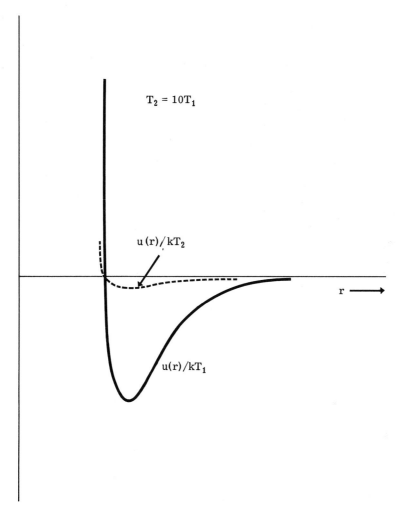

$$T_2 = 10T_1$$

$$u(r)/kT_2$$

$$r \longrightarrow$$

$$u(r)/kT_1$$

Figure 4-3
A high temperature, in effect, "washes out" the attractive part of
an intermolecular pair potential.

as variables instead of p and T. The curves in the figure represent
the average behavior of a wide variety of molecules. Actual points
(various gases) are included for $T_R = 1.50$ to show the amount of
scatter or degree of approximation.

The physical significance of the superposition observed in Fig.
4-4 is this: many gases behave in essentially the same way if one

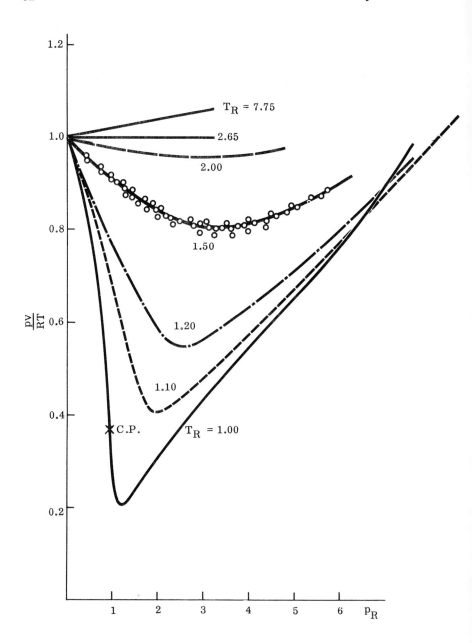

Figure 4-4
Identical behavior of different gases if reduced variables are used. For
simplicity, experimental points are included only for $T_R = 1.50$. The points
shown are a mixture of points for ten different gases.

takes into account the differences in magnitude of intermolecular forces. We have "reduced" T and p in Fig. 4-4 using critical constants, but Table 3-7 and the values of $p_c r^{*3}/\epsilon$ in Table 4-1 show that there is a direct connection between critical constants and intermolecular force parameters.

Incidentally, in the latter table, the most convenient units are p_c (atm), r^{*3} (cm^3 mole^{-1}), ϵ (cm^3 atm mole^{-1}), v_c (cm^3 mole^{-1}), and R(cm^3 atm deg^{-1} mole^{-1}). But the numbers in the table are dimensionless.

Figure 4-4 exemplifies what is known as the law of corresponding states: different substances behave in a similar manner if compared under corresponding conditions (e.g., at the same values of reduced variables T_R, p_R, and v_R). The values of $p_c v_c/RT_c$ in Table 4-1 provide a more quantitative example. The concept of corresponding states can also be extended to solids but more variation is observed in some properties because of sensitivity to details of crystal structure. This is illustrated in the next-to-last column of the table (T_t = triple point temperature).

Because of the proportionalities $RT_c \propto \epsilon$, $v_c \propto r^{*3}$ and $p_c \propto \epsilon/r^{*3}$, one can introduce the intermolecular force parameters ϵ and r^* into the law of corresponding states by using RT/ϵ, v/r^{*3}, and pr^{*3}/ϵ as reduced variables instead of T/T_c, v/v_c, and p/p_c. This is often done (see Eq. 4-7, for example).

Virial expansion. Experimental p-v-T data for imperfect gases are frequently put in the form

$$\frac{pv}{RT} = 1 + \frac{B(T)}{v} + \frac{C(T)}{v^2} + \frac{D(T)}{v^3} + \cdots \tag{4-3}$$

This is a power series in $1/v$ called the virial expansion. B(T) is the second virial coefficient, C(T) the third virial coefficient, etc. For a given temperature, the virial coefficients are all constants whose values can be deduced from the experimental data. Each gas is characterized by its own virial coefficients.

Table 4-1
Critical and Related Properties

Molecule	$p_c r^{*3}/\epsilon$	$p_c v_c/RT_c$	T_t/T_c	T_B/T_c
Ne	0.157	0.295	0.549	2.70
Ar	0.164	0.290	0.557	2.73
Xe	0.187	0.293	0.557	—
N$_2$	0.185	0.291	0.500	2.59
O$_2$	0.201	0.292	0.353	2.75
CH$_4$	0.178	0.288	0.477	2.58

For very large v (i.e., very small p), the terms in $1/v$, $1/v^2$, etc., drop out and we are left with the ideal gas law, $pv/RT = 1$. If v is decreased (p increased), the correction term B/v is the first one needed; if v is decreased further, the next term C/v^2 must be included; etc. A slightly imperfect gas is one which requires only the first correction term:

$$\frac{pv}{RT} = 1 + \frac{B(T)}{v} \qquad\qquad (4\text{-}4)$$

One can also expand pv/RT as a power series in p (instead of $1/v$). If only the linear term in p is necessary (slightly imperfect gas), we can find the required expression by replacing v in Eq. 4-4 by RT/p:

$$\frac{pv}{RT} = 1 + \frac{B(T)}{RT} p \qquad\qquad (4\text{-}5)$$

This linear equation in p applies to the initial (near $p = 0$) straight line part of the pv/RT curves in Figs. 4-1 and 4-2. Therefore the initial slope of these curves is $B(T)/RT$.

On examining the initial slopes in Fig. 4-1, we see that B for N_2 is positive at 100°C (repulsion more important), but negative at 0°C and −50°C (attraction more important). The initial slope is found to be zero at 52°C. Hence $B = 0$ at $T = 325°K$. The temperature at which $B = 0$ is known as the Boyle temperature of a gas, T_B. The last column in Table 4-1 indicates that T_B is another "corresponding" property.

We have just observed that B depends on the temperature. This is shown in more detail in Fig. 4-5 which gives experimental $B(T)$ curves for N_2, Ne, and Ar. But these separate curves can be brought together by use of the law of corresponding states. Since $B(T)$ has dimensions of a volume, we plot $B(T)/v_c$ against T/T_c in Fig. 4-6. The experimental points are a mixture of points for Ne, Ar, N_2, and CH_4.

The line drawn through the points in Fig. 4-6 is the theoretical curve calculated from statistical mechanics, using the Lennard-Jones potential for $u(r)$. The theory shows that $B(T)$ is determined by two-particle interactions, $C(T)$ by three-particle interactions, etc. The relation between $B(T)$ and $u(r)$ turns out to be

$$B(T) = -2\pi \int_0^\infty \left[e^{-u(r)/kT} - 1 \right] r^2\, dr \qquad\qquad (4\text{-}6)$$

Thus the intermolecular pair potential energy $u(r)$ and the temperature completely determine $B(T)$.

Some theoretical insight into the origin of the law of corresponding states is afforded by Eq. 4-6 if we introduce the dimensionless variable of integration $y = r/r^*$. Then we can write

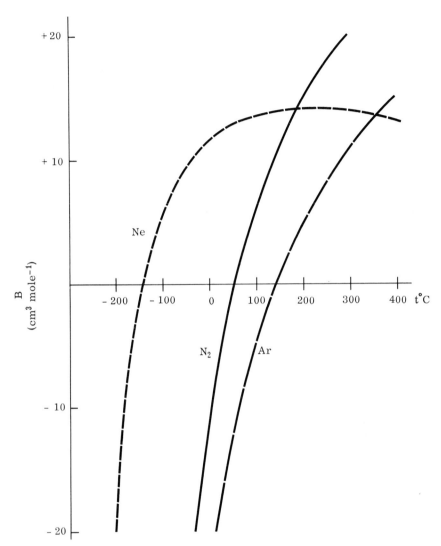

Figure 4-5
Second virial coefficient as a function of temperature for Ne, N_2, and Ar.

$$\frac{B(T)}{r^{*3}} = -2\pi \int_0^\infty \left[\exp\left(\frac{2\epsilon}{kT} y^{-6} - \frac{\epsilon}{kT} y^{-12}\right) - 1 \right] y^2 \, dy \qquad (4\text{-}7)$$

The significant point here is that $B(T)/r^{*3}$ is a function of kT/ϵ <u>only</u>. Thus, when $B(T)$ is "reduced" by r^{*3} and kT is "reduced" by ϵ, <u>all</u> gases with a Lennard-Jones intermolecular potential have the same second virial coefficient vs temperature curve (compare Fig. 4-6).

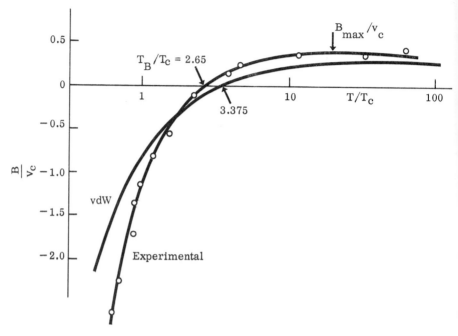

Figure 4-6
Reduced second virial coefficient as a function of reduced temperature.
Experimental points are a mixture of points for Ar, Ne, N_2, and CH_4.
The van der Waals curve is a plot of Eq. 4-21.

Second virial coefficient from experimental molar volume. Finally,
as a numerical exercise, we show how B can be calculated in a very
simple way from a careful measurement of v for a slightly imperfect
gas. Since $v_{ideal} = RT/p$, Eq. 4-5 can be rewritten as

$$\frac{v}{v_{ideal}} = 1 + \frac{B}{v_{ideal}} \tag{4-8}$$

or

$$B = v - v_{ideal} \tag{4-9}$$

The data given in Eqs. 4-1 and 4-2 furnish examples (compare the N_2
curve in Fig. 4-5):

$$B(N_2, 0°C) = 22{,}403\text{-}22{,}414 = -11 \text{ cm}^3 \text{ mole}^{-1}$$

$$B(NH_3, 0°C) = 22{,}090\text{-}22{,}414 = -324 \text{ cm}^3 \text{ mole}^{-1} \tag{4-10}$$

In using Eq. 4-8 to calculate B we are assuming that the next term in the power series is negligible compared with unity. The order of magnitude of the next term is $(B/v_{ideal})^2$. The magnitudes of the first three terms are then:

$$N_2: \ 1 + \left| \frac{11}{22,414} \right| + \left| \frac{11}{22,414} \right|^2 = 1 + 5 \times 10^{-4} + 2 \times 10^{-7}$$

$$NH_3: \ 1 + \left| \frac{324}{22,414} \right| + \left| \frac{324}{22,414} \right|^2 = 1 + 0.014 + 2 \times 10^{-4}$$

The assumption referred to is seen to be satisfied in both cases: no virial coefficients are needed for N_2; only the second is needed for NH_3.

4-2 VAN DER WAALS EQUATION

THE POINT OF VIEW of the preceding section (except for Eqs. 4-6 and 4-7) was basically empirical. We saw how experimental p-v-T data on different gases could be correlated through the law of corresponding states, and how such data for any one gas could be represented by a virial expansion.

This section is very different. It concerns an approximate theory of imperfect gases and liquids. Much better theories exist but we discuss this one because it is extremely simple and illustrates the most important qualitative ideas.

Equation of state. Our first task is to derive the equation of state. We start with the relation pV = NkT, appropriate for a fluid with no intermolecular forces, and then introduce two corrections to take these forces into account in a rough way.

For the first correction, we return to the concept of ''internal pressure'' mentioned on p. 60. In effect, there are two pressures that act to compress a fluid. One is the external pressure p and the other is the internal pressure, p_{int}, arising from attractive forces (the repulsive forces are dealt with separately in the second correction). The internal pressure is the force per unit area pulling the surface layer of fluid molecules inward (Fig. 4-7a). This force originates as follows. A molecule in the bulk of the fluid (Fig. 4-7b) is pulled equally in all directions, on the average. But a molecule within about 20 or 30Å of the surface (this being the range of attractive forces) has a net pull inward because some of its outward neighbors are missing. The net inward force on one molecule in the surface layer is proportional to the concentration of its neighbors, N/V. If the surface layer has a depth ℓ, and we consider a surface area α, the number of molecules in the layer is $\alpha \ell N/V$. The total net inward

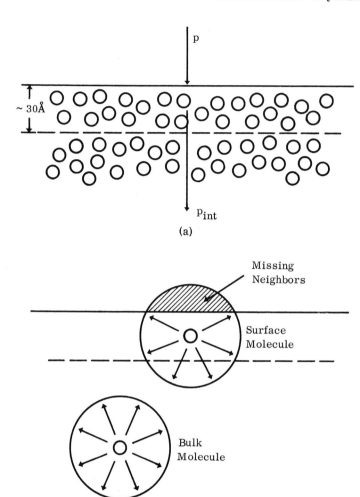

Figure 4-7
"Internal pressure" is due to missing neighbor interactions
near the surface of a fluid.

force on all molecules of the layer is then proportional to $\mathcal{a}\ell(N/V)^2$.
Therefore p_{int} is equal to $a'\ell(N/V)^2$, where a' is a proportionality
constant. But we combine a' with ℓ to give a new proportionality
constant, and write $p_{int} = a(N/V)^2$.

The first correction, therefore, amounts to replacing p in $pV = NkT$ by $p + a(N/V)^2$.

In the second correction, we take note of the fact that the equation pV = NkT implies that each of the N molecules is free to move through the entire volume V. Actually, because of the overlap repulsion, molecules themselves occupy space so that all of the volume V is not free for molecular wanderings. As a simple correction, let us say that one molecule fills an amount of space b and consequently N molecules fill a space Nb. Therefore the "free volume" is V − Nb, and not V. We remark, in passing, that a correction (Nb) proportional to N is strictly correct only for a slightly imperfect gas for which the "excluded volumes" b are additive. For a more dense fluid, this correction is too large because the excluded volumes overlap and therefore do not all contribute an amount b to the total.

In summary, the corrected equation of state, first obtained by J. D. van der Waals in 1873, is

$$\left(p + \frac{aN^2}{V^2}\right)(V - Nb) = NkT \tag{4-11}$$

where a and b are positive constants (the first being related to attractive forces and the second to repulsive forces). Other obvious ways to write this equation are

$$\left(p + \frac{an^2}{V^2}\right)(V - nb) = nRT \tag{4-12}$$

and

$$\left(p + \frac{a}{v^2}\right)(v - b) = RT \tag{4-13}$$

We shall use Eq. 4-13, primarily, with units cm^3 $mole^{-1}$ for b and cm^6 atm $mole^{-2}$ for a. We expect each gas to have its own pair of van der Waals constants (a and b) because of the relation of these constants to intermolecular forces.

Equation 4-13 has the necessary property that it reduces to pv = RT when v is very large. On the other hand, Eq. 4-13 also predicts critical behavior and the gas-liquid phase transition. This is shown in Fig. 4-8, which gives four different isotherms calculated from Eq. 4-13 with fixed values of a and b. The smooth curves are the ones calculated. The horizontal lines have been drawn in such a way[1] as to equalize the shaded areas above and below the horizontal lines. An experimental system, at equilibrium, would follow the horizontal lines, thus exhibiting a gas-liquid phase transition. In this respect, Fig. 4-8 should be compared with Fig. 1-12b.

---

[1]The justification for locating the horizontal lines in this way will appear at the end of Chapter 8.

The reason Eq. 4-13 produces smooth loops for $T < T_c$ rather than the horizontal lines observed experimentally is that the model from which the equation was derived makes no allowance for the simultaneous presence in the system of two regions (phases) with different densities. It was implicitly assumed, in the derivation, that the system had a uniform density throughout. Thus a loop represents a hypothetical system which is undergoing a phase transition but which is forced (unrealistically) to have a single density. The horizontal lines correct this shortcoming in the theory.

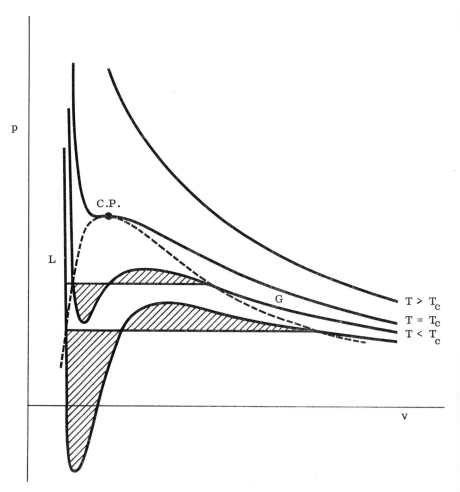

Figure 4-8
Isotherms calculated from van der Waals equation.

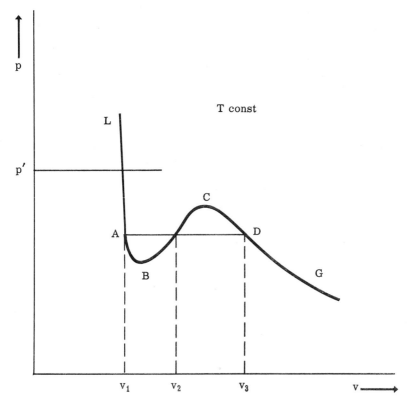

Figure 4-9
A van der Waals isotherm for $T < T_c$.

In Fig. 4-9, the p-v curve ($T < T_c$) LADG is the <u>stable</u>, equilibrium isotherm for the system. The segments AB and $\overline{DC}$ represent less stable behavior, called <u>metastable</u> (see p. 8), which might however be observed (e.g., DC corresponds to a supersaturated vapor). But the states represented by the segment BC are <u>unstable</u> and could never be observed because dp/dv $\le$ 0 for real systems (see p. 10).

Critical constants. Figure 4-8 indicates that a van der Waals fluid has a critical point. Let us find the critical constants T_c, p_c, and v_c in terms of a and b. Since the critical point is an inflection point, we could locate it by use of

$$\left(\frac{\partial p}{\partial v}\right)_T = 0, \quad \left(\frac{\partial^2 p}{\partial v^2}\right)_T = 0$$

An alternative method is the following. Equation 4-13 is a cubic equation in v:

$$v^3 - \left(b + \frac{RT}{p}\right)v^2 + \frac{a}{p}v - \frac{ab}{p} = 0 \tag{4-14}$$

For assigned values of a, b, p, and T, Eq. 4-14 is satisfied by three values of v (let us call them v_1, v_2, and v_3 — see Fig. 4-9). In terms of these "roots," the cubic equation can be written

$$(v - v_1)(v - v_2)(v - v_3) = 0 \tag{4-15}$$

For a value of p such as p′ in Fig. 4-9, there are one real root and two complex roots. As can be seen by letting $T \to T_c$ from below in Fig. 4-8, all three roots are real and have the same value, v_c, at the critical point (i.e., if we choose $p = p_c$ and $T = T_c$ in Eq. 4-14). Hence Eqs. 4-14 and 4-15 become in this special case

$$v^3 - \left(b + \frac{RT_c}{p_c}\right)v^2 + \frac{a}{p_c}v - \frac{ab}{p_c} = 0$$

$$(v - v_c)^3 = v^3 - 3v_c v^2 + 3v_c^2 v - v_c^3 = 0$$

These two cubic equations refer to the same system under the same conditions and so must be identical. Therefore we can equate coefficients of like powers of v:

$$b + \frac{RT_c}{p_c} = 3v_c, \quad \frac{a}{p_c} = 3v_c^2, \quad \frac{ab}{p_c} = v_c^3$$

These expressions can then be rearranged to give the final result:

$$v_c = 3b, \quad p_c = \frac{a}{27b^2}, \quad T_c = \frac{8a}{27bR} \tag{4-16}$$

If we combine Eqs. 4-16, we also find that $p_c v_c / RT_c = \frac{3}{8} = 0.375$. This should be compared with the experimental values in Table 4-1. The fact that $p_c v_c / RT_c$ is a pure number suggests that van der Waals equation obeys the law of corresponding states. To confirm this, we rewrite Eq. 4-13 as follows:

$$\frac{[p + (a/v^2)]}{p_c} \frac{(v - b)}{v_c} = \frac{RT}{p_c v_c} = \frac{RT}{\frac{3}{8}RT_c}$$

We then use Eqs. 4-16a and 4-16b to obtain

$$\left(p_R + \frac{3}{v_R^2}\right)(v_R - \tfrac{1}{3}) = \tfrac{8}{3}T_R \tag{4-17}$$

Therefore, since the coefficients here are pure numbers, p_R is the

Table 4-2
Van der Waals Constants for N_2

Source	a (cm^6 atm $mole^{-2}$)	b (cm^3 $mole^{-1}$)
From v_c and T_c	1.05×10^6	30.0
From v_c and p_c	0.81	30.0
From p_c and T_c	1.35	38.6

same function of v_R and T_R for all gases, or, similarly, v_R is a function of p_R and T_R, $v_R(p_R, T_R)$. From this it follows that pv/RT is a function of p_R and T_R (the same for all gases), for

$$\frac{pv}{RT} = \frac{p_R v_R(p_R, T_R)}{RT_R} \cdot \frac{p_c v_c}{T_c} = \frac{3}{8} \frac{p_R v_R(p_R, T_R)}{T_R}$$

In practice, van der Waals constants are usually evaluated from the experimental critical constants. Unfortunately, there is some ambiguity about this which is a consequence of the approximate nature of van der Waals equation. For Eqs. 4-16 lead to three different ways of calculating a and b from p_c, T_c, and v_c, and therefore three different sets of values:

(1) From v_c and T_c: $b = v_c/3$, $\quad a = 9v_c RT_c/8$

(2) From v_c and p_c: $b = v_c/3$, $\quad a = 3p_c v_c^2$

(3) From p_c and T_c: $b = RT_c/8p_c$, $\quad a = 27(RT_c)^2/64p_c$

To illustrate this, we use the critical constants for N_2 (p_c = 33.5 atm, v_c = 90.1 cm^3 $mole^{-1}$, T_c = 126.1°K) to calculate a and b (Table 4-2).

Table 4-3
Van der Waals Constants from p_c and T_c

Molecule	T_c°K	p_c (atm)	v_c (cm^3 $mole^{-1}$)	a (cm^6 atm $mole^{-2}$)	b (cm^3 $mole^{-1}$)
Ne	44.8	25.9	41.7	0.22×10^6	17.7
Ar	151.	48.0	75.2	1.35	32.3
N_2	126.1	33.5	90.1	1.35	38.6
O_2	154.	49.7	74.4	1.36	31.8
CH_4	190.	45.8	99.0	2.24	42.6

Table 4-3 gives van der Waals constants for several gases, all calculated from p_c and T_c.

Virial expansion. Equation 4-13 can be solved for p, and then the right-hand side expanded in powers of $1/v$:

$$p = \frac{RT}{v - b} - \frac{a}{v^2} = \frac{RT}{v[1 - (b/v)]} - \frac{a}{v^2}$$

$$= \frac{RT}{v}\left(1 + \frac{b}{v} + \frac{b^2}{v^2} + \cdots\right) - \frac{a}{v^2} \qquad (4\text{-}18)$$

where we have used

$$\frac{1}{1 - x} = 1 + x + x^2 + \cdots \qquad (|x| < 1)$$

Therefore

$$\frac{pv}{RT} = 1 + \left(b - \frac{a}{RT}\right)\frac{1}{v} + \frac{b^2}{v^2} + \cdots \qquad (4\text{-}19)$$

This is the virial expansion of van der Waals equation. The virial coefficients are

$$B(T) = b - \frac{a}{RT}, \quad C = b^2, \quad D = b^3, \text{ etc.} \qquad (4\text{-}20)$$

The "reduced" expression for the second virial coefficient is

$$\frac{B(T)}{v_c} = \frac{b}{3b} - \frac{a}{3bRT} = \frac{1}{3} - \frac{9}{8T_R} \qquad (4\text{-}21)$$

This function is included in Fig. 4-6. It resembles the true curve semi-quantitatively.

It was pointed out on p. 69 that one of the two corrections employed in deriving van der Waals equation is more accurate for a slightly imperfect gas than for a dense fluid. We might be inclined, then, to place more reliance on van der Waals constants deduced from $B(T)$ than on those found from critical constants. We describe next a method for finding a and b from $B(T)$.

According to Eq. 4-20a, the maximum value of B (which occurs when $T \to \infty$) is b: $B_{max} = b$. Also, the Boyle temperature (B = 0) is $T_B = a/Rb$. We therefore use <u>experimental</u> values of B_{max} (see Fig. 4-6) and T_B to obtain a and b:

$$b = B_{max} \text{ (expt)}, \quad a = RT_B \text{ (expt)} \, B_{max} \text{ (expt)} \qquad (4\text{-}22)$$

Incidentally, we note in Fig. 4-6 that, for real gases, $B(T)$ decreases slowly from B_{max} at high temperatures, whereas this does not occur with the van der Waals $B(T)$. The reason for this discrepancy is that "van der Waals molecules" are hard, like billiard balls, while real molecules are never completely hard. As $T \to \infty$, real molecules become smaller, in effect, because they can interpenetrate more when colliding at high speeds.

For spherical or almost spherical molecules, it may be convenient to use tabulated values of the Lennard-Jones parameters ϵ and r^* in place of B_{max} and T_B in Eqs. 4-22. The experimental corresponding states relations between these quantities are

$$B_{max} \text{ (expt)} = 0.864r^{*3}, \quad RT_B \text{(expt)} = 3.42\epsilon$$

so we have

$$b = 0.864r^{*3}, \quad a = 2.95\epsilon r^{*3} \tag{4-23}$$

Table 4-4 presents values of a and b derived from Eqs. 4-23, using Table 3-3. These values should be compared with Tables 4-2 and 4-3.

Having been obtained essentially from B_{max} (expt), the values of b in Table 4-4 are a good measure of the amount of space filled by a mole of molecules in a dilute gas. This is an additive or non-overlapping excluded volume (see p. 69). The space filled by closely packed molecules is rather different. The molar volume of a solid, v_S, corresponds rather well to packing at a nearest neighbor distance r^* (see Table 3-5). But tight packing, under compression, would be associated more appropriately with a nearest neighbor distance $r_0 = r^*/2^{1/6}$ (see p. 48). Since $r_0^3 = r^{*3}/2^{1/2}$, $v_S/2^{1/2}$ rather than v_S is a measure of the amount of space filled by a mole of tightly packed molecules (overlapping excluded volume). As expected (see Table 4-4), the overlapping excluded volume ($v_S/2^{1/2}$) is less than the

Table 4-4
Van der Waals Constants from B(T)

Molecule	a (cm^6 atm mole^{-2})	b (cm^3 mole^{-1})	v_S (cm^3 mole^{-1})	$v_S/2^{1/2}$ (cm^3 mole^{-1})	v_c/v_S
Ne	0.15×10^6	15.8	14.0	9.9	2.98
Ar	0.97	29.0	24.6	17.4	3.05
N$_2$	0.99	37.1	27.3	19.3	3.29
CH$_4$	1.70	40.7	30.9	21.8	3.20

nonoverlapping excluded volume (b). The two volumes differ by a factor of about two. The theoretical value of this factor for "hard
spheres" is 2.97.

Rather incidentally, the last column of Table 4-4 shows another experimental corresponding states relation. It also indicates that a fluid
at the critical point is about three times as expanded as the solid state.

Finally, we want to show that the van der Waals B(T) can be derived from the high temperature form of Eq. 4-6. The appropriate
(but unreal) potential function (Fig. 4-10a) for "van der Waals molecules" is

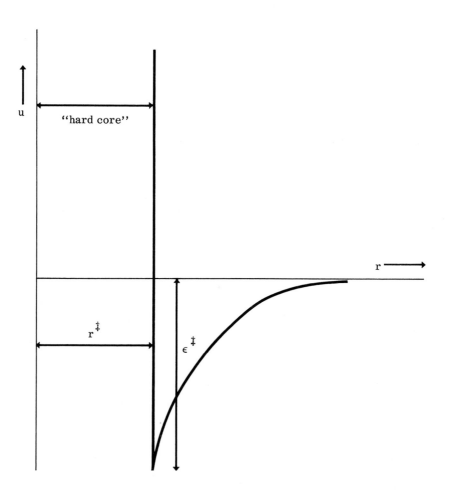

Figure 4-10a
Intermolecular pair potential for hard spheres with attraction.

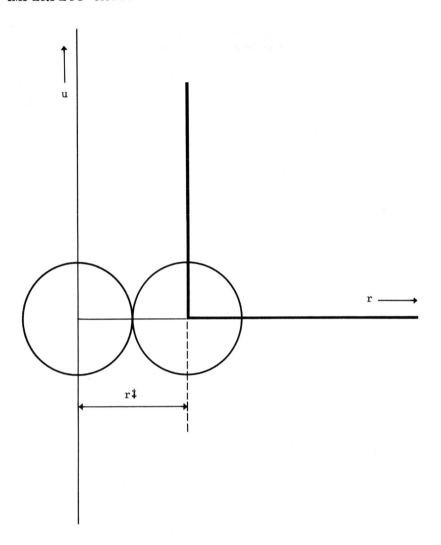

Figure 4-10b
Intermolecular pair potential for hard spheres.

$$u(r) = +\infty \qquad r < r^{\ddagger}$$

$$= -\epsilon^{\ddagger}\left(\frac{r^{\ddagger}}{r}\right)^{6} \qquad r \geq r^{\ddagger} \qquad \text{(4-24)}$$

This function has a "hard core" (vertical rise at $r = r^{\ddagger}$), an r^{-6}

attractive term, and $u = -\epsilon^\ddagger$ at $r = r^\ddagger$. As this is not a Lennard-Jones potential, $r^\ddagger$ and $\epsilon^\ddagger$ do not have the same significance as r^* and ϵ.

Because $u(r)$ comes in two "pieces," we break up the integral in Eq. 4-6 into two parts. Also, at high temperatures, $u/kT \ll 1$ so that $e^{-u/kT} = 1 - (u/kT)$. Therefore,

$$B(T) = -2\pi \int_0^{r^\ddagger} (-1) r^2 \, dr - 2\pi \int_{r^\ddagger}^\infty \frac{\epsilon^\ddagger}{kT} \left(\frac{r^\ddagger}{r} \right)^6 r^2 \, dr$$

$$= \frac{2\pi r^{\ddagger 3}}{3} - \frac{2\pi \epsilon^\ddagger r^{\ddagger 3}}{3kT} = b - \frac{a}{kT}$$

where

$$b = \frac{2\pi r^{\ddagger 3}}{3}, \quad a = \frac{2\pi \epsilon^\ddagger r^{\ddagger 3}}{3} \qquad\qquad (4\text{-}25)$$

Note the resemblance to Eqs. 4-23.

For hard spheres with no attraction (Fig. 4-10b), we have

$$\epsilon^\ddagger = 0, \quad a = 0, \quad B = b = \frac{2\pi r^{\ddagger 3}}{3} \qquad\qquad (4\text{-}26)$$

This value of B is four times the actual volume of a hard sphere (diameter $= r^\ddagger$).

PROBLEMS

4-1. Calculate the pressure in atm exerted by 10 g of N_2 in a 1 liter vessel at 25°C using: (a) the ideal gas equation and (b) van der Waals equation. Use a and b from Table 4-3. (c) Use the van der Waals constants to calculate the second virial coefficient B of N_2 at 25°C in units cm^3 $mole^{-1}$.

4-2. The density of gaseous HBr at 0°C and 1 atm is 3.644 g liter^{-1}. (a) What volume would be occupied by one mole of HBr under these conditions? (b) Use Eq. 4-9 to calculate B for HBr at 0°C in units cm^3 $mole^{-1}$.

4-3. Suggest a simple way of calculating the third virial coefficient C from experimental p, v data at the Boyle temperature of a gas.

4-4. H_2 gas at 0°C has pv/RT = 1.0330 at p = 50 atm and pv/RT = 1.1336 at p = 200 atm. Estimate B(T) and C(T) for H_2 at 0°C using Eq. 4-3.

4-5. Use $(\partial p/\partial v)_T = 0$ and $(\partial^2 p/\partial v^2)_T = 0$ to derive Eqs. 4-16 for van der Waals equation.

4-6. Use the van der Waals constants for H_2, a = 0.244 × 10^6 cm^6 atm mole^{-2} and b = 26.6 cm^3 mole^{-1}, to estimate B(T) and C(T) for H_2 at 0°C (see Eq. 4-20). Compare these results with the values found in Problem 4-4 from experimental data.

4-7. Explain how a plot of the experimental B(T) against 1/T could be used to find values of a and b.

CHAPTER 5

SOLIDS

THE UNIQUE CHARACTERISTIC of the solid state is the ordered
arrangement of the molecules ("molecule" here means molecule,
atom or ion). By contrast, liquids and especially gases have disordered structures (Fig. 1-1).

Matter tends to adopt the solid state at low temperatures. This
occurs because the molecular kinetic energy decreases with temperature leaving the potential energy to dominate the situation. The most
stable configuration of the molecules, as far as the potential energy
is concerned, is the one with minimum potential energy. This minimum is achieved through an ordered arrangement because such an
arrangement allows the largest number of favorable pair interactions.
A disordered structure is relatively inefficient in this respect.

The type of ordered structure and the intermolecular distances for
the given type are determined for each kind of molecule by the exact
nature of the intermolecular forces between the molecules. Consequently many different crystal structures are observed. In principle,
if the intermolecular force law for a given molecule is known, it is
possible to predict, theoretically, the stable crystal structure at 0°K
and, say, zero pressure (this is the structure giving the lowest

calculated potential energy). But this can be done, at present, for relatively few substances. In this chapter we shall confine ourselves very largely to a discussion of a few of the most important <u>observed</u> crystal structures, without getting involved in the theory. Also, we shall not consider at all the experimental method (X-ray diffraction) by which these structures are determined.

The molecules of a crystal vibrate (and, if polyatomic, may possibly rotate) about the positions or points of minimum potential energy (Fig. 5-1). These equilibrium points form a regular mathematical lattice that extends indefinitely in space. Crystal structures are described in terms of this point lattice, but it should always be kept in mind that the molecules in real crystals are never stationary. The situation is also complicated by the fact that lattice dimensions

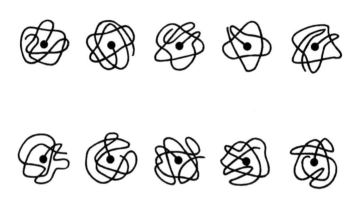

● = Point of Minimum Potential Energy

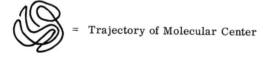 = Trajectory of Molecular Center

Figure 5-1
Molecular trajectories in a crystal (schematic).

depend slightly[1] on pressure and temperature (see Section 5-2), and
by the existence of imperfections of various sorts in all crystals (see
Section 5-6).

Not all "solids" are crystalline, by the way. Glass is the classic
example. Glass is a supercooled liquid. That is, it is in a disordered,
metastable state. The crystalline state is the stable state under ordinary conditions but the rate of the transition liquid → crystal is negligibly slow (compare p. 8). Glass is s liquid but we think of it as a
"solid" because its viscosity is virtually infinite. Despite this kind
of exception, we shall use the words "solid" and "crystal" as synonyms.

In Section 5-1 we give a brief classification of crystals based primarily on the kinds of force holding the crystal together. Then in
Sections 5-2 through 5-5 a few important types of crystal lattice are
examined, with primary emphasis on the simple cubic lattice (Section
5-2).

5-1   BINDING FORCES IN CRYSTALS

NO really sharp classification of crystal binding forces can be
made. Intermediate cases exist with any scheme adopted. Still,
such a classification is useful and one is given in Table 5-1. Figure
5-2 shows a few specific examples with atoms and ions drawn to
scale (see Section 5-2). To give an impression of the relative strength
of the forces holding the crystals together, Table 5-1 includes the
heat necessary to sublime the various crystals. For the ionic crystals
(and AgI), the heat refers to the process crystal → gaseous ions at
25°C; for the covalent crystals the process is crystal → gaseous
atoms at 25°C; and for the remaining examples the heat is the heat
of fusion at the normal melting point plus the heat of vaporization at
normal boiling point. A glance at the table confirms that van der
Waals forces (molecular crystals) are much the weakest, oriented
dipole-dipole forces (hydrogen bonded crystals) are somewhat stronger,
while covalent and ionic interactions are strongest. Metallic bonding,
which is related to covalent bonding (see below), is intermediate.

In the remainder of this section we make a few introductory comments on several of the crystal types listed in the table.

Ionic crystals. In these crystals, of which NaCl is the best known
example, there are no molecules—only ions. Ions of opposite sign
alternate in an ordered structure. There are strong interionic attractive and repulsive coulombic forces that are effective over large

---

[1]In many cases, different crystal structures are stable under different conditions of pressure and temperature. Examples are H_2O (Fig. 1-4), NH_4Cl, C
(Fig. 1-5), P, Fe, Sn, S, ZnS, etc.

Table 5-1
Classification of Crystal Types

Crystal Types	Heat of Sublimation (kcal mole^{-1})	Crystal Types	Heat of Sublimation (kcal mole^{-1})
Ionic		Metallic	
LiF	243	Na	24
NaCl	181	Ag	63
CaCl$_2$	525	Fe	94
CaO	722		
		Molecular	
Covalent		Ar	1.8
Diamond (C)	171	CH$_4$	2.5
SiC	283	N$_2$	1.5
AgI	207	C$_6$H$_6$ (benzene)	9.7
		Hydrogen Bonded	
		H$_2$O	11.1
		NH$_3$	7.0
		HF	7.1

distances (and many ions) because the coulombic potential energy falls off very slowly ($\sim 1/r$). As a result of the alternation in sign (each ion has ions of opposite sign as nearest neighbors), there is a very large net coulombic attraction holding the ions of the crystal together. There is, of course, also a small cohesive contribution from dispersion forces. As always, the closeness of packing is limited by the overlap repulsion.

Because the ionic attractive forces are much larger than dispersion forces (see Table 5-1), the ions of an ionic crystal are under great compression ("internal pressure"). Consequently, the nearest neighbor distance is approximately equal to r_0 (the sum of the van der Waals radii) rather than r^* (as in Table 3-5). In this connection Ar and NaCl should be compared in Fig. 5-2. Van der Waals radii in ionic crystals are called <u>ionic radii</u>. We shall have more to say about ionic radii in Section 5-2.

The ions of an ionic crystal vibrate about equilibrium positions but otherwise are almost immobile. Hence these crystals are poor electrical conductors. But when the ions achieve mobility by the crystal melting or by dissolving the crystal in a solvent such as water, the conductivity is much increased (though it is still not in the same class as that of a metal).

Covalent crystals. The atoms of a molecule are held together by chemical (covalent) bonds. Most molecules contain only a few atoms, but large molecules in which the bonding is extended more or less indefinitely are also well known (especially carbon compounds). Covalent crystals are three-dimensional examples of this. Thus, diamond is simply a giant molecule of carbon atoms in which each carbon atom is linked by tetrahedrally oriented covalent bonds to four other carbon atoms.

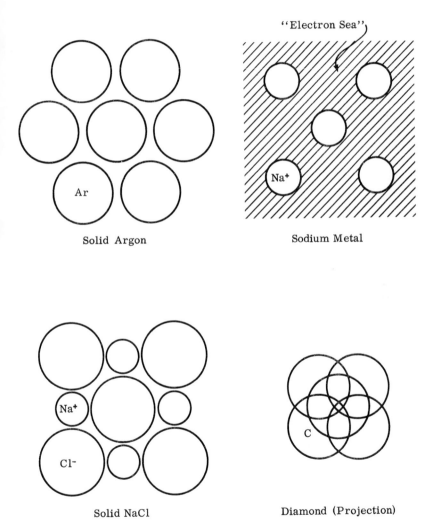

Solid Argon

Sodium Metal

Solid NaCl

Diamond (Projection)

Figure 5-2
Typical crystals with correct relative distances and atomic sizes.

In SiC and AgI, the structure is diamond-like and the bonding is primarily covalent. There is a transition from an ionic crystal to an atomic (covalent) crystal in the sequence AgF, AgCl, AgBr, and AgI. The first three of these compounds have an NaCl type of structure.

Metallic crystals. Excluding borderline cases, about sixty of the elements are metals. Metallic crystals are giant molecules, like diamond. But they differ from diamond in that the bonds involved are not ordinary directional, covalent bonds. Each metal atom has too many nearest neighbor atoms (usually eight or twelve) for the number of available valence electrons. Hence the covalent bonds must be shared (by "resonance") among the different nearest neighbor pairs of atoms. This results in covalent bonding that is weaker than one might expect (see Table 5-1) and to very mobile electrons. The electrical conductivity is therefore high (the small mass of an electron is of course an important factor in this connection).

For some theoretical purposes, an adequate model of a metal is a "sea" of free valence electrons swarming through a regular lattice of positive ions (Fig. 5-2). Because of the small mass of the electrons, it is essential with this model to use quantum rather than classical mechanics.

Molecular and hydrogen bonded crystals. Comments on the nature of the forces involved in these crystal types have already been made in Section 3-4 and need not be repeated here. Further information is contained in Sections 5-4 and 5-5, below.

5-2   SIMPLE CUBIC LATTICE

MANY salts of the type AB have the simple cubic structure shown in Fig. 5-3a. The best known example is NaCl.

In NaCl, each Na^+ has six Cl^- as nearest neighbors, and each Cl^- has six Na^+ as nearest neighbors. The number of nearest neighbors for this structure is therefore $n_1 = 6$. The nearest neighbor distance, as determined experimentally, is $a_1 = 2.82$ Å (Fig. 5-3b). The reader should verify by a study of Fig. 5-3 that each ion has: 12 second neighbors ($n_2 = 12$) of the same sign as itself, at a distance $a_2 = 2^{1/2}a_1 = 3.99$ Å; 8 third neighbors ($n_3 = 8$) of opposite sign at $a_3 = 3^{1/2}a_1$; etc. Table 5-2 gives the neighbor numbers $n_1, n_2, \ldots$, the distances $a_1, a_2, \ldots$, and the sign of the ions (assuming the central ion is +), for the simple cubic lattice. Table 5-3 lists experimental nearest neighbor distances a_1 for a number of compounds that exhibit the simple cubic structure.

Molar volume and density. There is a close relationship between a_1 and v (molar volume) or ρ (density) for a crystal. The reason is, of course, that all three of these quantities provide information about the closeness of packing of the ions, atoms, or molecules.

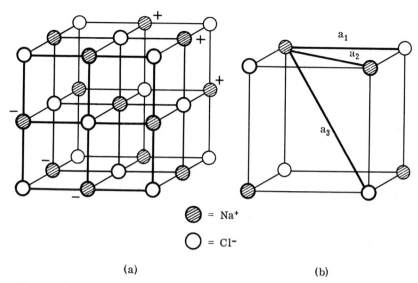

= Na⁺

= Cl⁻

(a)   (b)

Figure 5-3
Simple cubic lattice.

The exact connection between a_1 and v or ρ depends on the type of crystal lattice. We consider here a salt AB, of molecular weight M, with a simple cubic structure. Any one of the ions shown in Fig. 5-3b is shared by eight cubes, not just the cube shown in the figure. For counting purposes, we can therefore say that $\frac{1}{8}$ of each ion "belongs" to the cube shown. Therefore, we should assign a total of $4 \times \frac{1}{8} = \frac{1}{2}$ of an ion of each type to the cube. Thus the cube, of volume a_1^3, contains $\frac{1}{2}$ of a molecule. This is the basic fact needed. For the volume per molecule is then $2a_1^3$ and the molar volume is

Table 5-2
Simple Cubic Lattice (Central Ion = +)

i	n_i	a_i	Sign	i	n_i	a_i	Sign
1	6	a_1	−	8	30	$\sqrt{9}\,a_1$	−
2	12	$\sqrt{2}\,a_1$	+	9	24	$\sqrt{10}\,a_1$	+
3	8	$\sqrt{3}\,a_1$	−	10	24	$\sqrt{11}\,a_1$	−
4	6	$\sqrt{4}\,a_1$	+	11	8	$\sqrt{12}\,a_1$	+
5	24	$\sqrt{5}\,a_1$	−	12	24	$\sqrt{13}\,a_1$	−
6	24	$\sqrt{6}\,a_1$	+	13	48	$\sqrt{14}\,a_1$	+
7	12	$\sqrt{8}\,a_1$	+				

$$v(cm^3 \ mole^{-1}) = 2N_0 a_1^3 (cm^3) \qquad (5-1)$$

where N_0 is Avogadro's number. The density is (see p. 10)

$$\rho \ (g \ cm^{-3}) = \frac{M}{v(cm^3 \ mole^{-1})} = \frac{M}{2N_0 a_1^3 (cm^3)} \qquad (5-2)$$

If ρ or v is measured experimentally and the structure is known to be simple cubic, a_1 may be calculated. Or if a_1 is measured, ρ or v may be calculated. If both ρ (or v) and a_1 are measured, N_0 may be calculated. This is in fact the general method used to obtain the most accurate values of N_0. The limiting factor, as far as accuracy is concerned, is the presence of imperfections in the crystal (e.g., empty lattice points).

As a numerical example, let us calculate the density of NaCl, given that $a_1 = 2.82$ Å. From Eq. 5-2,

$$\rho = \frac{58.5}{2 \times 6.02 \times 10^{23} \times (2.82 \times 10^{-8})^3} = 2.16 \ g \ cm^{-3}$$

The experimental value is 2.165 g cm^{-3}.

Effect of temperature and pressure. The volumes of all solids, including simple cubic crystals, are rather insensitive to changes in temperature and pressure. The basic reason for this, in nonmathematical terms, is that the stable structure assumed by a solid, in response to intermolecular forces, is very stable indeed. Consequently the solid strongly resists any change in this structure. The insensitivity referred to can be seen from an examination of the experimental values of α (coefficient of thermal expansion) and β (compressibility) collected in Table 5-4. The exact mathematical definitions of α and β are:

Table 5-3
Compounds with Simple Cubic Structure

Compound	a_1 (in Å)	Compound	a_1 (in Å)
LiF	2.01	AgCl	2.77
NaCl	2.82	MgO	2.10
KCl	3.15	CaO	2.41
CsF	3.00	BaS	3.17
NH_4Cl	3.27	KCN	3.26

Table 5-4
Compressibility and Thermal Expansion Coefficients of Solids

Substance	α (deg^{-1})	β (atm^{-1})	Substance	α (deg^{-1})	β (atm^{-1})
LIF	10.2×10^{-5}	1.55×10^{-6}	Na	18.7×10^{-5}	16.1×10^{-6}
LiCl	13.2	3.52	Fe	2.72	0.63
LiBr	15.0	4.34	Ag	5.52	1.05
LiI	17.7	7.3	H_2O (ice)	15.3	12
Diamond	0.354	0.17			
Graphite	2.36	3.1			

$$\alpha = \frac{1}{v}\left(\frac{\partial v}{\partial T}\right)_p ; \quad \beta = -\frac{1}{v}\left(\frac{\partial v}{\partial p}\right)_T \qquad (5\text{-}3)$$

Thus, roughly speaking, α is the fractional increase in volume, $\Delta v / v$, per degree rise in temperature, while β is the fractional decrease in volume, $-\Delta v / v$, per atmosphere of pressure increase.

Let us take LiBr as a specific example. Suppose we start with a crystal of LiBr of volume exactly 1 cm^3 at 25°C and 1 atm. If we increase the temperature to 35°C, keeping the pressure constant, the volume increase will be

$$\Delta v = \alpha v \Delta T = 15.0 \times 10^{-5} \text{ deg}^{-1} \times 1 \text{ cm}^3 \times 10 \text{ deg}$$

$$= 0.0015 \text{ cm}^3$$

Thus the volume at 35°C is 1.0015 cm^3. Incidentally, since $v \propto a_1^3$, the value of a_1 at 35°C will be

$$a_1(35°C) = (1.0015)^{1/3} a_1(25°C) = 1.0005 a_1 (25°C)$$

which is a very small correction.

In another experiment on LiBr, suppose the pressure is increased by 100 atm, keeping the temperature constant at 25°C. The change of volume of the crystal will be

$$\Delta v = -\beta v \Delta p = -4.34 \times 10^{-6} \text{ atm}^{-1} \times 1 \text{ cm}^3 \times 100 \text{ atm}$$

$$= -0.00043 \text{ cm}^3$$

so that the final volume is 0.99957 cm^3. The corresponding change in a_1 is

$$a_1(101 \text{ atm}) = (0.99957)^{1/3} a_1 (1 \text{ atm}) = 0.99986 a_1 (1 \text{ atm})$$

Ionic radii. It has already been mentioned that van der Waals radii have the same significance for ions as for atoms and essentially spherical molecules. In the case of ions, these radii are called ionic radii. To a first approximation each ion has a radius with the same value in different crystals (e.g., Na$^+$ in NaCl and NaBr) and the sum of the two ionic radii in a crystal is equal to the nearest neighbor distance a_1. These remarks apply to all ionic crystals, not just simple cubic ones.

The concept of ionic radii in ionic crystals is somewhat more complicated than that of van der Waals radii in molecular crystals because there are two ions of different size in the lattice. Thus it is not usually possible to have all ions "in contact" with each other. The extent of noncontact will vary in a series such as NaF, NaCl, NaBr, etc. For this reason the first approximation referred to above ordinarily involves an error of a few percent and in some cases an error of as much as 10%.

There is another complication that follows from the presence in the crystal of two kinds of ion (rather than one kind of molecule). This complication becomes apparent when one tries to construct a table of ionic radii from experimental values of a_1. The difficulty is that, for any given crystal, there is not a unique way of dividing up a_1 into two parts (the two ionic radii). It is therefore necessary to assign the radius of some one ion on the basis of other information. The remaining ionic radii in the table (in the first approximation mentioned above) can then be filled in from experimental a_1 values.

As an example of "other information" that might be used, one would expect a decreasing sequence[2] of ionic and van der Waals radii for: (a) Cl$^-$, Ar, K$^+$; (b) Br$^-$, Kr, Rb$^+$; and (c) I$^-$, Xe, Cs$^+$. The basis of this expectation is that the substances in each group have the same number of electrons but increasing nuclear charge. The van der Waals radii ($r_0/2$) for Ar, Kr, and Xe are given in Table 3-3.

The most generally accepted table of ionic radii is that due to L. Pauling. Some of these radii are given in Table 5-5. The reader should compare a_1 values in Table 5-3 with ionic radii sums from Table 5-5.

Lattice energies. Because of their precisely known structures, ionic crystals are excellent systems on which to test our ideas concerning intermolecular forces. The potential energy of a number of

[2]We omit the neon sequence because of quantum mechanical effects in solid neon.

Table 5-5
Ionic Radii

Ion	Radius	Ion	Radius	Ion	Radius	Ion	Radius	Ion	Radius
				Li^+	0.60 Å	Be^{++}	0.31 Å	B^{+++}	0.20 Å
O^{--}	1.40 Å	F^-	1.36 Å	Na^+	0.95	Mg^{++}	0.65	Al^{+++}	0.50
S^{--}	1.84	Cl^-	1.81	K^+	1.33	Ca^{++}	0.99		
Se^{--}	1.98	Br^-	1.95	Rb^+	1.48	Sr^{++}	1.13		
Te^{--}	2.21	I^-	2.16	Cs^+	1.69	Ba^{++}	1.35	NH_4^+	1.48

these crystals at 0°K can be measured experimentally (in an indirect way) and compared with a theoretical calculation. The agreement is very good, as we shall see.

In the theoretical calculation, there are three additive contributions to the potential energy[3]. These can be calculated numerically if we use the experimental crystal structure to obtain the necessary interionic distances. The first and most important contribution is the sum of all the + +, + −, and − − coulombic interactions (Eq. 3-4) in the crystal. Because the coulombic interaction has a long range, special mathematical methods have to be employed to sum the series encountered. The second contribution is from r^{-6} dispersion interactions, and the third from overlap repulsion terms (Eq. 3-13). These latter two kinds of interaction have a short range, of course. The negative of the potential energy of the crystal is the work necessary to pull all the ions of the crystal apart to infinite separation: crystal → gaseous ions. This work is called the lattice energy. A few theoretical values of the lattice energy, calculated in the manner described, are given in Table 5-6.

To obtain an experimental value for the lattice energy of a crystal, the most convenient procedure is to break up the over-all process (crystal → gaseous ions) into a number of more elementary processes. The sum of the energies for the separate processes is then equal to the lattice energy. Let us consider NaCl as an example;

	Energy required
NaCl (solid) → Na (solid) + $\frac{1}{2}$ Cl_2 (gas)	99 kcal mole⁻¹
Na (solid) → Na (gas)	26
Na (gas) → Na^+ (gas) + e^- (gas)	117
$\frac{1}{2}$ Cl_2 (gas) → Cl (gas)	27
Cl (gas) + e^- (gas) → Cl^- (gas)	−88

Total: NaCl (solid) → Na^+ (gas) + Cl^- (gas)   181 kcal mole⁻¹

The experimental values in Table 5-6 have been found in this way.

---

[3]There is also a small quantum mechanical correction owing to the so-called zero-point vibrational energy (p. 138) of the crystal.

Table 5-6
Lattice Energies

Crystal	Lattice Energy (kcal mole^{-1})		Crystal	Lattice Energy (kcal mole^{-1})	
	Theory	Expt		Theory	Expt
NaCl	184	181	KI	153	151
NaBr	176	176	RbCl	162	159
NaI	164	166	RbBr	156	157
KCl	168	163	RbI	148	148
KBr	162	160			

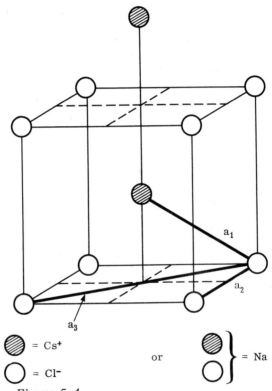

Figure 5-4
Body-centered cubic lattice.

5-3 BODY-CENTERED CUBIC LATTICE

FIGURE 5-4 shows the body-centered cubic structure which occurs in salts of the type AB, and also in a large number of metals.

In a salt with this structure, say CsCl, each Cs^+ has eight nearest neighbor Cl^- and also each Cl^- has eight nearest neighbor Cs^+. A little study of Fig. 5-4 shows that the structure is symmetrical with respect to Cs^+ and Cl^-. In fact, it is helpful to think of the CsCl structure as a simple cubic lattice of Cs^+ interpenetrating a second simple cubic lattice of Cl^-.

In a metal with body-centered cubic structure, all atoms are the same ($\bullet = \bigcirc$ in Fig. 5-4).

Table 5-7 gives neighbor numbers and distances for this lattice. The reader should verify some of these entries with the aid of Fig. 5-4. Because the body-centered cubic structure consists of two interpenetrating simple cubic lattices, the entries marked + in Table 5-7 can all be deduced from the entries i = 1 to i = 8 in Table 5-2.

A few crystals that have the body-centered cubic structure are listed in Table 5-8, together with the experimental nearest neighbor distances.

Molar volume and density. First consider a salt AB with molecular weight M. The cube in Fig. 5-4 contains one molecule of AB [one ion in center; $8 \times (\frac{1}{8}) = 1$ ion on corners]. The volume of the cube is a_2^3. But according to Table 5-7, $a_2 = (\frac{4}{3})^{1/2} a_1$. Therefore the volume per molecule is $(\frac{4}{3})^{3/2} a_1^3$, and the volume per mole is

$$v(cm^3 \text{ mole}^{-1}) = 8N_0 a_1^3 (cm^3)/3^{3/2} \tag{5-4}$$

As always,

$$\rho(g \text{ cm}^{-3}) = M/v(cm^3 \text{ mole}^{-1})$$

If all atoms in the crystal are alike, there are two atoms in the

Table 5-7
Body-Centered Cubic Lattice (Central Ion = +)

i	n_i	a_i	Sign	i	n_i	a_i	Sign
1	8	a_1	−	8	24	$\sqrt{20/3}\ a_1$	+
2	6	$\sqrt{4/3}\ a_1$	+	9	24	$\sqrt{24/3}\ a_1$	+
3	12	$\sqrt{8/3}\ a_1$	+	10	32	$\sqrt{27/3}\ a_1$	−
4	24	$\sqrt{11/3}\ a_1$	−	11	12	$\sqrt{32/3}\ a_1$	+
5	8	$\sqrt{12/3}\ a_1$	+	12	48	$\sqrt{35/3}\ a_1$	−
6	6	$\sqrt{16/3}\ a_1$	+	13	30	$\sqrt{36/3}\ a_1$	+
7	24	$\sqrt{19/3}\ a_1$	−				

Table 5-8
Substances with Body-Centered Cubic Structure

Salt	a_1 (in Å)	Element	a_1 (in Å)
CsCl	4.11	Ba	4.34
CsBr	4.29	Li	3.03
CsI	4.56	Na	3.71
NH_4Cl	3.87	Cs	5.24
TlCl	3.83	Cr	2.49

cube of volume a_2^3 (one at the center; one at the corners). The volume per atom is then $a_2^3/2$. Therefore

$$v(cm^3 \ mole^{-1}) = 4N_0 a_1^3 (cm^3)/3^{3/2} \qquad (5-5)$$

The reader may have noticed that NH_4Cl appears both in Table 5-3 and in Table 5-8. The explanation is that, at atmospheric pressure, the body-centered cubic structure for this salt is the stable one below 185°C while the simple cubic structure is stable above 185°C. There is a similar first order phase transition in NH_4Br at 138°C and in NH_4I at −17°C.

5-4 CLOSE-PACKED LATTICES

IF hard spheres are packed together as tightly as possible, each sphere will have 12 nearest neighbors rather than the 6 or 8 in the two lattices described so far. There are two different "close-packed" lattices: they are called face-centered cubic (fcc) and hexagonal close packed (hcp).

Both of these lattices can be generated starting from a close-packed set of lattice points in a plane. Figure 5-5a shows a two-dimensional close packed array of points. Each point has six nearest neighbors. The points form two kinds of equilateral triangles: $^\circ{}_\circ{}^\circ$ and $_\circ{}^\circ{}_\circ$. Let the circles in Fig. 5-5b be in the plane of the paper. Now place a lattice point, marked + (the + sign here means "above," not "positive charge"), in a plane above the paper, directly over the center of each triangle of type $^\circ{}_\circ{}^\circ$. The height of the new plane, above the paper, $(\frac{2}{3})^{1/2}a_1$, is such that the distance $\bigcirc{-}+$ is the same as the nearest neighbor distance a_1 in the plane of the paper (see Figs. 5-5bc). This same geometry is achieved if a hard sphere is set on top of a triangle of hard spheres in contact. Similarly, place a lattice point, marked −, in a plane below the paper, directly under the center of each triangle of type $_\circ{}^\circ{}_\circ$. The three two-dimensional lattices (O, +, −) thus formed are identical but are displaced horizontally relative to each other. Each point in the plane of the paper (O) now has twelve nearest neighbors at a distance a_1: six in the same plane (O); three above (+); and three below (−). If we make an infinite vertical stack of planes of these three kinds, as

Horizontal Arrangement

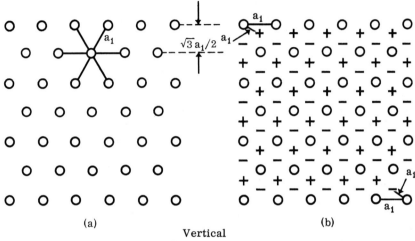

(a)   (b)

Vertical
Arrangement

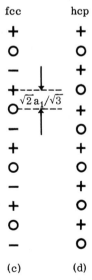

(c)   (d)

Figure 5-5
Close packed lattices.

Table 5-9
Face-Centered Cubic Lattice

i	n_i	a_i	i	n_i	a_i
1	12	a_1	8	6	$\sqrt{8}\,a_1$
2	6	$\sqrt{2}\,a_1$	9	36	$\sqrt{9}\,a_1$
3	24	$\sqrt{3}\,a_1$	10	24	$\sqrt{10}\,a_1$
4	12	$\sqrt{4}\,a_1$	11	24	$\sqrt{11}\,a_1$
5	24	$\sqrt{5}\,a_1$	12	24	$\sqrt{12}\,a_1$
6	8	$\sqrt{6}\,a_1$	13	72	$\sqrt{13}\,a_1$
7	48	$\sqrt{7}\,a_1$	14	48	$\sqrt{15}\,a_1$

indicated in Fig. 5-5c, we will have produced the three-dimensional fcc lattice. If on the other hand, we construct the stack of planes shown in Fig. 5-5d, we will have an hcp lattice. The distance between planes is the same in the two lattices. Also, in both cases $n_1 = 12$.

Molecules with forces of short range tend to adopt a close packed structure because of the large number of nearest neighbors. On the other hand, as a result of the long range of coulombic forces, ionic crystals can afford, so to speak, to pay less attention to the nearest neighbor number. The common values of n_1 chosen by ionic crystals are 8, 6, or even 4. But a close-packed lattice ($n_1 = 12$) is not a real possibility for an ionic crystal because of the fact that an ion of given sign cannot always have ions of opposite sign as nearest neighbors in such a lattice (as is possible, for example, in simple cubic, body-centered cubic, and diamond lattices).

The fcc lattice is closely related to the simple cubic lattice. Consider, for example, just the sodium ions in Fig. 5-3a (ignore the chloride ions). The central Na^+ has three nearest neighbors marked $-$, three marked $+$, and six unmarked (the same as ○ in Fig. 5-5b). This is the same arrangement of lattice points as in Fig. 5-5b except that the planes are tilted. Note that the $-$ and $+$ points in Fig. 5-3a are not in equivalent positions relative to the unmarked points so the structure is fcc (Fig. 5-5c) and not hcp (Fig. 5-5d). Conclusion: the positive ions in a simple cubic lattice form an fcc lattice.

The simple cubic structure is symmetric with respect to the two kinds of ions. Therefore the negative ions, by themselves, also form an fcc lattice. An inspection of the negative ion arrangement in Fig. 5-3a indicates the origin of the term "face-centered cubic." The large cube shown in the figure has a chloride ion at each corner and also one in the center of each face.

Table 5-9 lists neighbor numbers and distances for the fcc lattice. The entries through i = 7 follow directly from the $+$ entries in Table 5-2 ($2^{1/2}a_1 \rightarrow a_1$; $4^{1/2}a_1 \rightarrow (4^{1/2}/2^{1/2})a_1 = 2^{1/2}a_1$; etc.). Table 5-10 is the corresponding table for the hcp lattice.

Table 5-10
Hexagonal Close-Packed Lattice

i	n_i	a_i	i	n_i	a_i
1	12	a_1	8	12	$\sqrt{17/3}\,a_1$
2	6	$\sqrt{6/3}\,a_1$	9	6	$\sqrt{18/3}\,a_1$
3	2	$\sqrt{8/3}\,a_1$	10	6	$\sqrt{19/3}\,a_1$
4	18	$\sqrt{9/3}\,a_1$	11	12	$\sqrt{20/3}\,a_1$
5	12	$\sqrt{11/3}\,a_1$	12	24	$\sqrt{21/3}\,a_1$
6	6	$\sqrt{12/3}\,a_1$	13	6	$\sqrt{22/3}\,a_1$
7	12	$\sqrt{15/3}\,a_1$	14	12	$\sqrt{25/3}\,a_1$

Examples of substances crystallizing in one of the close-packed lattices are given in Table 5-11.

Molar volume and density. Because the distance between planes (Figs. 5-5bcd) is the same, fcc and hcp lattices that have the same value of a_1 will have the same number of molecules per unit volume. So we can use either lattice to deduce the relation between v and a_1. We choose the fcc lattice. Consider one of the small cubes in Fig. 5-3a and let the sodium ions in the figure be the molecules in the fcc crystal (ignore the chloride ions). The cube has molecules at four of its corners and therefore it contains $4 \times (\frac{1}{8}) = \frac{1}{2}$ of a molecule. The nearest neighbor distance a_1 in the fcc lattice is a diagonal of the face of the cube. The length of the edge of the cube is therefore $(1/2^{1/2})a_1$ and the volume of the cube is $a_1^3/2^{3/2}$. Since the cube contains one-half of a molecule, the volume per molecule is $a_1^3/2^{1/2}$ and

$$v\,(\text{cm}^3\ \text{mole}^{-1}) = N_0 a_1^3\,(\text{cm}^3)/2^{1/2} \tag{5-6}$$

Relative packing of spheres. Suppose a large number of identical hard spheres of diameter a_1 are packed together, with surfaces in

Table 5-11
Substances with Close-Packed Structure

Substance	a_1 (in Å)	Lattice	Substance	a_1 (in Å)	Lattice	Substance	a_1 (in Å)	Lattice
He	3.57	hcp	Xe	4.41	fcc	Al	2.86	fcc
Ne	3.20	fcc	H_2	3.88	hcp	Zn	2.66	hcp
Ar	3.83	fcc	N_2	4.00	fcc	Ca	3.93	fcc
Kr	3.94	fcc	CH_4	4.17	fcc	Cu	2.55	fcc

Table 5-12
Packing of Spheres

Lattice	v	v/v (close-packed)	n_1	% space filled
Close packed	$N_0 a_1^3 / 2^{1/2}$	1	12	74
Body centered	$4\ N_0 a_1^3 / 3^{3/2}$	$2^{5/2}/3^{3/2} = 1.088$	8	68
Simple cubic	$N_0 a_1^3$	$2^{1/2} = 1.414$	6	52
Diamond or ice	$8\ N_0 a_1^3 / 3^{3/2}$	$2^{7/2}/3^{3/2} = 2.176$	4	34

contact, in: (a) a simple cubic lattice; (b) a body-centered cubic lattice; (c) either type of close-packed lattice; and (d) a diamond or ice lattice (see the next section). What are the relative volumes per molecule? Table 5-12 provides the answer to this question. A close-packed lattice is seen to be more than twice as dense as the diamond or ice lattice. The factor of two in Eq. 5-1 is omitted in the table because there is only one type of sphere instead of two (compare Eqs. 5-4 and 5-5).

Another related question is this: in the close-packed case above, what percentage of the volume is actually filled by spheres and what percentage is empty space? The volume filled by a mole of spheres is $N_0 (\frac{4}{3}) \pi (a_1/2)^3$. The ratio of this volume to the volume of the lattice is

$$\frac{N_0 (\frac{4}{3}) \pi (a_1/2)^3}{N_0 a_1^3 / 2^{1/2}} = \frac{\pi}{3\sqrt{2}} = 0.74$$

Therefore 74% of the space is filled and 26% is empty. The last column in Table 5-12 shows the results for other lattices as well.

5-5 DIAMOND, GRAPHITE, AND ICE

DIAMOND, graphite, and ice have important and interesting structures that deserve some comment.

Diamond. In very many organic molecules, carbon forms covalent bonds with tetrahedral symmetry. Diamond is a super-molecule of this type. It consists of carbon atoms only, each covalently bonded to four others. The symmetry about each carbon is tetrahedral, and the $C-C$ bond distance is 1.54 Å, just as in ethane ($H_3 C - CH_3$).

The diamond structure is probably most simply viewed as a body-centered cubic structure with one-half of the atoms missing.

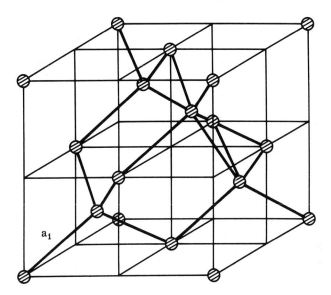

Figure 5-6
Structure of diamond.

Figure 5-6 shows a stack of eight body-centered cubes, but in each row of atoms (both corner rows and center rows) alternate atoms are omitted. Covalent bonds are indicated by darker lines. The only bonds drawn in the figure are those involving the four atoms at the centers of cubes. This structure can be carried on in all directions without limit.

Because many strong bonds must be broken in order to fracture the crystal, diamond is extremely hard—possibly the hardest substance known. The diamond structure is a relatively open one (see Table 5-14.

Table 5-13
Diamond Lattice

i	n_i	a_i	i	n_i	a_i
1	4	a_1	8	12	$\sqrt{32/3}\ a_1$
2	12	$\sqrt{8/3}\ a_1$	9	24	$\sqrt{35/3}\ a_1$
3	12	$\sqrt{11/3}\ a_1$	10	24	$\sqrt{40/3}\ a_1$
4	6	$\sqrt{16/3}\ a_1$	11	12	$\sqrt{43/3}\ a_1$
5	12	$\sqrt{19/3}\ a_1$	12	8	$\sqrt{48/3}\ a_1$
6	24	$\sqrt{24/3}\ a_1$	13	24	$\sqrt{51/3}\ a_1$
7	16	$\sqrt{27/3}\ a_1$			

Table 5-14

Substances with the Diamond Structure

Substance	a_1 (in Å)	Substance	a_1 (in Å)	Substance	a_1 (in Å)
C	1.54	AgI	2.81	CuI	2.62
Si	2.35	AlP	2.35	ZnS	2.35
Ge	2.43	SiC	1.88	CdS	2.52
Sn (gray)	2.80	CuCl	2.34	HgS	2.53
		CuBr	2.46		

Table 5-12) but this is countered, as far as the density is concerned, by the fact that the nearest neighbor distance, $a_1 = 1.54$ Å, is very small.

Because a diamond lattice contains just one-half as many atoms as a body-centered cubic lattice with the same nearest neighbor distance a_1, the molar volume of diamond is twice that given by Eq. 5-5. That is,

$$v\,(\text{cm}^3\ \text{mole}^{-1}) = 8N_0\,a_1^3\,(\text{cm}^3)/3^{3/2} \tag{5-7}$$

Table 5-13 presents neighbor numbers and distances for this lattice. It might be noticed that all of the a_i distances for the diamond lattice are included in Table 5-7 (body-centered cubic lattice). Also, values of n_i for diamond when i is odd are equal to one-half the corresponding n_i in Table 5-7, while the diamond n_i values for i even are the same as the corresponding n_i in Table 5-7. "Corresponding" here means at the same distance a_i.

Some other elements and a number of compounds of type AB also have the diamond structure. One form of ZnS, zincblende, is the best known of these compounds. The atoms or ions (in AB) alternate so that the nearest neighbors of A are B, and vice versa. Table 5-14 presents a number of examples. The elements listed are all in the same group of the periodic table. But lead, which is also in the group, crystallizes in the fcc structure. Silicon carbide, as well as diamond, is famous for its hardness.

Equation 5-7 applies to the elements in Table 5-14. For the compounds AB,

$$v\,(\text{cm}^3\ \text{mole}^{-1}) = 16N_0\,a_1^3\,(\text{cm}^3)/3^{3/2} \tag{5-8}$$

Graphite. Just as diamond is an extreme example of a saturated, aliphatic organic molecule, graphite is an extreme form of unsaturated, aromatic organic molecule. Benzene (C_6H_6) is the prototype, or "monomer," for graphite (5-I):

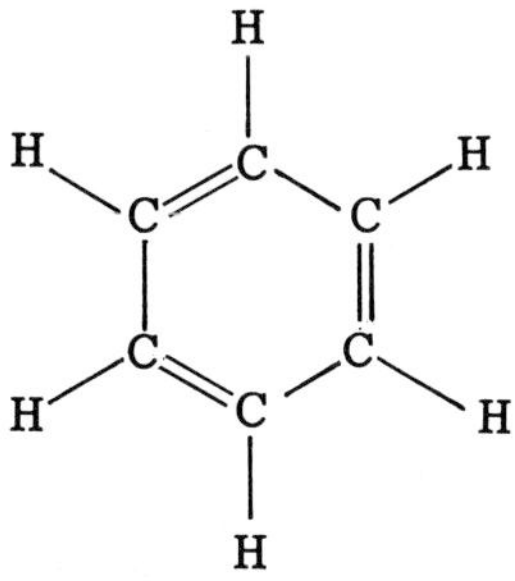

(5-I)

Because of resonance each carbon-carbon bond is a hybrid between a single bond and a double bond. The basic element in graphite is an extended flat sheet of carbon atoms with an hexagonal arrangement as in benzene (5-II):

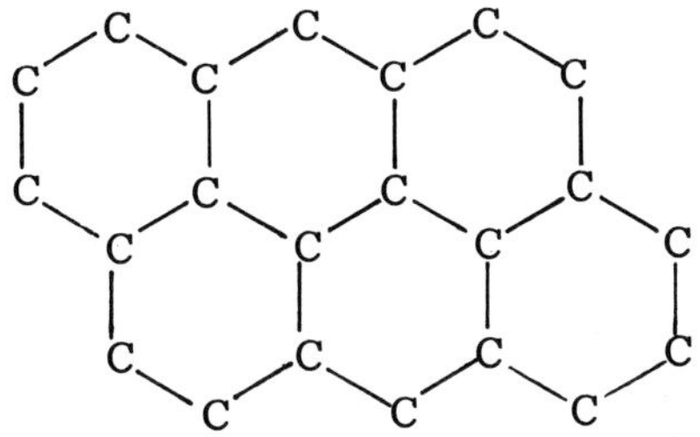

(5-II)

Each carbon atom has three nearest neighbors in the plane. One third of the bonds in each resonance structure are double bonds (not shown above). Therefore each bond has one-third double bond character. The single bond $C-C$ distance in diamond and ethane is 1.54 Å; the $C-C$ bond distance in graphite (33% double bond; 67% single bond) is 1.42 Å; The $C-C$ bond distance in benzene (50% double bond; 50% single bond) is 1.40 Å; and the double bond $C=C$ distance in ethylene ($H_2C=CH_2$) is 1.33 Å.

The carbon atoms within a sheet of graphite are held together by chemical bonds, as just described. But the sheets themselves are stacked vertically (Fig. 5-7) and attracted to each other by relatively weak dispersion forces. The distance between sheets is 3.35 Å, more than twice the $C-C$ distance of 1.42 Å.

The sheets in graphite can slip over one another rather easily. Hence graphite is flaky and is a well known solid lubricant.

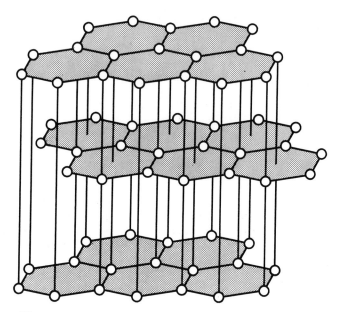

Figure 5-7
Structure of graphite.

Ice. Every oxygen atom in ice has four nearest neighbor oxygen atoms arranged tetrahedrally. But the structure is not the same as in diamond. Figures 5-8ab show how the oxygen lattice is constructed. We start with a two dimensional array (marked O) of oxygen atoms with hexagonal symmetry (as in Fig. 5-5). Above the center of each triangle of type $^\circ{}_\circ{}^\circ$ is placed another oxygen atom (marked +). Each +. has three nearest neighbors in the plane below at a distance a_1. For ice, a_1 = 2.76 Å. The O—O distance in the O plane is $(\frac{8}{3})^{1/2} a_1$. Another plane of oxygen atoms is placed <u>directly</u> above the + plane to provide the fourth nearest neighbor to each +. This new plane is therefore also a + plane; the +—+ interplanar distance is a_1. The stacking of planes is shown in Fig. 5-8b. Unlike Figs. 5-5cd, the interplanar distances are not all the same.

In summary: each + has three nearest neighbor O atoms and one nearest neighbor +, and each O has three nearest-neighbor + atoms and one nearest-neighbor O.

The hydrogen atoms are on lines joining the oxygen atoms, as shown on p. 45. Each oxygen is covalently bonded to two hydrogen atoms with O—H distance 0.99 Å (stretched by electrostatic forces from the value 0.96 Å in the gas phase). Also, each oxygen participates in two hydrogen bonds with O—H distance 1.77 Å.

Horizontal Arrangement

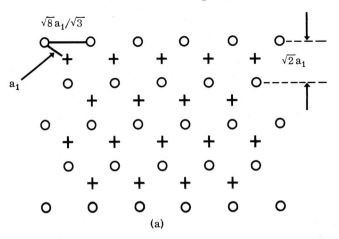

(a)

Vertical Arrangement

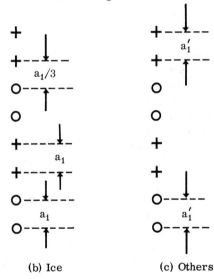

(b) Ice   (c) Others

Figure 5-8
Structure of ice, wurtzite (ZnS), etc.

Table 5-15
Substances with Structure Similar to Ice

Substance	a_1 (in Å)	a_1' (in Å)
NH_4F	2.76	2.63
BeO	1.60	1.64
ZnO	2.04	1.94
ZnS	2.36	2.36
CdS	2.56	2.52
CdSe	2.64	2.63

The tetrahedral structure of ice is stable because it allows efficient utilization of all possible hydrogen bonds (p. 45). But a tetrahedral structure is a relatively open one. Hence ice has an unusually low density. The density increases on melting (a very unusual occurrence[4]), because of the partial collapse and deterioration of this open, ordered structure.

Some substances of type AB have essentially the same structure as the oxygen atoms in ice. Each A has four B nearest neighbors, and vice versa. Wurtzite, a form of ZnS, is an example. However, in these substances the interplanar O—O and +—+ distances (a_1' in Fig. 5-8c) are not necessarily the same as a_1. Table 5-15 lists a few compounds of this type.

Finally, let us outline a calculation of the relation between v and a_1 for the ice lattice. The reader should verify each step, as an exercise. Each O or + (Fig. 5-8a) represents a molecule since there is one molecule per oxygen atom. The distance per molecule along a row of molecules (say those marked O) is $(\frac{8}{3})^{1/2}a_1$. The distance between rows of O molecules is $2^{1/2} a_1$. Therefore the area per molecule in a sheet of molecules is $2^{1/2} a_1 \times (\frac{8}{3})^{1/2} a_1 = (4/3^{1/2})a_1^2$. The vertical intersheet distance alternates between the values a_1 and $a_1/3$, with the average value $2a_1/3$. Therefore the volume per molecule is $(2a_1/3) \times (4/3^{1/2})a_1^2 = (8/3^{3/2})a_1^3$. Hence, finally,

$$v\,(cm^3\ mole^{-1}) = 8N_0 a_1^3\,(cm^3)/3^{3/2} \qquad (5\text{-}9)$$

This is the same as the formula for diamond, Eq. 5-7. If we put a_1 = 2.76 Å in this equation, we find v = 19.5 cm³ mole⁻¹ for ice, or a density ρ = 0.925 g cm⁻³. The measured density at the normal melting point is 0.917 g cm⁻³.

---

[4] Other examples: Sb, Bi, Ga.

5-6 LATTICE IMPERFECTIONS

Real crystals have imperfections in their lattice structures. These imperfections are responsible for many of the most important properties of some solids, such as electrical conductivity, diffusion, color, tensile strength, etc. Although this is a very extensive subject, we confine ourselves to a brief outline of the more important types of imperfections.

(1) Impurities. This is perhaps the most obvious kind of imperfection. No substance is absolutely pure. For example, in an NaCl crystal, an occasional Na^+ may be replaced by a K^+, or a Cl^- by a Br^-; or in solid N_2 there may be an occasional O_2 or CO in place of N_2; etc.

(2) Vacancies. An occasional lattice site may simply be vacant. Vacancies ordinarily originate at the surface of a crystal and move to the interior by diffusion (Fig. 5-9). A typical frequency of occurrence (or concentration) for vacancies is one site in 10^5. This frequency increases with temperature and may often be of the order of one site in 10^2 at the melting point.

(3) Frenkel defects. These are vacancies combined with interstitial ions, in crystals such as AgCl (Fig. 5-10). A vacancy is created simultaneously with and adjacent to an interstitial ion, but then the two imperfections can diffuse apart. A typical frequency for Frenkel defects is one vacancy (plus interstitial ion) in 10^7 sites.

(4) Nonstoichiometry. Example: an FeO crystal may contain fewer iron ions than oxygen ions ($O^=$). This would result from defects of the following type: two Fe^{++} ions are Fe^{+++} instead; and one Fe^{++} ion is missing (a vacancy). The combination leaves the crystal electrically neutral. Another example: in NaCl, there may be more sodium than chlorine as a consequence of defects in which one Na is uncharged and one Cl^- is missing (a vacancy).

(5) Dislocations. In contrast to the "point" defects mentioned so far, these are defects in the crystal structure that extend over hundreds of Angstrom units. There are several kinds; one is shown in Fig. 5-11.

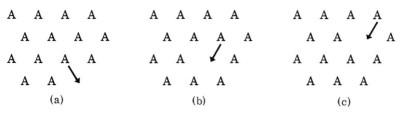

(a)   (b)   (c)

Figure 5-9
Diffusion of a vacancy.

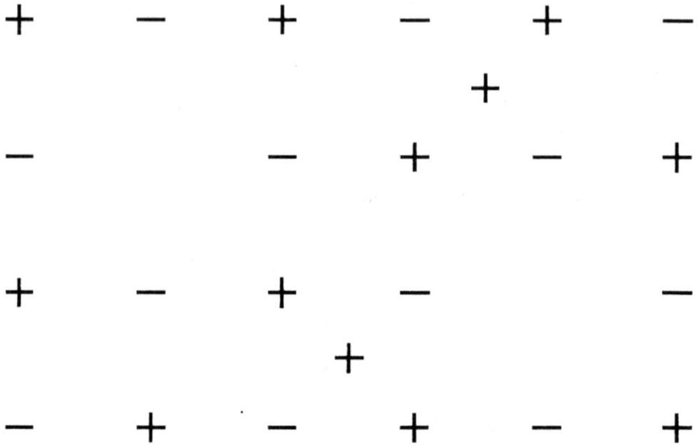

$+$ $-$ $+$ $-$ $+$ $-$

$+$

$-$ $-$ $+$ $-$ $+$

$+$ $-$ $+$ $-$ $-$

$+$

$-$ $+$ $-$ $+$ $-$ $+$

Figure 5-10
Frenkel defects.

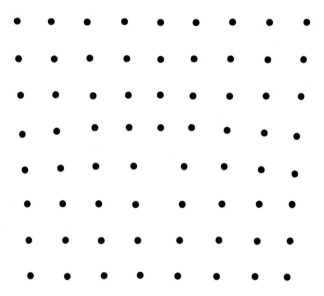

Figure 5-11
A dislocation defect.

(6) <u>Surface distortion.</u> Compared to the bulk of a crystal, the interionic, interatomic, or intermolecular distances will be different in a
few molecular layers near each surface of the crystal. This is because of unbalanced intermolecular forces at the surface. The distortion of the surface layer will affect the second layer a little, which
in turn will affect the third layer a little less, etc.

PROBLEMS

5-1. Make a table like Table 5-2 for a simple "cubic" lattice in <u>two</u> dimensions only. Include i = 1 through i = 5.

5-2. Prove that $a_2 = (\frac{4}{3})^{1/2} a_1$ for a body-centered cubic lattice.

5-3. (a) Start with $\rho = 0.917$ g cm^{-3} for ice and calculate a value of a_1 from
Eq. 5-9. (b) Assume that the discrepancy between $\rho = 0.925$ g cm^{-3}
from the measured a_1 and $\rho = 0.917$ g cm^{-3} is due to missing water
molecules in the ice lattice. What fraction of the lattice sites is
empty?

5-4. Calculate the $C-C-C$ bond angle in diamond using Table 5-13.

5-5. Calculate the density of graphite in g cm^{-3} from the crystal structure. Look up the experimental value and compare.

5-6. MgO has a simple cubic structure. Its density is 3.58 g cm^{-3}. Calculate a_1 in Å and compare with Table 5-3.

5-7. Use Table 5-11 to calculate the molar volume of solid aluminum (in
cm^3 $mole^{-1}$).

5-8. A metal has a body-centered cubic structure. If the second neighbor
distance is 4.0Å and the atomic weight of the metal is 80, what is the
density of the metal?

5-9. Use Eqs. 5-3 to find expressions for α and β for an ideal gas.

5-10. Use Tables 5-3 and 5-8 to calculate Δv in cm^3 $mole^{-1}$ for the phase
transition in solid $NH_4 Cl$ at 185°C.

CHAPTER 6

LIQUIDS

AS WE HAVE MENTIONED BEFORE, in all matter at equilibrium there exists a competition between the ordering tendency of the intermolecular forces or potential energy and the disordering tendency of the kinetic or thermal motion of the molecules. A molecular system "likes" a low potential energy; but it also likes random and uninhibited molecular motion. The vigor of the molecular motion increases with temperature. Hence the disordering tendency dominates at sufficiently high temperatures while the ordering tendency dominates at low temperatures. As a result, the gas state is stable at high temperatures and the solid state is stable at low temperatures.

One might expect matter always to exist in one or the other of these two states. But, as we know, this idea is too simple. There also exists a compromise form of matter, the liquid state, which is stable in an intermediate temperature range. The essential characteristics of a liquid are: (a) the crystalline order is broken down but (b) the molecular packing is about as dense as in the solid. Hence a liquid tries, so to speak, to realize simultaneously the stabilizing tendencies of both gas and solid. It has molecular disorder as in a gas, but it also has close intermolecular interactions as in a solid.

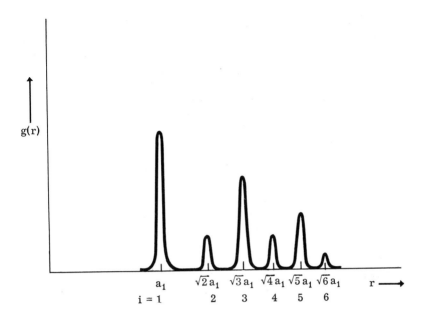

Figure 6-2b
Schematic radial distribution function for solid argon.

neighbor shells are not clearly definable because of spreading and overlapping. However, a second small and broad peak in g(r) is discernable at about r = 7.4Å; this peak can be attributed to third, fourth, and fifth neighbors. After about 15Å the order around any given molecule (the "central" molecule) can be said to have disappeared completely.

We note that in this particular case the nearest neighbor distance in the liquid (3.85Å) is essentially the same as in the solid (Table 3-5; a_1 = 3.83Å). Therefore holes are much more important here than lattice expansion. In fact, by a study of the area under the first peak in Fig. 6-2a, it can be deduced that n_1 = 10.5 in the liquid. This is in close agreement with the value n_1 = 10.4, mentioned above, which would entirely account for the expansion of argon on melting.

Figure 6-2b shows (semi-schematically) how g(r) would look for a ccp crystal with a_1 = 3.85Å. The peaks are associated with successive neighbor shells. The periodicity in g(r) persists to arbitrarily large r. This extended periodicity illustrates long range order. The peaks are not completely sharp because vibration about equilibrium positions smears the structure a little bit.

Comparison of Figs. 6-2a and 6-2b shows the extent to which

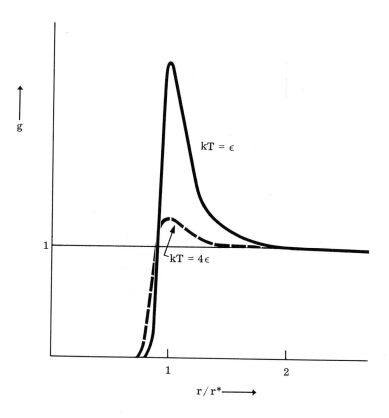

Figure 6-2c
g(r) for a dilute gas at two different temperatures.

crystalline order has been retained in liquid argon at this temperature and pressure.

Figure 6-2c presents g(r) for a very dilute gas. The reader
should be able to deduce that $g(r) = e^{-u(r)/kT}$ in this case, where
u(r) is the intermolecular pair potential energy. The figure has been
calculated using a Lennard-Jones potential for u(r), at two temperatures: $kT = \epsilon$ and $kT = 4\epsilon$. The peak in g(r) occurs at the minimum
in u(r); that is, at $r = r^*$. Of course, as Eq. 6-1 shows, g(r) gives a
relative number or density at r. For a very dilute gas, the actual
density is near zero for all values of r.

In summary: the radial distribution function g(r) provides a precise and detailed way in which to express the structure of a liquid
(or gas, or solid). The average numbers and distances of all neighbors
are implicit in g(r). This method shows that liquids have short range
order left over from crystalline order, but no long range order.

6-4 STRUCTURE OF LIQUID WATER

UNLIKE MOST SOLIDS, ice contracts when it melts. This is due to a break-down in the open, tetrahedral structure of ice. X-ray studies show that the nearest neighbor distance (a_1) increases on melting, but this tendency toward expansion is more than offset by an increase in the number of nearest neighbors (n_1). The fact that these two changes have opposite effects on the density is what leads to the well-known maximum in density at 4°C. Ice at the melting point has $a_1 = 2.76$Å and $n_1 = 4$. Liquid water is found to have $a_1 = 2.88$Å, $n_1 = 4.4$ at 1.5°C and $a_1 = 3.0$Å, $n_1 = 4.9$ at 83°C. The tetrahedral structure deteriorates progressively with increasing temperature but still it is quite apparent from the low value of n_1, even at 83°C, that there is considerable residual, local tetrahedral structure in the liquid.

6-5 POTENTIAL ENERGY OF A LIQUID

WE HAVE ALREADY USED, in Table 3-6, the sum of the heat of fusion at the normal melting point and the heat of vaporization at the normal boiling point as an approximate measure of the negative potential energy of a solid. In the same way, the heat of vaporization, by itself, is an approximation to the negative potential energy of a liquid. If the main difference between a liquid and a solid is the presence of lattice vacancies in the liquid, then the quantity

$$\frac{\text{heat of vaporization}}{\text{heat of vaporization} + \text{heat of fusion}} \times 12$$

should give us an estimate of n_1 for the liquid for substances that have $n_1 = 12$ in the solid state. Table 6-1 contains this calculation for Ne, Ar, Kr, and Xe. The fact that we find about the same n_1 from the heats as we do from the expansion on melting (see p. 109) is another

Table 6-1
Estimate of Nearest-Neighbor Number

Molecule	Heat of Fusion (cal mole^{-1})	Heat of Vaporization (cal mole^{-1})	n_1
Ne	80	420	10.1
Ar	270	1550	10.2
Kr	330	2160	10.4
Xe	430	3020	10.5
Average			10.3

indication that the picture of a liquid, far from the critical point, as an imperfect crystal with many holes is a rather good one.

Incidentally, it is quite easy to derive an exact expression for the potential energy of a monatomic fluid in terms of the radial distribution function. As we have seen, the central molecule has, on the average, $(N/V) \cdot g(r) \cdot 4\pi r^2 \, dr$ neighbors between r and r + dr. The potential energy of interaction between the central molecule and these neighbors is $u(r) \cdot (N/V) \cdot g(r) \cdot 4\pi r^2 \, dr$. The potential energy of interaction between the central molecule and all other molecules is then

$$\frac{4\pi N}{V} \int_0^\infty u(r)g(r)r^2 \, dr$$

The integrand goes to zero when r is greater than about 20Å because $u(r) \to 0$. Therefore the upper limit can be written as $r = \infty$, for convenience (instead of stopping the integration at the walls of the container). Any one of the N molecules can be chosen as "central." Therefore the total potential energy of the whole fluid is the above expression multiplied by N/2. We have to divide by two in order not to count each pair interaction twice (see p. 54).

The velocity distribution and average kinetic energy of the molecules is not affected by intermolecular forces. That is, there are independent Boltzmann distributions in kinetic and potential energy. This follows because (a) the total energy of the monatomic fluid at any instant is the sum of kinetic energy plus potential energy, and (b) the kinetic energy depends only on the velocities of the molecules, while the potential energy depends only on the positions of the molecules. The upshot of all this is that the average kinetic energy of a monatomic fluid (gas or liquid) is 3NkT/2, just as in Eq. 2-8 for an ideal gas. Finally, then, the total energy of the fluid is

$$E = \text{kinetic energy} + \text{potential energy}$$

$$= \tfrac{3}{2}NkT + \frac{2\pi N^2}{V} \int_0^\infty u(r)g(r)r^2 \, dr \tag{6-2}$$

We remind the reader that g(r) depends on N/V and T. As an example of the application of Eq. 6-2, one could use the experimental g(r) for argon in Fig. 6-2a and the Lennard-Jones u(r) (Table 3-3) to calculate the energy of liquid argon at 91.8°K and 1.8 atm.

6-6   SURFACE PROPERTIES

THE SURFACE ENERGY of a liquid is closely related to but not quite the same thing as the surface tension. If we start with a sample of bulk liquid and create an additional amount of surface of area α

(keeping the temperature constant), the surface energy E^S of the liquid is defined as

$$E^S = \frac{\text{Energy of liquid with additional area } \alpha \; - \; \text{Energy of liquid without area } \alpha}{\alpha}$$

The two samples of liquid differ only in potential energy, not kinetic energy (because they both have the same temperature). The potential energy of the sample with new area is larger than that of the original sample because the molecules at the newly created surface have lost some of their pair interactions (which have negative potential energy).

Let us make a rough and easy calculation of E^S for liquid argon, as an exercise. We assume that liquid argon has $a_1 = 3.85\text{Å}$ and $n_1 = 10.5$ (see above). From Fig. 5-5a, we see that the area per molecule at the surface of a ccp crystal is $3^{1/2} a_1^2/2$. But because of vacancies in the liquid, the area per surface molecule is larger:

$$\frac{12}{10.5} \cdot \frac{\sqrt{3}\,a_1^2}{2} = 14.7\text{Å}^2 \text{ molecule}^{-1}$$

Now each surface molecule has lost $\frac{1}{4}$ of its nearest-neighbor interactions ($12 \to 9$ in the crystal; $10.5 \to 0.75 \times 10.5$ in the liquid). If we take the heat of vaporization as a rough estimate of the negative potential energy of the liquid, then the increase in potential energy per surface molecule when new surface is created is $(\frac{1}{4}) \times$ heat of vaporization per molecule. For argon, this quantity is

$$\frac{1}{4} \times \frac{1550 \times 4.18 \times 10^7}{6.02 \times 10^{23}} = 2.69 \times 10^{-14} \text{ erg molecule}^{-1}$$

where 4.18×10^7 is the number of ergs per calorie. Finally,

$$E^S = \frac{\text{increase in potential energy per surface molecule}}{\text{area per surface molecule}}$$

$$= \frac{2.69 \times 10^{-14}}{14.7 \times 10^{-16}} = 18.4 \text{ ergs cm}^{-2}$$

The experimental value at $90°K$ is 35 ergs cm^{-2}. This much discrepancy between theory and experiment is not surprising with such a simple model and calculation.

As a final topic, we treat a quite unrelated <u>kinetic</u> surface property. The question is: at what rate do molecules evaporate from the surface of a liquid (or solid)? This would be a difficult question to answer if we approached it in a straightforward way. Instead, let us use an indirect argument. The rate of evaporation of molecules from a liquid into the space above it will depend on the temperature T of the liquid but will be practically independent of the gas pressure p, provided it is not too large (to insure this, T should be well below T_c). That is, the rate of evaporation from the liquid will be the same whether p = 0 (vacuum), p = p_0 (the vapor pressure at T), or p has some value between zero and p_0.

In an experiment, one would likely start with liquid at T in an otherwise evacuated container. The rate of evaporation from the liquid would proceed at a constant rate, causing p to increase from the initial value p = 0 to the final equilibrium value p = p_0. The rate of condensation of gas molecules onto the surface of the liquid increases with p, and of course the equilibrium pressure p_0 is the pressure at which the rate of condensation exactly equals the rate of evaporation.

This last remark allows us to answer the original question for we can use the rate of condensation at the particular pressure p_0 as a measure of the rate of evaporation at any p. The number of gas molecules that hit the liquid surface (which we count as entering the liquid phase) per unit time per unit area when p = p_0 is, according to Eq. A4-14,

$$\frac{p_0}{(2\pi mkT)^{1/2}}$$

This, then, is also the required rate of evaporation. The calculation following Eq. A4-14 shows that in a case with rather large vapor pressure (0°C, p_0 = 1 atm) about 10^{24} molecules leave a liquid surface per sec per cm². This is about 1 mole per sec per cm². If the vapor pressure is 0.01 atm at 0°C, the number is 10^{22}, etc.

PROBLEMS

6-1. Suppose a liquid of surface area α and at temperature T vaporizes into a vacuum of volume V = $\alpha \times h$, beginning at t = 0. (a) Find an equation for dp/dt, where p is the gas pressure in V at time t. (b) Verify that the solution of this differential equation is

$$\frac{p_0 - p(t)}{p_0} = e^{-\bar{v}t/4h}$$

where p_0 = vapor pressure at T and $\bar{v}$ is the average molecular velocity. That is, p = p_0 at t = ∞ (equilibrium). Make a rough plot of the function p(t) and indicate an approximate time scale (using reasonable values for $\bar{v}$ and h).

CHAPTER 7

FIRST LAW OF THERMODYNAMICS

THE REMAINDER of this book will be devoted to an elementary introduction to thermodynamics. Only a few of many possible topics will be included. Our object is to try to give the reader a general understanding of what thermodynamics is about, and to stimulate his interest in the further study of thermodynamics and statistical mechanics (the molecular interpretation of thermodynamic data). The typical chemistry student will encounter these subjects again in a physical chemistry course.

The books by Mahan, Klotz, and Slater[1] (in order of increasing difficulty) are recommended for supplementary reading. The first two of these are on chemical thermodynamics. The third starts off with thermodynamics but is concerned primarily with statistical mechanics, states of matter, and related topics.

---

[1] B. H. Mahan, Elementary Chemical Thermodynamics, W. A. Benjamin, Inc., New York, 1963. I. M. Klotz, Introduction to Chemical Thermodynamics, W. A. Benjamin, Inc., New York, 1964. J. C. Slater, Introduction to Chemical Physics, McGraw-Hill Book Co., New York, 1939.

117

At this point the reader should review Section 1-1 which contains
a few introductory remarks about thermodynamics.

Thermodynamics is basically an experimental subject. The experiments are carried out on equilibrium systems. It has been found
that results in this field, obtained during the last century and this one,
are consistent with and can be systematized by just three basic laws
or postulates — the three laws of thermodynamics. Of course the experiments — or many of them — came first and the laws were conceived later in order to synthesize the observations. But we shall
take the logical rather than the historical approach to thermodynamics.
The laws will be stated at the outset and then deductions will be made
from the laws. The real test of the laws is whether these and other
deductions agree with the observed facts. This is especially important in connection with the second law because the law itself is rather
abstract and not related to experience in an obvious way. But deductions from the law make sense intuitively and agree with experiment.
The first law, on the other hand, seems almost self-evident.

In the above connection, the author can assure the reader that up
to the present time no exceptions to the laws of thermodynamics are
known, and that thermodynamics is one of the most solidly established
disciplines in physics or chemistry.

We introduce the first law in the present chapter and the other two
laws in Chapter 8.

7-1   FIRST LAW OF THERMODYNAMICS

THE FIRST law of thermodynamics is simply the familiar law of
conservation of energy as applied at the macroscopic level to equilibrium systems.

In principle, we separate the universe into two parts: (a) the system (i.e., the sample of matter whose equilibrium properties are being studied); and (b) its surroundings (e.g., a large heat bath and its
surroundings). If the equilibrium state[2] of the system is altered (e.g.,
by varying its temperature, pressure, etc.), its energy will in general
change. But, according to the law of conservation of energy, the energy of the system is neither created nor destroyed; it has to be
furnished by or given to some other source. The other source in this
case is the surroundings. The system can vary its energy only by
energy exchange with the surroundings. On the macroscopic level

---

[2]The word "state" is often used in the sense "states of matter" - gas, liquid, and solid. Here the term is much more general. For example, a mole of
gas at 1.0 atm and 0°C is an equilibrium state for the gas, a mole of the same
gas at 1.1 atm and 0°C is another equilibrium state, etc.

there are two ways[3] to do this: <u>heat</u> can flow from system to surroundings, or vice versa (this would occur if there is any temperature difference between the two bodies, however slight); or the system
can do mechanical <u>work</u> on the surroundings, or vice versa (e.g., by
means of a piston—see Fig. 1-7—which may be connected to a machine of some sort in the surroundings).

Let us now state the first law in the form of an equation and then
make some explanatory comments about the quantities that appear in
the equation. Suppose a thermodynamic system is in some (<u>initial</u>)
equilibrium state 1 and through any kind of process[4] the system
reaches a different (<u>final</u>) equilibrium state 2. Then the change in
energy of the system in the process is given by

$$\Delta E \equiv E_2 - E_1 = Q - W \qquad (7\text{-}1)$$

where E = energy of the system, Q = heat absorbed <u>by</u> the system
<u>from</u> the surroundings during the process, and W = work done <u>by</u> the
system <u>on</u> the surroundings during the process. The symbol Δ means
"change in." It will be used in connection with a number of properties, not just the energy. ΔX is shorthand for $X_{final\ state}$ −
$X_{initial\ state}$, whatever X is.

In Eq. 7-1, there is a positive sign in front of Q and a negative
sign in front of W because absorption of heat by the system increases
the energy of the system while work done by the system uses up some
of its energy.

Q and W themselves may be positive <u>or</u> negative. Q is positive
when the system absorbs heat, negative when it evolves heat (heat is
absorbed by the surroundings). W is positive when the system does
work on the surroundings, negative when the surroundings do work on
the system.

The first law is a sort of "bookkeeping" law. The three quantities
ΔE, Q, and W, must always satisfy Eq. 7-1. Usually two of these are
measured and the third calculated from the equation. Experimental
or theoretical applications of the first law are exercises in energy
bookkeeping.

From a molecular point of view, the thermodynamic energy E of
a system is the sum of the average kinetic energy plus average potential energy of the molecules in the system. But there is no purely

---

[3]The system is assumed to be closed: no molecules enter or leave the
system. If the system is open an additional term must be added to Eq. 7-1
and to many later equations.

[4]"Process" is a general term that refers to the procedure used to alter the
thermodynamic state of a system. For example, we might change the state of
a system by increasing its temperature while keeping the pressure constant;
or by increasing its volume keeping the temperature constant; etc.

thermodynamic way of distinguishing between these two kinds of energy; we deal only with the complete energy E.

The first law tells us nothing about the absolute value of E for a system; it has to do only with the difference in energy of the same system in two different states (e.g., a gas at 0°C vs the same gas at 10°C; gas vs liquid; or NH_3 vs a mixture of N_2 and H_2; etc.). This is a reflection of the fact that only differences in E can be measured and is consistent with our comments in Section 3-1: an absolute value for E does not exist because the choice of the zero of potential energy for a system of molecules is arbitrary.

The state of a thermodynamic system can be specified by giving the values of a set of variables sufficient to allow another scientist to prepare exactly the same system in the same equilibrium state. For example, we might designate the mole numbers n_1, n_2, . . . of the various substances introduced into the container together with the volume V and temperature T. Other common choices are p, T, n_1, n_2, . . . ; or V, T, c_1, c_2, . . . (where $c_i = n_i/V$); etc. The same state can be specified in many different ways. It is obvious from a molecular point of view that a given collection of molecules (n_1, n_2, . . .) at equilibrium, with particular values of V and T, will always have the same average kinetic and potential energies (the same choice of zero is always made), and therefore the same value of E, regardless of how the system was prepared (e.g., cooled down from a higher temperature than T or heated up from a lower one; expanded from a smaller volume up to V, or compressed to V; etc.). In other words, E is a property of the state of the system but not of its past history. Such a property is called a state function. Examples of other state functions already encountered are V, p, T, n_1, n_2, . . ., c_1, c_2, ... The concept of a state function proves to be very important in thermodynamics.

We have just appealed to the molecular point of view in order to see that E is a state function. But the science of thermodynamics can be (and, in fact, was originally) constructed without resort to molecular theory. To take care of this point of logic we shall say that the first law or postulate of thermodynamics consists of Eq. 7-1 together with the statement that the quantity E appearing in this equation is a state function.

The reason a Δ is not used with Q and W in Eq. 7-1 is that heat and work are not state functions—but more on this later. From its definition, it is obvious that the symbol Δ can be applied to state functions only.

If a system starts in state 1 and goes to state 2 by two different processes (in two different experiments), the values of E_1 and E_2 are the same for both processes because these values depend on states only. Therefore ΔE has the same value in the two processes. ΔE depends only on initial and final states; it is independent of the process (or <u>path</u>) used to pass between the two states. This is true for any state function.

If the initial and final states in Eq. 7-1 differ from each other only infinitesimally,[5] the notation used is

$$dE = DQ - DW \qquad (7\text{-}2)$$

The general physical significance of the terms here is the same as in Eq. 7-1. The quantity dE is a conventional differential quantity, but special notation (''D'') is used for DQ and DW because, as we shall see later, DQ is not the differential of some property of the state of the system (i.e., DQ is not the differential of a state function), nor is DW.

The notation dX for an infinitesimal variation in any state function is mathematically equivalent to the notation ΔX for a finite change. For if a system passes from an initial state 1 to a final state 2 (finite change) by a succession of infinitesimal changes in state, and if we sum over all of these infinitesimal steps, we get (regardless of the path used)

$$\int_1^2 dX = X \Big|_1^2 = X_2 - X_1 = \Delta X \qquad (7\text{-}3)$$

Work. There are many types of work by means of which a system can exchange energy with its surroundings: pressure-volume, gravitational, surface, length-tension, electrical, magnetic, etc. Pressure-volume work is the most important and the only kind we shall take into account.

Consider a system of volume V (Fig. 1-7) that exerts a pressure p on a piston of cross-sectional area α. The piston, which is part of the surroundings and may be connected to a machine or engine, exerts the same pressure on the system. Thus, at equilibrium, there is a balance of forces. Now suppose the pressure exerted by the piston is reduced infinitesimally so that the system expands by an amount dV. The system does work on the surroundings in this expansion. The piston moves outward a distance dV/α against a force[6] $p\alpha$. Therefore

DW = work done on the surroundings by the system

= force × distance

$$= p\alpha \times (dV/\alpha) = pdV \qquad (7\text{-}4)$$

---

[5]An example: the initial state is characterized by V, T, n_1, n_2, . . . and the final state by V + dV, T + dT, n_1, n_2, ...

[6]Strictly speaking, the force is (p - dp) α and the work is pdV - dpdV. But the second term is of no consequence (dp → 0).

This same equation is obtained for a compression (dV and DW are both negative). Hence, when the only kind of work is p-V work, Eq. 7-2 becomes

$$dE = DQ - pdV \qquad (7\text{-}5)$$

It is possible for the system to change its volume when the piston, or external, pressure p_{ex} is different from the pressure p inside the system. For example, in Fig. 7-1, $p > p_{ex}$ but the piston is held in place by pins. If the pins are moved upward slightly, to new positions, resulting in a volume increase dV, then clearly

$$DW = p_{ex}\,dV \qquad (7\text{-}6)$$

since the contact with the surroundings is through p_{ex}, not p. Thus, if $p \neq p_{ex}$, p_{ex} determines the work. But we shall almost always be interested in the "balanced force" situation, $p = p_{ex}$ and DW = pdV.

If the volume of a system is gradually changed from V_1 to V_2, always keeping the pressure balanced as just mentioned, then the total work W done by the system in the process is the sum of the infinitesimal quantities p(V) dV between V_1 and V_2, where the notation p(V) emphasizes the fact that ordinarily the pressure will change as the volume changes. Thus

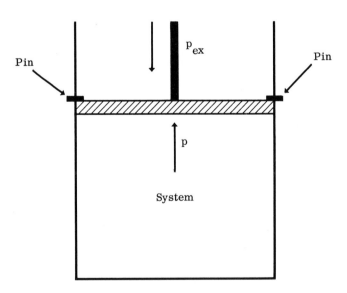

Figure 7-1
Thermodynamic system discussed in text.

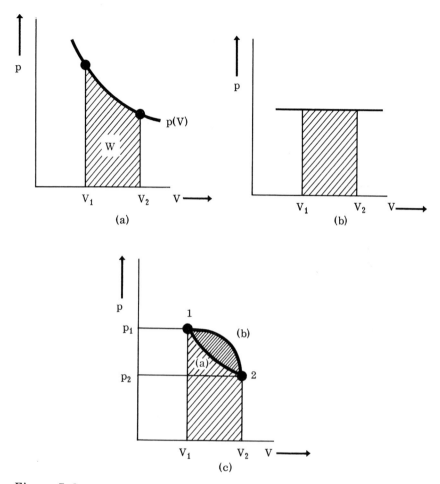

Figure 7-2
Work as the area under a p(V) curve.

$$W = \int_{V_1}^{V_2} p(V) \, dV \qquad (7\text{-}7)$$

This is illustrated in Fig. 7-2a. The curve is a plot of the function p(V). According to Eq. 7-7, the area under the curve between V_1 and V_2 is equal to the work W. In the special case (Fig. 7-2b) that p is constant between V_1 and V_2 (e.g., in a phase transition),

$$W = p \int_{V_1}^{V_2} dV = p(V_2 - V_1) = p\Delta V \qquad (p \text{ const}) \qquad (7\text{-}8)$$

Equations 7-7 and 7-8 are to be used, when appropriate, in Eq. 7-1.

It is now possible to see that W in Eq. 7-1 depends on the process or path and not on initial and final states only. For suppose a system proceeds from state 1 to state 2 by two different p-V paths, (a) and (b), in Fig. 7-2c. This could be accomplished by varying the temperature in two different ways as the volume is changed from V_1 to V_2. The quantities ΔE, ΔV, Δp, and ΔT have the same values in both processes because initial and final states are the same and E, V, p, and T are all state functions. But W is equal to the area under the p-V path or curve. Hence W has different values for paths (a) and (b). W depends on the curve, not just the end points of the curve.

Q also has different values for paths (a) and (b). This follows because ΔE is the same for the two paths, W is different for the two paths, and $Q = \Delta E + W$. Therefore neither W nor Q is a state function. Work and heat are properties associated with processes, not with thermodynamic states.

Whenever a finite process is constructed by putting together a succession of infinitesimal processes, the quantities DQ add up to Q and the DW add up to W: $\int_1^2 DQ = Q$ and $\int_1^2 DW = W$. But we cannot write $\int_1^2 DQ = Q_2 - Q_1$, etc.

We also note, at this point, the mathematically equivalent fact that DW = pdV is not the differential of a state function. That is, DW cannot be written in the form d (state function). The quantities dV = DW/p, dp, and d(pV) are differentials of state functions, but not pdV or Vdp. As we shall see in Section 8-2, DQ resembles DW in this respect.

Reversible and irreversible processes. There are in principle an infinite number of processes by means of which a system can pass between any two thermodynamic states. These processes fall into two classes: reversible processes and irreversible processes. The distinction turns out to be very significant, especially in connection with the second law of thermodynamics.

The initial and final states in any thermodynamic process are equilibrium states (otherwise thermodynamics cannot be applied). In a reversible process, the system passes through a succession of equilibrium states in going from the initial to the final state; every intermediate state is an equilibrium state. This requires that the process be carried out extremely slowly (strictly, infinitely slowly) so that the system can come to equilibrium at each infinitesimal stage of the process. The expansion from V_1 to V_2 in Fig. 7-2a is an example. In order that the system in this figure should have a well defined pressure p and that $p = p_{ex}$ at each V between V_1 and V_2, the system must be in equilibrium at each V.

In an irreversible process, not all of the intermediate states, between initial and final states, are equilibrium states. Sometimes none of them is an equilibrium state. Processes taking place at a finite rate may not allow time for equilibrium always to be maintained. An example is the expansion of the system in Fig. 7-1 that would occur if $p > p_{ex}$ and if the pins are suddenly raised a finite distance to new positions.

We shall be dealing almost entirely with reversible processes in this chapter. Irreversible processes play a leading role in Chapter 8.

The law of conservation of energy, Eq. 7-1 or 7-2, applies to any thermodynamic process, reversible or irreversible. The same is true of $DW = p_{ex} dV$. But $DW = pdV$ is applicable to reversible processes only.

Special cases of the first law. Here we apply the first law to a few general classes of processes. The analysis is simple but important. Section 7-3 contains more explicit examples.

Isolated system. An isolated system has no thermodynamic "contact" with the surroundings, whatever: the walls of the system are thermally insulated and the volume is held constant. Therefore $Q = 0$ and $W = 0$. We then deduce from Eq. 7-1 that $\Delta E = 0$. Many different kinds of process can take place in an isolated system, but in every case $\Delta E = 0$ or $E_1 = E_2$. The energy stays constant because there is no way for it to change. For example, a chemical reaction may occur which gives off a lot of heat. But the heat cannot escape so the temperature of the system will rise. On the molecular level, potential energy is converted to kinetic energy, but the total energy remains constant.

Adiabatic process. An adiabatic process is one that takes place without any flow of heat between system and surroundings (the system is thermally insulated): $Q = 0$. Then, according to the first law, $\Delta E = -W$, or $dE = -DW$. The change in the energy of the system is determined entirely by the work done. An example will be considered in Section 7-3.

Constant volume process. For any process occurring in a container with fixed volume, $W = 0$ and $\Delta E = Q$. Therefore measurement of Q tells us the energy change in the system during the process.

Constant pressure process. Many experiments are done under a constant pressure (often the pressure of the atmosphere). Chemical reactions, phase transitions, and the mixing of two pure substances to form a solution are important examples. Using Eq. 7-8,

$$\Delta E = Q - p\Delta V$$

or

$$Q = \Delta E + p\Delta V \quad \text{(p const)} \tag{7-9}$$

This result suggests the definition of a new thermodynamic state function, defined in terms of "old" functions by

$$H \equiv E + pV \tag{7-10}$$

H is called the <u>heat</u> <u>content</u>, or <u>enthalpy</u>. In a constant pressure process,

$$H_2 - H_1 = (E_2 + pV_2) - (E_1 + pV_1)$$

or

$$\Delta H = \Delta E + p\Delta V \qquad (p \text{ const}) \qquad (7\text{-}11)$$

Therefore, from Eq. 7-9,

$$Q = \Delta H \qquad (p \text{ const}) \qquad (7\text{-}12)$$

Just as measurement of Q at constant volume gives ΔE, we observe here that measurement of Q at constant pressure gives ΔH. This fact alone makes the definition of a new function H worth the trouble.

Numerical example: vaporization of water. Let us apply some of the above ideas to the reversible vaporization of water at the normal boiling point.[7] The process we consider is

One mole of liquid H_2O , $\rightarrow$ One mole of gaseous H_2O
at 1 atm and 100°C   at 1 atm and 100°C.

This can be carried out by gradually introducing heat into the system from the heat bath. The liquid vaporizes and the volume increases, with p and T const.

The experimental data (besides n, p, and T, already given) are[8]

$$v_L = 0.0188 \text{ liter mole}^{-1}, \quad v_G = 30.6 \text{ liters mole}^{-1},$$

$$Q = 9.71 \text{ kcal mole}^{-1}$$

where Q is the heat of vaporization. We have $\Delta H = Q = H_G - H_L = 9.71$ kcal mole^{-1}, and $\Delta v = 30.6$ liter mole^{-1}. We can also calculate ΔE , a quantity not so easy to measure for this process:

$$\Delta E = \Delta H - p\Delta v$$

$$= 9.71 \text{ kcal mole}^{-1} - 1 \times 30.6 \times .0242 \text{ kcal mole}^{-1}$$

$$= 9.71 - 0.74 = 8.97 \text{ kcal mole}^{-1}$$

---

[7]The reader might want to review Section 1-3 in connection with this and the following example.

[8]We shall use a small capital letter for molar quantities generally: $v = V/n$, $E = E/n$, $H = H/n$, etc.

where we have used the fact that 1 liter atm = 0.0242 kcal (Appendix 1). Since $\varepsilon_G - \varepsilon_L$ = 8.97 kcal mole^{-1}, the energy of the gas is higher than the energy of the liquid by this amount. This is because the potential energy of the liquid is less than that of the gas.

If we write the first law as $Q = \Delta E + p\Delta v$, we can interpret the above results as follows. In the vaporization process, 9.71 kcal of heat are absorbed by the system from the bath. Of these 9.71 kcal, 0.74 kcal are required to increase the volume of the system against the atmospheric pressure (work done by the system[9]) and 8.97 kcal is the energy necessary to overcome the intermolecular forces and pull the liquid molecules apart. In Chapter 6 we used the heat of vaporization ($Q = \Delta H$) as an estimate of the negative potential energy of the liquid. We now see that ΔE is the more proper quantity to use, though the difference between ΔH and ΔE is not serious in very approximate calculations.

We have here a good illustration of the relation between thermodynamics and statistical mechanics. From thermodynamic equations and measurements, we are able to conclude that $\varepsilon_G - \varepsilon_L$ = 8.97 kcal mole^{-1}. But this is the end of the line as far as thermodynamics is concerned. It is then the task of statistical mechanics to explain or deduce the number 8.97 kcal mole^{-1} from the molecular properties of H_2O. In fact, the main contribution to this energy comes from hydrogen bond interactions in the liquid. But a complete theory would be very complicated and has not yet been achieved.

There is one final point worth mentioning. In phase transitions of the type $L \rightarrow G$ or $S \rightarrow G$, it is often true (as above) that the volume of the condensed phase is negligible compared to the volume of the gas, and furthermore that the gas is ideal to within experimental error. If this is the case,

$$p\Delta V = pV_G = nRT \tag{7-13}$$

and

$$\Delta H = \Delta E + nRT \tag{7-14}$$

As a check in the above problem,

$$nRT = \frac{1 \times 1.987 \times 373.1}{1000} = 0.74 \text{ kcal}$$

Numerical example: melting of ice. The reversible process to be analyzed here is

---

[9]If the piston is connected to an engine, this is the useful work obtained from the process.

One mole of ice at $\rightarrow$ One mole of liquid H_2O
1 atm and 0°C   at 1 atm and 0°C.

Again, heat is gradually transferred into the system from the bath to induce the phase transition, which occurs at constant temperature and pressure. It is observed that

$$v_S = 19.7 \text{ cm}^3 \text{ mole}^{-1}, \quad v_L = 18.0 \text{ cm}^3 \text{ mole}^{-1}$$

$$Q = 1.436 \text{ kcal mole}^{-1}$$

where Q is the heat of fusion. Therefore,

$$\Delta H = Q = H_L - H_S = 1.436 \text{ kcal mole}^{-1}$$

$$\Delta v = -1.7 \text{ cm}^3 \text{ mole}^{-1}$$

and

$$\Delta E = \Delta H - p\Delta v$$

$$= 1.436 \text{ kcal mole}^{-1} + 1 \times 0.0017 \times .0242 \text{ kcal mole}^{-1}$$

$$= 1.436 + 4 \times 10^{-5} = 1.436 \text{ kcal mole}^{-1}$$

The term $p\Delta v$ is seen to be negligible; $\Delta H \cong \Delta E$. This is usually the case in processes involving condensed phases only: because of the relatively small volumes of condensed phases, pV terms are negligible compared with other energy terms.

Since $E_L - E_S = 1.436$ kcal mole^{-1}, the liquid has a higher energy than the solid. The main reason for this is that the solid has more hydrogen bonds and hence a lower potential energy than the liquid. It is estimated in Problem 8-4 that 12% of the hydrogen bonds are broken when ice melts at the triple point.

7-2 HEAT CAPACITY

IF a system absorbs heat, its temperature either rises or stays constant. A system undergoing a phase transition at constant pressure (see the examples above) is a case in which the temperature stays constant. But an increase in temperature is the usual thing. If a very small amount of heat DQ is absorbed and causes a temperature rise dT, the ratio DQ/dT is called the heat capacity C. The temperature rise dT is proportional to DQ; the proportionality constant is $1/C$.

If a system can absorb a lot of heat without affecting its temperature much, C will be large. Roughly speaking, the heat capacity is a measure of the capability of the molecules of a system to "store energy." Large molecules with many atoms can put energy into the form of rotational, vibrational, and translational kinetic and potential energy. Hence systems made up of such molecules have higher molar heat capacities than systems of monatomic molecules, under comparable conditions.

The value of DQ/dT depends on the conditions under which the heat is absorbed. Consequently, there are many different kinds of heat capacity, not just one. We shall discuss the two most important cases.

If the heat is absorbed with the volume of the system held constant, we have

$$C_V = \left(\frac{DQ}{dT}\right)_V \qquad (7\text{-}15)$$

This is called the heat capacity at constant volume. We see from Eq. 7-5 that DQ = dE when V is constant (dV = 0). Therefore,

$$C_V = \left(\frac{\partial E}{\partial T}\right)_V \qquad (7\text{-}16)$$

Thus C_V is very closely related to E. Since E is a state function, it follows from Eq. 7-16 that C_V is also. For a pure substance, E may be regarded as a function of n, V, and T. Therefore C_V also depends on n, V, and T. Strictly speaking, we should indicate in Eq. 7-16 that n is held constant in the differentiation as well as V. But this will always be understood because the only processes we consider take place in closed containers that do not allow exchange of matter between system and surroundings.

Experimental data on pure substances are usually quoted for the molar heat capacity, $c_V = C_V/n$, with units cal deg^{-1} mole^{-1}. The specific heat is the heat capacity per gram.

For given n and V, C_V is a function of T, $C_V(T)$. If we measure C_V for a substance between temperatures T_1 and T_2, we can calculate the quantity $E(T_2) - E(T_1)$ for the substance by integrating Eq. 7-16:

$$dE = C_V(T)\, dT \qquad (n, V\ const)$$
$$\int_{T_1}^{T_2} dE = E(T_2) - E(T_1) = \int_{T_1}^{T_2} C_V(T)\, dT \qquad (n, V\ const)$$
$$(7\text{-}17)$$

In this way, information about the energy can be obtained by measuring C_V.

The heat capacity at constant pressure is more convenient to measure and is used more than C_V. This quantity is defined as

$$C_p = \left(\frac{DQ}{dT}\right)_p \qquad (7-18)$$

One is tempted to assume from Eq. 7-12 that $DQ = dH$ for an infinitesimal constant pressure process. This can be verified by combining Eqs. 7-5 and 7-10:

$$dH = d(E + pV) = dE + pdV + Vdp$$

$$= DQ + Vdp \qquad (7-19)$$

When $p = \text{const}$ ($dp = 0$), Eq. 7-19 gives $dH = DQ$. Therefore

$$C_p = \left(\frac{\partial H}{\partial T}\right)_p \qquad (7-20)$$

C_p is also a state function: the units for $c_p = C_p/n$ are the same as
for c_V.

A system in a given state has definite values of both C_V and C_p,
and these values usually differ (though not by much for condensed
systems). As a specific example, let us find the difference between
C_p and C_V for an ideal gas.

Although in general E for a pure substance is a function of n, V,
and T, in the case of an ideal gas E is independent of V and a function of n and T only. This is because the dependence of E on V,
when it exists, arises from the effect of V on the intermolecular potential energy of the molecules (a change in V results in different
average intermolecular distances). But intermolecular forces are
negligible in an ideal gas. Alternatively, if we regard E as a function of n, p, and T (the choice of independent variables is a matter
of convenience), we conclude by the same kind of argument that E
for an ideal gas is a function of n and T only, and independent of p.
Therefore, since $H = E + nRT$ for an ideal gas,

$$C_p = \left(\frac{\partial H}{\partial T}\right)_{p,n} = \left(\frac{\partial E}{\partial T}\right)_n + nR$$

Also,

$$C_V = \left(\frac{\partial E}{\partial T}\right)_{V,n} = \left(\frac{\partial E}{\partial T}\right)_n$$

Hence,

$$C_p = C_V + nR \quad \text{(ideal gas)}$$

or, per mole of gas,

$$c_p = c_V + R \quad \text{(ideal gas)} \tag{7-21}$$

This is a very simple result. It holds for any ideal gas at any temperature. We have included the variable n in the derivatives above to avoid confusion.

In following the logic of thermodynamics, it should be noticed that we have invoked a molecular (nonthermodynamic) argument above to show that E is a function of n and T only, for an ideal gas. But this property can be proved from thermodynamics alone after the second law is available (Chapter 8), if we define an ideal gas as one with equation of state pV = nRT.

Returning now to Eq. 7-20, integration over a temperature range yields

$$H(T_2) - H(T_1) = \int_{T_1}^{T_2} C_p(T)\, dT \quad \text{(n,p constant)} \tag{7-22}$$

H(T) − H(0) for a pure substance. Equation 7-22 suggests that if experimental C_p data are available for a pure substance between T = 0 and, say, temperature T = T′, at a constant pressure, then integration of $C_p(T)$ should give H(T′) − H(0), where H(0) is the heat content at absolute zero. There is, however, one important complication. If there are any phase transitions between T = 0 and T = T′, there will be an additional contribution to H(T′) − H(0) from each phase transition. For example, suppose the only transition between T = 0 and T = T′ is melting of the solid at $T_m < T'$ (compare Fig. 1-10). Then

$$H_L(T') - H_S(0) = \int_0^{T_m} c_p^S(T)\, dT + [H_L(T_m) - H_S(T_m)]$$

$$+ \int_{T_m}^{T'} c_p^L(T)\, dT \tag{7-23}$$

where L = liquid and S = solid. The first integral on the right is equal to $H_S(T_m) - H_S(0)$, where $H_S(T_m)$ is the heat content of the solid at the melting point. If $c_p^S(T)$ is plotted as ordinate against T, the integral can be evaluated by finding the area under the curve between T = 0 and T = T_m. The term [ ] is the heat of fusion (Q = ΔH). The second integral is equal to $H_L(T') - H_L(T_m)$. It can be found as the area under the $C_p^L(T)$ curve between T = T_m and T = T′.

The implied reversible process in Eq. 7-23 is

n moles of solid   →   n moles of liquid
  at T = 0 and p   at T = T′ and p

The process is carried out by absorption of heat from a heat bath whose temperature is gradually increased, keeping the pressure of the system constant. Since $DQ = dH$ for a constant pressure process, the quantity $H_L(T') - H_S(0)$ is equal to the total amount of heat Q absorbed by the system in the above process.

Note that experimental measurements give $H_L(T') - H_S(0)$, and not $H_L(T')$ by itself. This is because absolute values of E and H do not exist; in theoretical work these quantities always involve an arbitrary assignment of the zero of energy, as has been mentioned before.

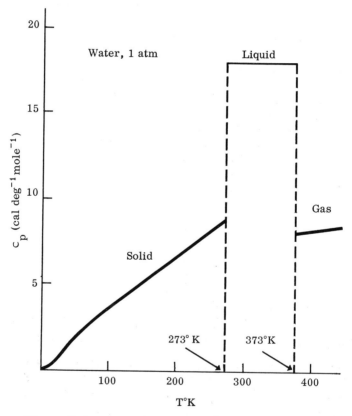

Figure 7-3
Experimental heat capacity of water.

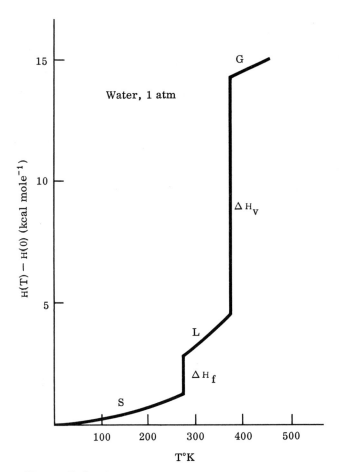

Figure 7-4
Heat content (enthalpy) of water.

A similar calculation can be made for E instead of H, using C_V in place of C_p and ΔE rather than ΔH at phase transitions. For condensed phases, there is usually very little difference between $E(T) - E(0)$ and $H(T) - H(0)$.

Numerical example: water. Let us calculate and plot the heat content of one mole of H_2O from $T = 0$ to $T = 400°K$, at 1 atm pressure. The experimental data needed are the heat of fusion ($\Delta H_f = 1.436$ kcal mole^{-1}; f = fusion), the heat of vaporization ($\Delta H_v = 9.71$ kcal mole^{-1}; v = vaporization), and c_p at 1 atm for solid, liquid, or gas between $0°K$ and $400°K$. The heat capacity is given in Fig. 7-3. We can then calculate $H(T) - H(0)$, as in Eq. 7-23. For $T < 273.1°K$, $H(T) - H(0)$

is the area under the c_p^S curve from $T = 0$ to T. ΔH_f is added at 273.1°K. Then the area under c_p^L between 273.1°K and T is added for T in the range 273.1°K < T < 373.1°K. Next, ΔH_v is added at 373.1°K. Finally, the area under c_p^G between 373.1°K and T is added if $T > 373.1$°K. The result is shown in Fig. 7-4, where $H(T) - H(0)$ is plotted against T.

The same kind of curve for CCl_4 is given in Fig. 7-5. There is a change in the crystal structure of CCl_4 at 225.4°K. Hence an extra phase transition appears in the diagram.

As final topics in this section, we discuss the experimental and

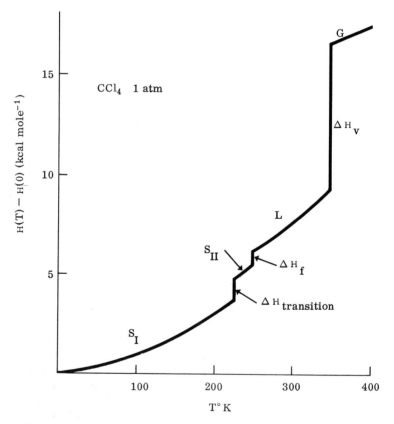

Figure 7-5
Heat content (enthalpy) of CCl_4. There is a Solid I → Solid II transition before melting.

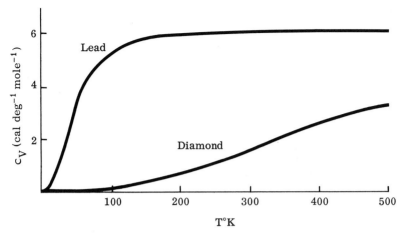

Figure 7-6
Experimental heat capacities of solid lead and diamond.

theoretical heat capacities of simple solids and ideal gases. The heat
capacity of liquids is too difficult a problem to be included in an elementary book. The theory is complicated and far from complete.

Heat capacity of monatomic solids. Figure 7-6 gives the experimental c_V as a function of T for lead (solid) and diamond. There
does not seem to be a close relationship between the two curves. But
if we plot c_V against T/Θ instead of T, where Θ is the temperature
at which c_V has reached one-half of its maximum value, we find that
the two curves in Fig. 7-6, as well as many others, fall on top of each
other. This is demonstrated in Fig. 7-7. The maximum c_V is 3R =
5.96 cal deg^{-1} mole^{-1}. We have here a law of corresponding states
for monatomic solids, or solids with single atoms at lattice points,
such as NaCl, etc. (compare Section 4-1).

The approximate theoretical explanation of the behavior in Fig.
7-7 is due to A. Einstein (1907). His theory was later refined by P.
Debye (1912). In a monatomic crystal, each atom can vibrate in three
dimensions (x, y, z) about its equilibrium position. Einstein pointed
out that the vibrational motion of the N atoms in a crystal is approximately equivalent to the vibrational motion of a collection of 3N independent and identical one-dimensional oscillators.[10] A one-dimensional oscillator in classical mechanics can have any amount of
energy, $\epsilon \geq 0$ (Fig. 7-8). The new and essential step taken by Einstein

---

[10] A one-dimensional oscillator is a particle of mass m, confined to motion
along a line (say tne x axis), and under the influence of a force f = -ax, where
a is a positive constant. This force law is called Hooke's law.

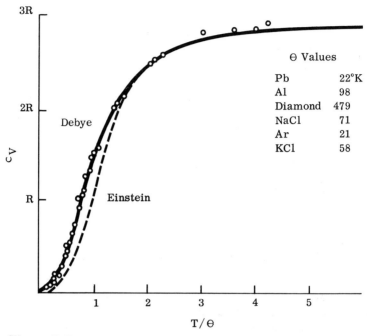

Θ Values	
Pb	22°K
Al	98
Diamond	479
NaCl	71
Ar	21
KCl	58

Figure 7-7
Heat capacity plotted against a reduced temperature: the experimental points are for Ag, graphite, Al, $Al_2 O_3$, and KCl; the curve through the points is from the Debye theory.

was to apply quantum theory (which was in its infancy at the time) rather than classical mechanics to the oscillator problem. In quantum theory, only certain discrete, equally spaced values of the energy are possible for a one-dimensional oscillator (Fig. 7-8). These values are given by

$$\epsilon_n = h\nu(n + \tfrac{1}{2}) \qquad n = 0, 1, 2, 3, \ldots \qquad (7\text{-}24)$$

where n is the quantum number, ν is the classical frequency of the vibration, and h is a fundamental, natural constant, Planck's constant (see Appendix 1), which always has a characteristic role in atomic phenomena.

An oscillator sitting still at its equilibrium position has no energy ($\epsilon = 0$) in classical mechanics (Fig. 7-8). But in quantum mechanics, the lowest possible energy is $\epsilon_0 = h\nu/2$. This is the ground state energy, which is incomprehensible in classical terms.

The probability P_n that any one oscillator will have an energy ϵ_n

at T is proportional to $e^{-\epsilon_n/kT}$, the Boltzmann factor. The probability itself is

$$P_n = \frac{e^{-\epsilon_n/kT}}{\sum\limits_{n=0}^{\infty} e^{-\epsilon_n/kT}}$$

Therefore the average energy of an oscillator is (see Appendix 3 for details)

$$\bar{\epsilon} = \sum_n \epsilon_n P_n = \sum_n \epsilon_n e^{-\epsilon_n/kT} / \sum_n e^{-\epsilon_n/kT}$$

$$= \tfrac{1}{2}h\nu + \frac{h\nu}{e^{h\nu/kT} - 1} \qquad (7\text{-}25)$$

and the energy of the crystal is $E = 3N\bar{\epsilon}$. Each crystal has its own

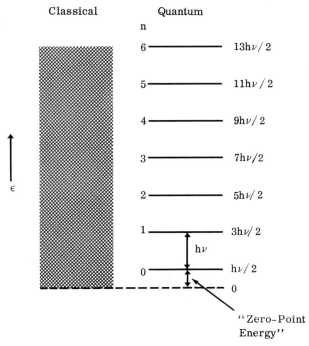

Figure 7-8
Possible values of the energy of a one-dimensional oscillator.

value of ν, which depends on the intermolecular forces. The term $3Nh\nu/2$ in E is the zero-point energy of the crystal. This amount of energy remains even at $T = 0$.

The heat capacity of the crystal is

$$C_V = \frac{\partial E}{\partial T} = \frac{3Nk \; e^{h\nu/kT} \; (h\nu/kT)^2}{(e^{h\nu/kT} - 1)^2} \tag{7-26}$$

For one mole, we put $Nk = R$. As indicated in Fig. 7-7, this function represents the experimental observations quite well, except at low temperatures (Debye's theory corrects this). The essential facts are all satisfactorily explained: (a) the high temperature limit of c_V is 3R; (b) the low temperature limit is zero; and (c) c_V is the same function of $kT/h\nu$ for all substances (law of corresponding states). Clearly ν is proportional to Θ, as defined above. Θ values for a few substances are given in Fig. 7-7. Strong intermolecular forces lead to large values of ν and Θ.

In classical mechanics, as already mentioned, any $\epsilon \geq 0$ is possible. The probability that an oscillator has an energy between ϵ and $\epsilon + d\epsilon$ is

$$\frac{e^{-\epsilon/kT} \; d\epsilon}{\int_0^\infty e^{-\epsilon/kT} \; d\epsilon}$$

Integration replaces summation because a continuous energy "spectrum" replaces a discrete one (Fig. 7-8). The average energy of an oscillator is then

$$\bar{\epsilon} = \frac{\int_0^\infty \epsilon \; e^{-\epsilon/kT} \; d\epsilon}{\int_0^\infty e^{-\epsilon/kT} \; d\epsilon} = kT \frac{\int_0^\infty y \; e^{-y} \; dy}{\int_0^\infty e^{-y} \; dy}$$

where we have put $y = \epsilon/kT$. Both integrals are equal to unity. Hence $\bar{\epsilon} = kT$, $E = 3NkT$, $C_V = 3Nk$, and $c_V = 3R$. These classical results are the same as the high temperature limit of the quantum results. Before Einstein's application of quantum theory to this problem, it was a mystery why experimental values of $c_V < 3R$ were found at low temperatures; $c_V = 3R$ was expected at all temperatures.

It is easy to see qualitatively why a set of discrete energy levels leads to the limit $C_V \rightarrow 0$ as $T \rightarrow 0$. At $T = 0$, all oscillators are in their ground state ($n = 0$, $\epsilon_0 = h\nu/2$). This is a consequence of the Boltzmann distribution: the ratio of the probability of quantum state n to quantum state $n = 0$ is

$$\frac{P_n}{P_0} = \frac{e^{-(n + \frac{1}{2})\,h\nu/kT}}{e^{-h\nu/2kT}} = e^{-nh\nu/kT}$$

and this quantity goes to zero as $T \rightarrow 0$ for $n = 1, 2, 3, \ldots$. As the temperature is raised, the population of oscillators in quantum states $n = 1, 2, 3, \ldots$ gradually increases (see Appendix 3). But practically all of the oscillators are still in the ground state at temperatures like 5 or 10°K. The basic reason why the oscillators are "stuck" in the ground state in this way is that an oscillator can absorb energy only in sizeable chunks (or quanta) of size $h\nu$ (see Fig. 7-8). If the temperature of a crystal is increased from, say, 5°K to 6°K, by changing the temperature of its heat bath, practically no heat will be absorbed by the crystal ($DQ \cong 0$) because very few of the oscillators will take in chunks of energy $h\nu$ at such a low temperature. Therefore $DQ/dT = C_V$ is practically zero. In classical mechanics an oscillator can increase its energy by <u>infinitesimal</u> amounts. Hence there is no "resistance" to heat absorption, of the above type, even at low temperatures. This leads to a classical C_V which is independent of temperature.

Heat capacity of monatomic and diatomic ideal gases. Molecules of an ideal gas can absorb energy in three essentially independent ways: (a) translational motion; (b) internal vibrational motion; and (c) rotational motion. Only the first of these applies to monatomic molecules. The situation is more complicated for imperfect gases because of the existence of intermolecular potential energy and because of the effect of intermolecular forces on the rotational motion.

<u>Monatomic ideal gases</u>. Each atom of the gas has three translational degrees of freedom (see p. 107): free motion in x, y, and z directions. The velocity and kinetic energy distributions have already been considered in Chapter 2 and Appendix 4, using classical mechanics. According to quantum mechanics, there are actually discrete translational energy levels but for an atom moving in a macroscopic volume these levels are so close together as to be practically continuous. Hence it is legitimate to use classical mechanics for the translational motion.

Equation A4-8 states that a gas of N atoms at temperature T has an energy

$$E = N\bar{\epsilon} = \tfrac{3}{2}NkT \tag{7-27}$$

where $\bar{\epsilon}$ is the average energy per atom. Therefore

$$C_V = \frac{\partial E}{\partial T} = \tfrac{3}{2}Nk, \quad c_V = \tfrac{3}{2}R \tag{7-28}$$

and, from Eq. 7-21,

$$c_p = \tfrac{5}{2}R \tag{7-29}$$

Both c_V and c_p are independent of temperature (Fig. 7-9). These theoretical values are confirmed experimentally.

Diatomic ideal gases. Because of the almost complete independence of the translational, rotational, and vibrational motion, the energy of an ideal diatomic gas can be written in the form

$$E = E_{trans} + E_{rot} + E_{vib}$$

where trans = translation, etc. Then

$$C_V = \frac{\partial E}{\partial T} = C_{V\,(trans)} + C_{V\,(rot)} + C_{V\,(vib)} \tag{7-30}$$

The translational heat capacity is just $3Nk/2$, as in Eq. 7-28 for a monatomic gas.

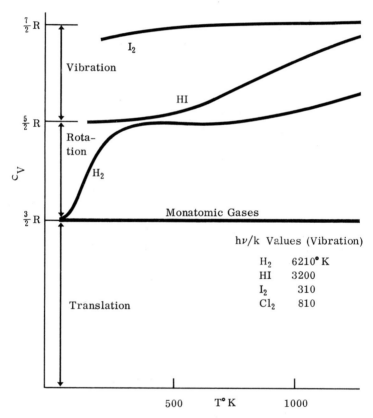

Figure 7-9
Experimental heat capacities of various dilute gases.

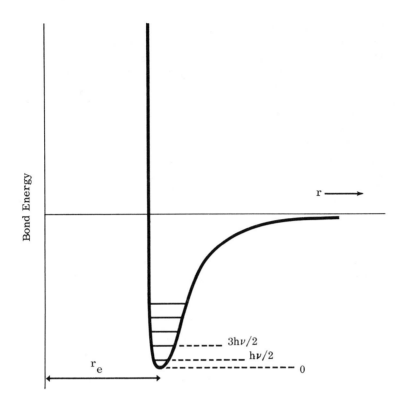

Figure 7-10
Vibrational energy levels of a diatomic molecule.

    The theoretical interpretation of $C_{V\,(vib)}$ for a diatomic gas is
virtually the same as in the Einstein theory for C_V of a monatomic
solid. The essential point is that each diatomic molecule is itself a
one-dimensional oscillator: the two atoms vibrate toward and away
from each other, and the interatomic distance r oscillates about the
equilibrium interatomic distance r_e. Figure 7-10 shows the chemical
bond energy (which serves as the potential energy for the vibrational
motion) of a typical diatomic molecule plotted as a function of interatomic distance. This curve resembles the Lennard-Jones potential
(Fig. 3-8) superficially, but only superficially. Usually r_e is only 1
or 2Å and the depth of the potential well (the <u>bond energy</u>) is ordinarily in the range 50 to 150 kcal mole^{-1}—very much larger than for
intermolecular forces. The vibration takes place in the neighborhood
of r_e (near the bottom of the well). The first few vibrational energy
levels are shown (compare Fig. 7-8).

The conclusion we reach is that, as far as the vibrational motion is concerned, a gas of N diatomic molecules may be treated as a collection of N one-dimensional oscillators. E_{vib} is equal to $N\epsilon$, where ϵ is given by Eq. 7-25. $C_{V(vib)}$ is the same as C_V in Eq. 7-26, except that the factor of three is omitted. The Einstein functions are correct in this case. The Debye refinement is unnecessary and inapplicable because it has to do with the coupling of the vibrations of the atoms of a crystal. In a diatomic gas, each molecule carries out its own independent vibrations.

Because chemical bond forces in diatomic molecules are much stronger than the intermolecular forces in most crystals, the frequency ν here is usually about ten times typical vibrational frequencies in solids. Hence the quanta of energy $h\nu$ which have to be absorbed are large and $C_{V(vib)}$ is often practically zero up to $300-400°K$ (Fig. 7-9).

The rotational motion of a diatomic molecule is equivalent from a theoretical point of view to the free motion of one particle on the surface of a sphere. There is in effect only one free particle, not two, because the two atoms of a molecule are "attached" to each other, as in a dumbbell, by the chemical bond between them. One atom may be thought of as moving freely on the sphere, but then the other has no freedom at all. As usual, there will be a Boltzmann distribution in the rotational energy (all kinetic). This is a two dimensional analogue of the translational motion of a particle in a three dimensional space. Without going into any further details, we have immediately, in classical mechanics, that

$$E_{rot} = NkT, \quad C_{V(rot)} = Nk \tag{7-31}$$

because the average energy per dimension and per particle is $kT/2$ (see p. 299).

The rotational energy levels are discrete but rather close together: the rotational quanta of energy are much smaller than the vibrational quanta. Except for H_2 (see Fig. 7-9), the classical value of $C_{V(rot)}$ is attained for common diatomic gases at temperatures in the range 10 to 60°K, depending on the gas.

Despite the resemblance, pointed out above, between translational and rotational motion, the translational energy quanta are very much smaller than the rotational quanta because the translational motion takes place in a macroscopic volume while the rotational motion occurs on a "surface" of molecular dimensions.

Typical values of the three kinds of energy quanta[11] in a diatomic molecule are:

---

[11]Typical vibrational quanta in a monatomic solid: 0.5 kcal mole^{-1}.

Vibration: 4 kcal mole^{-1}
Rotation: 0.02 kcal mole^{-1}
Translation: 10^{-17} kcal mole^{-1}

These energies can be derived from quantum mechanics, or in the first two cases, from experimental spectroscopy. A rough estimate of the temperature at which the classical value of the heat capacity is reached, in each of the three cases, may be made by putting RT equal to, say, two times the energy above. This is because the Boltzmann factor $e^{-\epsilon/kT}$ has practically the same value for adjacent energy levels if kT is much larger than the energy level difference. When this is the case, the discrete energy levels become <u>effectively</u> continuous (as in classical mechanics). Let us calculate the above mentioned temperature:

Vibration: RT = 2 × 4,000 cal mole^{-1} deg^{-1}; T = 4000°K
Rotation: RT = 2 × 20 cal mole^{-1} deg^{-1};   T = 20°K
Translation: RT = 2 × 10^{-14} cal mole^{-1} deg^{-1}; T = 10^{-14}°K

Let us now summarize the above results, for a typical molecule. At temperatures between 20°K and 400°K, translation and rotation are both classical while $c_{V(vib)}$ is still practically zero:

$$c_V = c_{V(trans)} + c_{V(rot)} + c_{V(vib)}$$

$$= \tfrac{3}{2}R + R + 0 = \tfrac{5}{2}R$$

Below 20°K, $c_{V(rot)} < R$ and $c_V < 5R/2$. Above 400°K, $c_{V(vib)} > 0$ and $c_V > 5R/2$. At about 4000°K, vibration is also classical and

$$c_V = \tfrac{3}{2}R + R + R = \tfrac{7}{2}R \tag{7-32}$$

Figure 7-9 gives c_V as a function of T for the ideal gases I_2, HI, and H_2. Of these, HI is typical while the other two gases are unusual (because of their weights).

In all of these cases, $c_p = c_V + R$.

There is one final point that must be mentioned. The reader may have noticed that the <u>classical</u> $c_{V(trans)} = 3R/2$ (three degrees of freedom), $c_{V(rot)} = \overline{2R/2}$ (two degrees of freedom), but $c_{V(vib)} = 2R/2$ (<u>one</u> degree of freedom). The explanation of the "double value" for vibration is that translation and rotation have only kinetic energy associated with them, but the vibrational degree of freedom has in addition an average <u>potential</u> energy equal to the average kinetic energy.

7-3   REVERSIBLE AND IRREVERSIBLE EXPANSIONS
OF AN IDEAL GAS

THE OBJECT of this section is to apply the first law to a few simple
processes, as illustrations. There is quite a bit of unavoidable
mathematics here, but it is not complicated.

A precautionary comment: An ideal gas is used in the following,
and most of the equations are valid for an ideal gas only. But thermodynamics applies to <u>any</u> sample of matter in equilibrium. Ideal gas
equations must not be confused with <u>general</u> thermodynamic equations.

We choose as our system an ideal gas with heat capacity $C_V(T)$.
We shall apply the first law to four different processes, all starting
from the state n, p_1, V_1, T_2 and ending at the state n, p_2, V_2, T_2.
In Fig. 7-11, the processes are labeled A, B + C, D + F, and G. The
first three are reversible processes proceeding along different paths
in the p-V diagram, but the fourth is an irreversible process.

Before examining each of these processes in turn, let us make a
few general deductions that necessarily apply to all of them. The
energy of an ideal gas depends on T only (with n constant, as
usual), and in all of these processes the initial temperature is the
same as the final temperature. Therefore $\Delta E = 0$. It then follows
that Q = W. Although we must have Q = W for each process, the
values of Q and W will depend on the process (because Q and W are
not state functions). Incidentally, since $p_1 V_1 = p_2 V_2$ and H = E + pV,
$\Delta H = 0$ as well.

For any process with initial and final states n, p_1, V_1, T_2 and
n, p_2, V_2, T_2, respectively, carried out on a system <u>other</u> than an
ideal gas (imperfect gas, liquid, or solid), we would expect $\Delta E \neq 0$,
$\Delta H \neq 0$, and $Q \neq W$. But the values of ΔE and ΔH would be independent of the process.

Process A: Reversible isothermal expansion. The gas is kept in a
heat bath at T_2 and its volume gradually increased from V_1 to V_2.
Since E depends only on T, and T is constant,

$$dE = 0 = DQ - DW$$

$$DQ = DW = pdV = \frac{nRT_2}{V} dV$$

Therefore, in this process (subscript A),

$$Q_A = W_A = nRT_2 \int_{V_1}^{V_2} \frac{dV}{V}$$

$$= nRT_2 \ln \frac{V_2}{V_1}$$

$$= 2.303 \ nRT_2 \log \frac{V_2}{V_1} \qquad (7\text{-}33)$$

$$\Delta E_A = Q_A - W_A = 0 \qquad (7\text{-}34)$$

(see Appendix 1 concerning logarithms). In process A, the system takes in heat from the bath and converts it into work. The energy of the system itself does not change. The gas merely passes the energy from the bath to whatever machine is linked to the piston.

Process B + C: reversible adiabatic expansion. In this process the gas is first (B) expanded reversibly and adiabatically (DQ = 0) from V_1 to V_2 by placing thermal insulation around the system. As we shall see, the temperature decreases during this expansion. Let the temperature reached at V_2 be called T_α. We then (C) have to heat the gas gradually from T_α to T_2, keeping V_2 constant (Fig. 7-11). This could be done by removing the thermal insulation, placing the system in a heat bath at T_α, and slowly raising the temperature of the bath to T_2.

In the adiabatic expansion,

$$DQ = 0 \text{ and } dE = -DW$$

Since E is a function of T only,

$$dE = \left(\frac{\partial E}{\partial T}\right)_V dT = C_V(T) \, dT = -p \, dV \qquad (7\text{-}35)$$

In the expansion, the system does work (dV > 0) on the surroundings. As there is no heat bath in this case, this energy must come from the system itself. That is, dE < 0. This results in a decrease in temperature (dT < 0). Since C_V and p are both positive quantities, Eq. 7-35 verifies that dV and dT have opposite signs.

Integration of Eq. 7-35 over the path B leads to

$$\Delta E_B = \int_{T_2}^{T_\alpha} C_V(T) \, dT = -W_B \qquad Q_B = 0 \qquad (7\text{-}36)$$

In process C, dV = 0 and

$$dE = C_V(T) \, dT = DQ$$

Integration gives

$$\Delta E_C = \int_{T_\alpha}^{T_2} C_V(T) \, dT = Q_C \qquad W_C = 0 \qquad (7\text{-}37)$$

For the whole process, then,

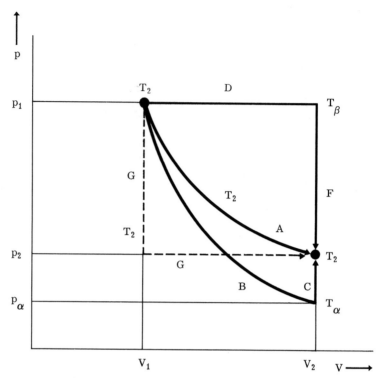

Figure 7-11
Thermodynamic processes discussed in text.

$$Q_{B+C} = W_{B+C} = \int_{T_\alpha}^{T_2} C_V(T)\, dT \qquad (7\text{-}38)$$

$$\Delta E_{B+C} = Q_{B+C} - W_{B+C} = 0 \qquad (7\text{-}39)$$

Process D + F. Process D is a reversible expansion at constant pressure p_1. This could be accomplished by gradually heating the system, keeping a constant weight (pressure) on the piston. Let T_β be the final temperature ($T_\beta = p_1 V_2/nR$). We have

$$dE = C_V(T)\, dT = DQ - p_1\, dV$$

On integration of this equation, we find

$$\Delta E_D = \int_{T_2}^{T_\beta} C_V(T)\, dT$$

$$W_D = p_1(V_2 - V_1)$$

$$Q_D = \int_{T_2}^{T_\beta} C_V(T)\, dT + p_1(V_2 - V_1)$$

Process F is practically the same as process C. We have

$$\Delta E_F = \int_{T_\beta}^{T_2} C_V(T)\, dT = Q_F \qquad W_F = 0$$

For the complete process,

$$Q_{D+F} = W_{D+F} = p_1(V_2 - V_1) \tag{7-40}$$

$$\Delta E_{D+F} = Q_{D+F} - W_{D+F} = 0 \tag{7-41}$$

Process G: irreversible expansion at p_2. In this process we start with the system in a heat bath at T_2 and a sufficient weight on the piston to give a pressure p_i. This weight is suddenly exchanged for a smaller one which produces a pressure p_2. The heat bath is not changed. The gas will then expand spontaneously and irreversibly from V_1 to V_2, with $p_{ex} = p_2$ (see Eq. 7-6). Because there are no intermolecular forces, the temperature inside the system will remain at T_2 despite the sudden expansion. The pressure inside the system will be ill-defined until final equilibrium is reached at p_2, V_2, T_2. This process is indicated by the dashed path G in Fig. 7-11.

Since ΔE depends only on initial and final states,

$$\Delta E_G = 0 = Q_G - W_G \tag{7-42}$$

Furthermore,

$$W_G = p_{ex}(V_2 - V_1) = p_2(V_2 - V_1) = Q_G \tag{7-43}$$

In summary, we see that W_A, W_{B+C}, W_{D+F}, and W_G all have different values. In each case, W is equal to the area under the appropriate curve in Fig. 7-11. Also, $Q = W$ and $\Delta E = 0$.

The integral of DQ/T. As a final topic in this chapter, we make a calculation involving the above processes that will prove useful in the next chapter.

First, consider the reversible processes A, B + C, and D + F only. We have seen that $\int DQ = Q$ depends on the path: $Q_A \neq Q_{B+C} \neq Q_{D+F}$. But if we calculate $\int DQ/T$ instead of $\int DQ$, we get a result that is the $\underline{same}$ for all three paths! This suggests that a new state function might be defined by d (state function) = $(1/T)DQ$ (reversible). This idea is used in the next chapter.

Let us now verify the statement that $\int DQ/T$ is the same for the paths A, B + C, and D + F.

In process A, T has the constant value T_2. Therefore

$$\int_A \frac{DQ}{T} = \frac{1}{T_2} \int_A DQ = \frac{Q_A}{T_2} = nR \ln \frac{V_2}{V_1} \qquad (7\text{-}44)$$

In process B, $\int_B DQ/T = 0$. But, in connection with this process, let us derive a relation needed below. If we divide Eq. 7-35 by T and then integrate, we find that

$$\int_{T_2}^{T_\alpha} \frac{C_V(T)}{T}\, dT = -nR \int_{V_1}^{V_2} \frac{dV}{V} = -nR \ln \frac{V_2}{V_1} \qquad (7\text{-}45)$$

This equation allows one to calculate T_α if $C_V(T)$ is known and n, V_1, V_2, and T_2 are given. In process C,

$$\int_C \frac{DQ}{T} = \int_{T_\alpha}^{T_2} \frac{C_V(T)}{T}\, dT = nR \ln \frac{V_2}{V_1}$$

where we have used Eq. 7-45 in the last step. Thus

$$\int_{B+C} \frac{DQ}{T} = nR \ln \frac{V_2}{V_1} \qquad (7\text{-}46)$$

In process D,

$$\int_D \frac{DQ}{T} = \int_{T_2}^{T_\beta} \frac{C_V(T)}{T}\, dT + p_1 \int_{V_1}^{V_2} \frac{dV}{T}$$

The equation of state along path D is $p_1 V = nRT$. We use this in the last term above and obtain

$$\int_D \frac{DQ}{T} = \int_{T_2}^{T_\beta} \frac{C_V(T)}{T} \, dT + nR \ln \frac{V_2}{V_1}$$

In process F,

$$\int_F \frac{DQ}{T} = \int_{T_\beta}^{T_2} \frac{C_V(T)}{T} \, dT$$

We add the last two equations to get

$$\int_{D+F} \frac{DQ}{T} = nR \ln \frac{V_2}{V_1} \tag{7-47}$$

On comparing Eqs. 7-44, 7-46, and 7-47, we see, indeed, that $\int DQ/T$ does have the same value in the three cases.

Finally, we calculate $\int DQ/T$ for the irreversible path G. Since T has the constant value T_2,

$$\int_G \frac{DQ}{T} = \frac{1}{T_2} \int_G DQ = \frac{Q_G}{T_2}$$

$$= \frac{p_2(V_2 - V_1)}{T_2} = nR\left(1 - \frac{V_1}{V_2}\right) \tag{7-48}$$

This result, for an irreversible path, is <u>not</u> the same as for the three reversible paths above. There are several ways to prove that ln (V_2/V_1) is larger than $1 - (V_1/V_2)$ when $V_2/V_1 > 1$. But this is left to the reader.

PROBLEMS

7-1. Calculate the heat capacity in cal deg^{-1} mole^{-1} of a liquid 10.0 cm^3 of which is increased in temperature by $0.50°$C on absorption of 6.00 cal of heat. Density = 1.20g/cm^3. Molecular weight = 60.

7-2. 100 liters of gaseous helium at STP are gradually (reversibly) heated to 100°C at constant volume. Calculate, for this process, Q, W, ΔV, Δp, ΔE and ΔH. Assume the gas is ideal with $c_V = 3R/2$.

7-3. Calculate the heat Q required gradually to raise the temperature of one mole of HBr gas (ideal) at 1 atm pressure (held constant) from 0° to 500°C. Also calculate ΔH and ΔE for the process. The heat capacity of HBr in this temperature range is c_p (cal deg^{-1} mole^{-1}) $= a + bT + cT^2$, where a = 6.578, b = 0.955×10^{-3}, c = 1.581×10^{-7}.

7-4. The heat of vaporization of liquid Na at 1 atm and 1172°K (normal boiling point) is 23,700 cal mole^{-1}. Calculate ΔE for the process:

10 g liquid Na at normal boiling point → 10 g vapor at normal boiling point.

CHAPTER 8

SECOND LAW
OF THERMODYNAMICS

THE FIRST LAW or postulate of thermodynamics has to do with energy transfer into and out of a thermodynamic system. It is a very practical and useful law, but not particularly interesting because it is a little too obvious. But the second law is rather strange and somewhat more difficult to comprehend. Furthermore, the scope of thermodynamics is very considerably broadened by the introduction of the second law.

From the point of view of physical chemistry or molecular physics,[1] the second law is concerned, basically, with the subject of the relative stability of different thermodynamic states, and with the related questions of the direction of spontaneous processes between states and the criteria for stable equilibrium in thermodynamic systems. Examples: (1) if we start with a certain liquid at a given p and T, will it remain a liquid or will it change spontaneously into gas, or into solid? (2) If H_2 gas and Cl_2 gas are mixed under definite conditions, with a catalyst present, to what extent will HCl molecules be formed and what thermodynamic principle determines

---

[1]An engineer would probably have a somewhat different point of view.

this extent? (3) Why is it that a gas mixture does not spontaneously
unmix? The remainder of the book will be devoted largely to answer-
ing questions of this sort. The basic principles involved are introduced in this chapter.

The third law of thermodynamics is by no means as significant
and far reaching as the first two laws. It will be mentioned rather
briefly in Section 8-4.

The second law will be stated in Section 8-2. But instead of pro-
ducing it out of thin air, so to speak, we devote Section 8-1 to an intuitive kind of argument that will make the statement of the law at
least plausible. This is <u>not</u> a derivation but rather a train of thought
which suggests our statement of the second law in Section 8-2 as a
reasonable possibility. That the "reasonable possibility" in fact turns
out to be the truth has been ascertained by comparing deductions
from the second law with experiment.

The above is a very common procedure in research in theoretical
physics and chemistry. Intuition, half-baked arguments, and vague
presentiments lead to the suggestion of a proposition or theory; the
theory is then checked against experiment, usually with negative results; but occasionally the guess as to how nature really works turns
out to be right!

8-1 INTRODUCTION

IF MORE than one state[2] is conceivable for a thermodynamic system
with specified variables (e.g., p, T, n_1, n_2, ...), what <u>thermodynamic</u>
criterion determines the particular state that is most stable? In other
words, if the system is able to pass from one to another of these
states, in which state will it end up? This is one way to put the question we wish to pursue in this chapter. Of course it is possible that
no general criterion (or criteria) of this sort exists, but we shall proceed on the assumption that it does.

If two states, say 1 and 2, are possible and 2 is the more stable
state, then state 1 will tend to go over into state 2 spontaneously, although in some cases the rate of the process may be slow or even
practically zero. By "spontaneous," we mean a process that occurs
without any assistance or restraint from the outside. The process is
therefore uncontrolled and irreversible. In fact, any irreversible
process may be conceived of as a succession of one, a few, or many
spontaneous, internal adjustments or responses of the system that
follow upon changes in its condition imposed from outside. For example: a catalyst might be added allowing a chemical reaction to

---

[2]We mean "state" in the general sense (p. 118), not just gas vs liquid vs
solid.

proceed; a partition might be removed allowing a gas to expand into a larger volume; the temperature of the heat bath surrounding a system might be increased steadily and at a finite rate; a piston might be pushed into a system at a finite rate forcing its compression; etc. We shall use the terms "spontaneous" and "irreversible" more or less interchangeably.

Clearly, an alternative criterion, equivalent to the one mentioned above, would indicate the direction (e.g., 1 → 2, above) of spontaneous processes between possible states.

We have already noted several times (pp. 79, 106) that for temperatures near 0°K an apparent stability criterion is that the stable state is the one with lowest potential energy. Since we seek a thermodynamic criterion, and potential energy, by itself, does not appear in thermodynamics, we surmise that the low temperature criterion is actually: the stable state is the one with lowest E. This is reasonable because there is practically no difference between U and E at 0°K. The kinetic energy is very small; only the zero point kinetic energy remains.

According to this criterion, a spontaneous process between two possible states at very low constant temperature will occur in such a direction that E decreases: $dE < 0$. For example: liquid → solid at 0°K. Or one could say that the spontaneous process takes place in such a direction that E approaches its minimum possible value: E → minimum. After all possible spontaneous processes have occurred, the final (stable) equilibrium state of the system is the one with minimum energy; the other states passed through are metastable relative to the final state.

It is perfectly clear, however, that the criterion E = minimum is not a general criterion for relative stability of states nor is $dE < 0$ or E → minimum a general criterion for the direction of spontaneous processes. To see this, we need only look at a few special cases.

(1) Under certain conditions of p and T the gas (or liquid) state for any substance exists. That is, the gas is more stable than the solid. For such values of p and T, solid → gas spontaneously. But E increases in this process!

(2) There is a distribution of N_2 and O_2 molecules in the earth's gravitational field. But according to the principle E → minimum, all of the N_2 and O_2 would condense on the surface because that is where the (potential) energy is lowest.

(3) At very high temperatures, gaseous H_2 molecules dissociate somewhat into H atoms. But H_2 has a lower energy than 2H (because of the chemical bond).

(4) Spontaneous processes of all sorts can occur in isolated systems. For example: mixing of two gases; chemical reaction; expansion of a gas into a vacuum; etc. But E = const in isolated systems.

If we look over the above examples, and many more like them, we observe that besides the tendency dE $<$ 0 or E $\rightarrow$ minimum in spontaneous processes, there is a second and quite different tendency in operation. Namely, the molecules or atoms of the system tend to seek as random or disordered an arrangement as possible. The fundamental reason for this is very simple. There are many more ways for a collection of molecules or atoms to be disordered than to be ordered; consequently, if we ignore the energy, disordered structures have a higher probability than ordered ones. For example, if a large number of billiard balls are dumped into a barrel, the chance that the balls would be observed in an ordered (crystal-like) structure is practically zero. An almost equivalent statement is that a crystal has an extremely improbable molecular arrangement compared to a liquid. But the other effect, the energy, swings the stability balance in favor of the crystal at low temperatures.

In Example (1), above, the gas is more disordered than the solid, but the solid has the lower energy. In Example (2), the actual distribution of N_2 and O_2 molecules in the atmosphere (see Problem 10-9) represents a more disordered state than if all the molecules were on the earth's surface. The observed distribution is clearly some kind of compromise between low energy and high disorder. In Example (3), a gas of 2N hydrogen atoms is more disordered than a gas of N hydrogen molecules. For in the former case all of the 2N atoms move freely in the container while in the latter case N atoms move freely but each of the other N atoms has to stay within about 1Å of one of the first group of N atoms. But the molecules have a lower energy than the atoms. The actual amount of dissociation observed is again a compromise between low energy and high disorder.

There appears to be a sort of competition between energy and disorder, with low energy dominating in the stability criterion at low temperatures and high disorder dominating at high temperatures (e.g., solid $\rightarrow$ gas, $H_2 \rightarrow$ 2H, etc., at high temperatures). Energy and disorder seem equally important. By analogy with E, we are thus led to anticipate or surmise that a disorder state function should exist with the property d (disorder) $>$ 0, disorder $\rightarrow$ maximum in spontaneous processes at high temperatures.

We therefore seek a new disorder state function. After we have it, or think we have it, the next problem will be to combine it properly with the energy to give a general stability criterion, or criteria.

Disorder state function. We associate molecular disorder with chaotic ''thermal'' motion. The more heat a system has absorbed, the more chaotic or disordered it is. Example: solid $\rightarrow$ liquid $\rightarrow$ gas if heat is put steadily into a system, initially solid, at constant pressure. As a first guess, therefore, we might be inclined to use Q itself for the new disorder function. The difficulty with this is that Q is not a state function. But still heat and disorder seem so intimately related we look next for some modification of Q, if we cannot use Q itself.

This is a general problem but let us see if we can get a hint or suggestion from a simple special case. Consider a reversible, infinitesimal change in the volume and temperature of an ideal gas. We have, since E is independent of V,

$$dE = C_V(T) \, dT = DQ - p \, dV$$

or

$$DQ = C_V(T) \, dT + \frac{nRT}{V} \, dV \tag{8-1}$$

If Q were a state function, the right-hand side of Eq. 8-1 could be written as the differential of a state function. This can be done with the first term on the right, for it is a function of one variable only and can be written as $d(\int C_V(T) \, dT + c)$ (see Eq. A2-5b), where c is an integration constant. But the combination $(T/V) \, dV$ in the second term is like $p \, dV$ on p. 124. It cannot be put in the form d (function of T and V). However, we notice a very simple thing: if we divide Eq. 8-1 through by T, we get

$$\frac{DQ}{T} = \frac{C_V(T)}{T} \, dT + \frac{nR}{V} \, dV$$

and now the right-hand side <u>is</u> the differential of a state function! Specifically,

$$\frac{DQ}{T} = d\left[\int \frac{C_V(T)}{T} \, dT + nR \ln V + c \right] \tag{8-2}$$

The quantity in square brackets is a function of the state variables V, T, and n.

At this point it should be recalled that we found a closely related result in Eqs. 7-44 to 7-47: the integral of DQ/T, for an ideal gas, along several reversible paths connecting the same end points gives a result independent of path. Equation 8-2 is a little more general, for <u>any</u> reversible path connecting an initial state T_1, V_1 and a final state T_2, V_2 may be used, with the result:

$$\int_1^2 \frac{DQ}{T} = \int_{T_1}^{T_2} \frac{C_V(T)}{T} \, dT + nR \ln \frac{V_2}{V_1} \tag{8-3}$$

Note that the integration constant cancels.

For an ideal gas, then, DQ/T = d (state function), in a reversible process. We shall postulate in Section 8-2, as part of the second law, that this is true for any substance, not just an ideal gas. It is at any rate certain that in a general law, T^{-1} is the only possible function of T which, when multiplied by DQ, converts DQ into the differential of a state function. This follows because T^{-1} is the only such possibility in Eq. 8-1 for an ideal gas.

Since T, as well as Q, is associated with the extent of thermal motion and disorder in a system, it is not surprising to find T combined with Q in the expression DQ/T. If we define disorder through the equation DQ/T = d (disorder), we see that an amount of heat DQ put into a system at a high temperature increases the disorder less than the same amount of heat put in at a low temperature. This is not unreasonable, for the lower the temperature the more ordered the system and hence the greater the opportunities for the heat DQ to mess up the order.

We have indicated that DQ/T = d (disorder), for a reversible process, will be used below as part of our second postulate or law. But the disorder state function so introduced is usually called the entropy and given the symbol S. We shall use this nomenclature from now on.

Entropy in irreversible processes. We have seen above that both energy and entropy (disorder), are ordinarily involved in determining the direction of spontaneous processes in thermodynamic systems. But only energy is important at very low temperatures. It should be a help in understanding the role of entropy if we could look at some special cases in which only entropy is important. There are a number of choices. For example, in any spontaneous process taking place in an isolated system [see (4), p. 153], the entropy must be the crucial variable because the energy is necessarily constant.

Let us therefore consider any infinitesimal spontaneous process in an isolated system. Since the energy cannot change, the driving force for the spontaneous process is the tendency of the disorder or entropy of the system to increase. That is, in the process, $dS > 0$. The heat absorbed in the process is $DQ_{irrev} = 0$, since the system is isolated. So instead of $dS = DQ_{irrev}/T$ we have that $dS > DQ_{irrev}/T$. If the system (no longer isolated) had gone reversibly from the same initial to the same final state as in the spontaneous process, dS would have the same value (S is supposed to be a state function) and $dS = DQ_{rev}/T$. Therefore $DQ_{rev} > 0$ and[3] $DQ_{rev} > DQ_{irrev}$.

The inequality $dS > DQ_{irrev}/T$ applies to any spontaneous infinitesimal process in an isolated system. In a reversible process

---

[3]Compare Eq. 7-48 and the comments following this equation.

with $DQ > 0$, S increases because heat (with its attendant disorder) is brought into the system from outside. But in an isolated system $DQ_{irrev} = 0$. No heat enters the system, yet $dS > 0$. Conclusion: entropy is <u>produced</u> or <u>created</u> <u>inside</u> the system by the spontaneous (irreversible) process itself.

Although we have had in mind here a spontaneous process in an isolated system, this last remark is just as appealing intuitively when applied to <u>any</u> infinitesimal reversible or irreversible process (in an isolated system or not). Let us try out this idea. That is, we think of there being two contributions to dS in <u>any</u> infinitesimal process. One is equal to DQ/T, where DQ is the heat absorbed by the system from its surroundings (this could be positive or negative). We call this $(dS)_{ext}$ (ext = external). The other is the entropy produced or disorder created inside the system, $(dS)_{int}$ (int = internal) owing to any irreversibility in the process. For an irreversible process $(dS)_{int} > 0$; for a reversible process $(dS)_{int} = 0$. Putting this together:

Any process: $\qquad\qquad dS = (dS)_{int} + (dS)_{ext} = (dS)_{int} + (DQ/T)$

Reversible process: $\quad (dS)_{int} = 0, \ dS = DQ_{rev}/T$

Irreversible process: $(dS)_{int} > 0, \ dS > DQ_{irrev}/T$

In an isolated system, $DQ = 0$ and $dS = (dS)_{int} \geq 0$.

This scheme appears to be satisfactory as far as it goes, but what about combining E and S to furnish a general criterion for the direction of spontaneous processes? This seems to work too. For we have, in a spontaneous process,

$$dE = DQ_{irrev} - pdV$$

$$< TdS - pdV$$

since $TdS > DQ_{irrev}$. If we rearrange terms,

$$dE - TdS + pdV < 0 \qquad\qquad\qquad (8\text{-}4)$$

Here we see a combination of E and S in a single criterion of the type sought. There is an additional term, pdV, to complicate matters slightly but we might anticipate that this term is relatively

unimportant. We also note that certain special cases of 8-4 are essentially[4] those previously referred to a number of times:

$$dE < 0 \quad \text{if } T = 0 \text{ and } V = \text{const}$$

$$dS > 0 \quad \text{if } T = \text{large and constant, and } V = \text{const}$$

$$dS > 0 \quad \text{if } E = \text{constant and } V = \text{const (isolated system)}$$

In the high temperature case, we are assuming (and this turns out to
be correct) that in the expression $d(E - TS) < 0$, E becomes small
compared to TS as $T \to \infty$ because both T and S increase with T.

We shall not pursue this subject any further here because, it will
be recalled, the whole argument in this section is supposed to be sug-
gestive only. In this argument we have followed one guess or intuitive step by another. But the over-all structure we have built is
just the sort of thing we originally set out to find. Therefore, in the
next section, we formulate the second law of thermodynamics in accordance with the ideas of the present section. There is every
reason to believe that this particular version of the law happens to
be an actual law of nature, because up to the present time deductions
from it have all been found to be consistent with experimental observations. Furthermore, the molecular theory of the equilibrium
properties of matter—which rests on an entirely different foundation—proves to be in full accord with this second postulate of thermodynamics. Section 8-4 will give some indication of this.

8-2 SECOND LAW OF THERMODYNAMICS

WITH THE above background in mind, we now state the second law
or postulate of thermodynamics. We emphasize that the postulate applies to any kind of macroscopic substance in equilibrium—gas,
liquid, solid, solution (of any type), chemical equilibrium mixture,
etc. The second law has been tested successfully with a great variety of thermodynamic systems; but we postulate that it will apply to all substances—including those not yet tested or even discovered.

Any macroscopic, equilibrium system possesses a state function
called the entropy, S, with the following properties: (a) in an infinitesimal, reversible process

---

[4]We shall not worry about the difference between V = const and p = const at
this preliminary stage. See Section 8-5.

$$dS = \frac{DQ_{rev}}{T} \qquad\qquad (8\text{-}5)$$

(b) in an infinitesimal, irreversible process

$$dS > \frac{DQ_{irrev}}{T} \qquad\qquad (8\text{-}6)$$

Although we consider S to be a measure of the amount of disorder in a system, this interpretation of S is not part of the postulate. The concept of molecular disorder was essential as an intuitive aid in Section 8-1, but now we want to separate logic from intuition. The subject of entropy as disorder will be taken up again in Section 8-4.

As we shall see, the inequality 8-6 will allow us to predict the direction of spontaneous processes in macroscopic systems and hence is of major importance in science. However 8-6 is not useful unless we have a quantitative way to measure the difference in entropy between two states; but such a way is provided by Eq. 8-5. The two relations are often combined:

$$dS \geq \frac{DQ}{T} \qquad\qquad (8\text{-}7)$$

where the equality holds for a reversible process and the inequality for an irreversible process. DQ may be positive or negative.

Still another way to express the second law is the following. For any infinitesimal process,

$$dS = (dS)_{int} + (dS)_{ext}$$
$$\qquad\qquad (8\text{-}8)$$
$$(dS)_{int} \geq 0, \quad (dS)_{ext} = \frac{DQ}{T}$$

There are two contributions to dS: heat DQ entering or leaving the system from outside is responsible for the entropy change $(dS)_{ext} = DQ/T$; in addition, if the process is irreversible, the irreversibility itself, inside the system, contributes to an increase in disorder or entropy, $(dS)_{int} > 0$. Thus, for a reversible process,

$$(dS)_{int} = 0, \quad (dS)_{ext} = \frac{DQ_{rev}}{T}, \quad dS = \frac{DQ_{rev}}{T} \qquad (8\text{-}9)$$

while for an irreversible process,

$$(dS)_{int} > 0, \quad (dS)_{ext} = \frac{DQ_{irrev}}{T}, \quad dS > \frac{DQ_{irrev}}{T} \qquad (8\text{-}10)$$

Experimental tests of the second law are usually rather indirect. But direct tests are possible in principle. For example, take any macroscopic sample of matter at p_1, T_1 and, in separate experiments, slowly change the state of the sample to p_2, T_2 by several different processes, or paths (see Fig. 7-11, for example). Along each path measure the heat exchange with the surrounding bath. Then, if $\int DQ/T$ is calculated for each path, the same value should be found in all cases (the more slowly the processes are carried out, the closer will be the agreement). This kind of result verifies that the entropy, as introduced in Eq. 8-5, is indeed a state function.

To test 8-6 on the same sample of matter, any irreversible process is used to pass from p_1, T_1 to p_2, T_2. Again the heat exchange with the surroundings is measured. It should be found that $\int DQ_{irrev}/T$ is <u>less</u> than the value of $\int DQ/T$ obtained from the (almost) reversible paths referred to above. This follows because: (a) ΔS has the same value for <u>any</u> process, reversible or irreversible, connecting the states p_1, T_1 and p_2, T_2 (S is a state function); (b) any reversible path can be used to measure ΔS by means of the relation $\Delta S = \int DQ/T$; (c) for any irreversible path $\Delta S > \int DQ_{irrev}/T$; therefore (d) $\int DQ/T$ for any reversible path is greater than $\int DQ_{irrev}/T$ for any irreversible path connecting the same two states.

Indeed, we have the general, practical rule: the value of ΔS for any <u>irreversible</u> process cannot be found directly from $\int DQ_{irrev}/T$ but rather ΔS is equal to $\int DQ/T$ measured along <u>any reversible</u> path connecting the initial and final states of the irreversible process.

Isolated system. The above discussion is necessarily rather abstract because we have been introducing a <u>general</u> law. We turn now to the special case of isolated systems. The physical significance of the entropy is relatively easy to understand in relation to this special class of systems. We shall begin to see here that at least some deductions from the second law do agree with common experience or intuition.

We recall (p. 125) that an isolated system has a constant volume (W = 0) and is thermally insulated from the outside world (Q = 0). Therefore, for any process taking place in an isolated system, $\Delta E = 0$ or E = const. But the entropy is not necessarily constant. In fact the second law states, for such a system, that

$$(dS)_{int} = 0, \ (dS)_{ext} = 0; \quad dS = 0 \quad \text{(reversible process)}$$

$$(dS)_{int} > 0, \ (dS)_{ext} = 0; \quad dS > 0 \quad \text{(irreversible process)}$$

$$(8\text{-}11)$$

The implication of these relations is that if any spontaneous process whatever can occur in an isolated system, the entropy or disorder will increase $(dS > 0)$ during the process. If several different spontaneous processes can occur, together or successively, S will increase during all of them. When the system finally exhausts all available spontaneous processes, that is, when it reaches equilibrium, the entropy or disorder will have attained its highest possible value consistent with the way the system was made up in the first place (volume, mole numbers, etc.).

At equilibrium, then, S = const and dS = 0. Any small spontaneous fluctuation in the state of the system at equilibrium amounts to a reversible process with dS = 0. This is the only kind of re-versible process possible in an isolated system because outside controls on what is taking place inside the system are not permitted (or the system would not be isolated).

Figure 8-1 illustrates the above comments schematically. The entropy of an isolated system is plotted against time. The entropy increases as time passes until equilibrium is finally reached. Then $S = S_{max}$ = const. In summary: S → maximum in an isolated system.

Suppose a sample of matter has a higher entropy in state 2 than in state 1 $(S_2 - S_1 > 0)$, but E and V have the same values in the two states $(E_1 = E_2, \ V_1 = V_2)$. The entropy difference $S_2 - S_1$ would have to be measured, incidentally, using a reversible process with the sample not isolated. Now the second law predicts that if the sample is isolated in state 1, and maintained in isolation, it is possible for it to pass spontaneously into state 2, because the entropy would increase in this case. But the second law also predicts that if the sample is isolated in state 2 it will never pass spontaneously into state 1, because this would involve an entropy decrease. Of course the first process, 1 → 2, may not actually be observed within a reasonable period of time because its rate might be extremely slow.

This is an example of what we mean by the second law of thermodynamics predicting the direction of spontaneous processes. In an isolated system, the entropy is the state function that determines the direction $(dS > 0)$ of spontaneous processes. In nonisolated systems, other state functions are involved in a similar way (Section 8-5).

The condition $dS > 0$ for spontaneous processes in an isolated

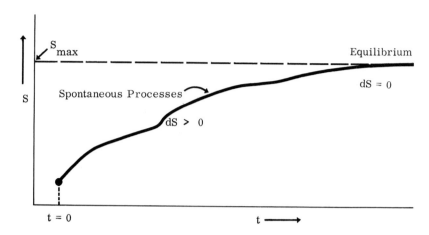

Figure 8-1
Schematic representation of entropy increase in isolated system.

system agrees with the qualitative discussion in Section 8-1. For in an isolated system the energy is forced to stay constant (because of the first law: conservation of energy). Hence the disorder or entropy is left as the only factor involved in the determination of the final stable or equilibrium state of a system. There is a natural tendency for the disorder of a molecular system to increase. In an isolated system the disorder does not have to reach a compromise with the energy. Therefore entropy or disorder will go spontaneously to its highest possible value (Fig. 8-1).

The final equilibrium state in an isolated system is characterized by $dS = 0$ or S = maximum (Fig. 8-1). Therefore the second law can be said to determine not only the direction of spontaneous processes ($dS > 0$) but it also furnishes the criterion for final equilibrium: S = maximum.

Examples. We indicate very briefly here a few examples of spontaneous processes in isolated systems. Some of these cases will be discussed quantitatively in Section 8-3. Figure 8-2 shows the systems we shall consider. In every case the volume is held constant and the outside walls are thermally insulated (indicated by double lines). For all these processes $\Delta E = 0$ and $\Delta S > 0$.

(a) In the initial state a gas is to the left of a removable partition and a vacuum is to the right. The process is initiated by suddenly pulling out the partition. The gas will diffuse spontaneously into the entire container. In the final state the gas density is uniform. If the gas is nonideal, its temperature will change in the process (though E = const). The final state is more disordered (has a higher entropy) than the initial state because each molecule can wander

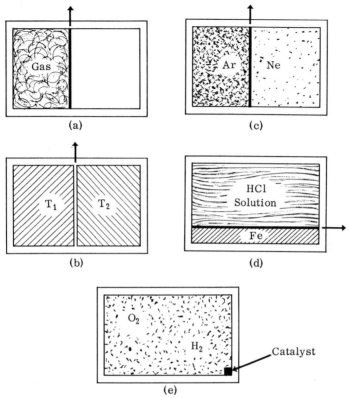

Figure 8-2
Irreversible processes in isolated systems. Double lines =
thermal insulation.

through a larger volume in the final state. The process indicated
occurs spontaneously (once the partition is removed). But the reverse process (all the gas molecules go back, spontaneously, to the
side from which they came) will never be observed (see Section
8-4). Here we certainly have a case in which our experience or
physical intuition agrees with the predictions of the second law.

(b) Two pieces of metal at temperatures T_1 and T_2 ($T_2 > T_1$)
are separated by a sheet of thermal insulation. This sheet is suddenly removed. The spontaneous process in this case is the flow
of heat from right (T_2) to left (T_1). Equilibrium will be reached
when both pieces of metal have the same temperature (somewhere
between T_1 and T_2). We shall verify in Section 8-3 that $\Delta S > 0$ for
this process. The reverse process would never be observed in
nature; that is, the two pieces of metal have the same temperature

to begin with, but then heat flows spontaneously from one side to the other to establish a significant temperature difference.

(c) Gaseous (or liquid) argon and neon are separated by a partition. The partition is removed. The mixing of the two substances to form a gaseous (or liquid) solution is the spontaneous process in this case. The final state, with the two kinds of molecules mixed together, is certainly more disordered than the initial state ($\Delta S > 0$). Spontaneous reversal of this process (unmixing) will never occur. Again the second law makes intuitive sense.

(d) A piece of iron is separated from an (excess of) aqueous HCl solution by an acid-proof partition. The partition is removed and a rather complicated series of events takes place spontaneously. The iron is dissolved to form Fe^{++} in the aqueous solution. A gas phase (H_2, HCl, H_2O) is produced at the top of the container. There will be extensive transport (diffusion) of heat, molecules, and ions within the system before equilibrium is finally reached. The temperature will rise considerably since the heat produced in the chemical reaction cannot escape. The final state is rather obviously more disordered than the initial state. For example: the iron atoms leave their ordered crystal structure and are dispersed throughout the solution; all the ions and molecules in the system undergo more violent motion because of the temperature rise; etc. The spontaneous reverse process is virtually inconceivable.

(e) To begin with we have a gaseous mixture of H_2 and O_2 in equilibrium. The temperature is such that the reaction between H_2 and O_2 to form H_2O will not proceed at a significant rate without a catalyst. A catalyst is added and the reaction occurs spontaneously, even explosively, to form a new equilibrium state that contains H_2, O_2 and H_2O at a higher temperature.

The universe as an isolated system. Since, by definition, the "universe" includes everything, it has no contact with surroundings. Hence the universe is an isolated system. All kinds of irreversible processes, many on a cosmic scale, are taking place in the universe. Therefore the entropy of the universe is increasing. Slowly but surely (according to the second law of thermodynamics) the universe is approaching a final equilibrium state, of maximum entropy or disorder, in which the temperature will be uniform (it is far from uniform now), matter distribution will be as uniform as it can get, etc. Life will of course be inconsistent with this final state of the universe since living organisms are not equilibrium systems. The way this is often put is that the second law predicts the eventual "running down" of the universe.

Incidentally, in this connection, entropy is sometimes referred to as "time's arrow"; the entropy tells time which way it can go. The only direction in which time can pass is that direction along which the entropy of the universe increases. Any attempt to run

the universe backward (reverse the direction of time) must fail because in this case the entropy of the universe would decrease.

A growing organism, for example an embryo, appears to offer a
contradiction to the second law because as time passes it certainly
becomes more ordered rather than more disordered. The fallacy
here is that a living organism is not an isolated system: it exchanges
heat, matter, and work with its surroundings. The requirement that
the entropy or disorder must increase in spontaneous processes applies only to isolated systems. The entropy (per unit mass) of an
embryo decreases with time, while the entropy of a mature, living
organism (a system in a steady state—see p. 2) remains about
constant. At death the entropy of an organism suddenly rises as the
various intricate mechanisms and structures ''run down.''

Measurement or calculation of entropy changes. We leave isolated
systems and return now to the general question of the evaluation of entropy changes. We have already emphasized that the entropy change
ΔS between two states is the same for any process connecting the
states, but that a reversible process must be used actually to evaluate ΔS from $\int DQ_{rev}/T$.

But direct application of $\Delta S = \int DQ_{rev}/T$ is tedious and unnecessary. In this subsection we show that it is easy to derive equivalent
but more practical equations for finding the change of entropy with
temperature, pressure, and volume (these are the most important
cases). We shall see that no particular reversible process need be
specified; the equations apply to any reversible process. The reason
for this is, of course, that S is a state function and hence ΔS is independent of the path used.

For any reversible process the equation

$$dE = DQ - DW$$

becomes, on introducing $DQ = T\,dS$ and $DW = p\,dV$,

$$dE = T\,dS - p\,dV \qquad (8\text{-}12)$$

This equation combines the first and second laws of thermodynamics.
Now if we regard E as a function of T and V (the mole numbers are
held constant as usual), we also have that

$$dE = \left(\frac{\partial E}{\partial T}\right)_V dT + \left(\frac{\partial E}{\partial V}\right)_T dV \qquad (8\text{-}13)$$

This last step is calculus, not thermodynamics. From Eqs. 8-12 and
8-13, we then have that

$$T \, dS = C_V \, dT + \left[p + \left(\frac{\partial E}{\partial V} \right)_T \right] dV \qquad \text{(8-14)}$$

Therefore we get the following equations that show how S changes with T at constant V, or vice versa:

$$\left(\frac{\partial S}{\partial T} \right)_V = \frac{C_V}{T}, \quad \left(\frac{\partial S}{\partial V} \right)_T = \frac{1}{T} \left[p + \left(\frac{\partial E}{\partial V} \right)_T \right] \qquad \text{(8-15)}$$

The first of these is very practical to use (because C_V and T are easy to measure), but not so for the second relation because $(\partial E / \partial V)_T$ is not readily available. We shall return to $(\partial S / \partial V)_T$ below.

If C_V for any substance is known as a function of T between T_1 and T_2 (with V const), integration of Eq. 8-15a gives

$$\Delta S = S(T_2) - S(T_1) = \int_{T_1}^{T_2} \frac{C_V(T)}{T} \, dT \qquad \text{(V const)} \qquad \text{(8-16)}$$

This is very similar to Eq. 7-17. It is assumed here that there is no phase change between T_1 and T_2. If C_V / T is plotted against T, ΔS is the area under the C_V / T curve between T_1 and T_2.

The variables p and T are more common in experimental work than V and T. To introduce these variables, we write

$$dH = d(E + pV) = dE + p \, dV + V \, dp$$

$$= T \, dS + V \, dp \qquad \text{(8-17)}$$

where we have used Eq. 8-12. Also,

$$dH = \left(\frac{\partial H}{\partial T} \right)_p dT + \left(\frac{\partial H}{\partial p} \right)_T dp \qquad \text{(8-18)}$$

Therefore

$$T \, dS = C_p \, dT + \left[\left(\frac{\partial H}{\partial p} \right)_T - V \right] dp \qquad \text{(8-19)}$$

which is analogous to Eq. 8-14. We then find, just as in Eq. 8-15

$$\left(\frac{\partial S}{\partial T} \right)_p = \frac{C_p}{T}, \quad \left(\frac{\partial S}{\partial p} \right)_T = \frac{1}{T} \left[\left(\frac{\partial H}{\partial p} \right)_T - V \right] \qquad \text{(8-20)}$$

Thus if $C_p(T)$ for any substance is available between T_1 and T_2 at some constant pressure,

$$\Delta S = S(T_2) - S(T_1) = \int_{T_1}^{T_2} \frac{C_p(T)}{T} \, dT \quad \text{(p const)} \qquad (8\text{-}21)$$

again assuming no phase change. Here ΔS is the area under the C_p/T vs T curve between T_1 and T_2. This equation will be applied to H_2O in Section 8-3.

Let us digress briefly to take care of a point mentioned in the footnote on p. 16. In the fundamental equation 8-12 we note that T and p appear in analogous ways, as do also S and $-V$. In Chapter 1 we made use of the fact that the quantity $[\partial(-V)/\partial p]_T$ is never negative. Similarly, $(\partial S/\partial T)_p$ is also never negative (because C_p is never negative): the disorder, S, increases with temperature, just as we would expect.

We now come back to $(\partial S/\partial V)_T$ and $(\partial S/\partial p)_T$. We can easily derive practical expressions for these derivatives by using some simple mathematical trickery. For the first of these two derivatives we would like V and T to be independent variables. We notice, in Eq. 8-17, that by adding pV to E the independent variables in Eq. 8-12 are changed from S and V to S and p. In a similar way we can switch variables from S and V to T and V:

$$d(E - TS) = dE - T \, dS - S \, dT$$

$$= -S \, dT - p \, dV \qquad (8\text{-}22)$$

Now we have that

$$\frac{\partial(E - TS)}{\partial T} = -S \quad \text{and} \quad \frac{\partial^2(E - TS)}{\partial V \partial T} = -\left(\frac{\partial S}{\partial V}\right)_T$$

Also,

$$\frac{\partial(E - TS)}{\partial V} = -p \quad \text{and} \quad \frac{\partial^2(E - TS)}{\partial T \partial V} = -\left(\frac{\partial p}{\partial T}\right)_V$$

But the two second derivatives are equal. Therefore

$$\left(\frac{\partial S}{\partial V}\right)_T = \left(\frac{\partial p}{\partial T}\right)_V \qquad (8\text{-}23)$$

This is the desired result. The derivative on the right can be found from p-V-T (equation of state) data. Hence the dependence of S on V at constant T (isothermal expansion or compression) may be obtained by integrating Eq. 8-23:

$$S(V_2) - S(V_1) = \int_{V_1}^{V_2} \left(\frac{\partial p}{\partial T}\right)_V dV \qquad \text{(T const)} \qquad (8\text{-}24)$$

Equation 8-23 applies to <u>any</u> equilibrium sample of matter. As a simple example, let us try it out on an ideal gas with equation of state pV = nRT. We have

$$\left(\frac{\partial p}{\partial T}\right)_V = \frac{nR}{V} = \frac{p}{T} \qquad (8\text{-}25)$$

and hence

$$S(V_2) - S(V_1) = \int_{V_1}^{V_2} \frac{nR}{V} dV = nR \ln \frac{V_2}{V_1}$$

$$= 2.303nR \log \frac{V_2}{V_1} \qquad (8\text{-}26)$$

Equation 8-26 shows that the entropy of an ideal gas (at constant temperature) increases with volume: if $V_2 > V_1$, $S(V_2) > S(V_1)$. This is what we expect because a larger volume allows more random (less restricted) motion for each molecule. The reader should go back to Eqs. 7-33 and 7-44 to see that direct application of $\int DQ/T$ gives the same result.

In Chapter 7 (p. 130) we made use of the fact that the energy of an ideal gas is independent of volume. We can now see that this follows from the second law. For if we use Eqs. 8-23 and 8-25 in Eq. 8-15, we have that $(\partial E/\partial V)_T = 0$.

We can find $(\partial S/\partial p)_T$ in exactly the same way. From Eq. 8-17,

$$d(H - TS) = -S\, dT + V\, dp$$

$$\frac{\partial(H - TS)}{\partial T} = -S, \qquad \frac{\partial^2(H - TS)}{\partial p \partial T} = -\left(\frac{\partial S}{\partial p}\right)_T$$

$$\frac{\partial(H - TS)}{\partial p} = V, \qquad \frac{\partial^2(H - TS)}{\partial T \partial p} = \left(\frac{\partial V}{\partial T}\right)_p$$

Therefore

$$\left(\frac{\partial S}{\partial p}\right)_T = -\left(\frac{\partial V}{\partial T}\right)_p \tag{8-27}$$

and

$$S(p_2) - S(p_1) = -\int_{p_1}^{p_2} \left(\frac{\partial V}{\partial T}\right)_p dp \quad (T \text{ const}) \tag{8-28}$$

Equations 8-27 and 8-28 allow us to determine how the entropy of any substance changes with pressure (at constant temperature).

We leave it to the reader to verify that if a substance has the equation of state $pV = nRT$, then

$$S(p_2) - S(p_1) = nR \ln \frac{p_1}{p_2} \tag{8-29}$$

and $(\partial H/\partial p)_T = 0$. Since $p_1 V_1 = p_2 V_2$ in an isothermal expansion, Eqs. 8-26 and 8-29 are clearly self-consistent.

Entropy change in a phase transition. Suppose that n moles of a pure substance undergo a reversible phase transition, at p and T, from phase 1 to phase 2. Let the measured heat of the process be Q. Since the process occurs at constant pressure, $\Delta H = H_2 - H_1 = Q$. Because the temperature is constant as well,

$$\Delta S = \int \frac{DQ}{T} = \frac{1}{T} \int DQ = \frac{Q}{T} = \frac{\Delta H}{T} \tag{8-30}$$

Therefore, ΔH and ΔS in a phase transition are simply related by $\Delta H = T \Delta S$. If either ΔH or ΔS is known, the other is easily calculated. Of course a phase transition is a very special kind of process; this relation between ΔH and ΔS is not generally true of other thermodynamic processes.

We can use Eq. 8-12 to verify Eq. 8-30. The infinitesimals dE, dS, and dV in Eq. 8-12 refer here to the conversion of a very small amount of phase 1 into phase 2. For the complete transition, since p and T are constant,

$$\Delta E = T \Delta S - p \Delta V$$

or

$$\Delta E + p \Delta V = \Delta H = T \Delta S$$

which agrees with Eq. 8-30.

Equation 8-30 will be illustrated in the next section. But we might make one general comment here. If Q is positive, heat is added to phase 1 to produce phase 2. We therefore expect phase 2 to be more disordered than phase 1. That is, phase 2 should have a higher entropy than phase 1. This is of course consistent with Eq. 8-30 which tells us that $S_2 - S_1$ is positive if Q is positive.

Pressure-temperature relation. In a phase diagram such as Fig. 1-4, a phase transition takes place at a point on one of the two-phase lines. The pressure p and temperature T, referred to in the preceding paragraphs, are the coordinates of the point. If the temperature is changed by an amount dT, while maintaining the two phases in equilibrium (that is, while staying on the two-phase line), the equilibrium pressure will change by, say, dp. The ratio dp/dT is the slope of the two-phase line at the point p, T (Fig. 8-3). What we want to do here is to find the connection between dp/dT and the entropy change ΔS for the transition at p, T.

Equation 8-23 is a general expression for $(\partial p / \partial T)_V$; what we require is a special case of this equation, valid at a phase transition. As can be seen, for example, in Fig. 1-12b, the pressure of a pure substance is ordinarily a function of both T and v. But in a phase transition region (for example, inside the coexistence curve in Fig. 1-12b), the p-v isotherm is flat. The flatness means physically that the equilibrium pressure p stays constant when the phase transition is carried out at constant T. Thus, in such a region, p depends on

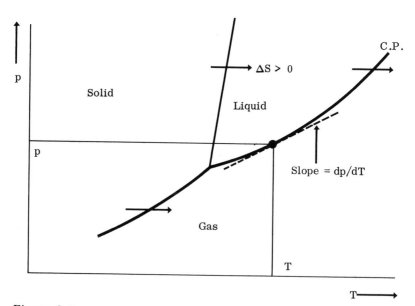

Figure 8-3
Typical phase diagram. Relation to entropy change at phase transitions.

T but not on v (or, not on V—since n is constant). Therefore, when two phases are in equilibrium, $(\partial p/\partial T)_V$ becomes simply dp/dT.

We turn next to $(\partial S/\partial V)_T$. At the beginning of the transition (to be carried out with p and T const), $V = nv_1$ and $S = ns_1$, while at the end of the transition $V = nv_2$ and $S = ns_2$. At an intermediate stage of the transition let n' be the number of moles in phase 2 and let $n-n'$ be the number of moles in phase 1. Then the volume of the two phase system is

$$V = (n - n')v_1 + n'v_2$$

Similarly,

$$S = (n - n')s_1 + n's_2$$

In other words, V and S are both linear functions of n'—the variable that can be used to tell us how far along we are in the transition. Since S and V are both linear functions of n', we may also regard S as a linear function of V (or vice versa). The exact relation is easily found by eliminating n' from the above two equations:

$$S - ns_1 = \frac{s_2 - s_1}{v_2 - v_1} (V - nv_1) \tag{8-31}$$

As a check, put $V = nv_1$ (beginning of transition). Then $S = ns_1$. Or, put $V = nv_2$ (end of transition). Then $S = ns_2$.

Now v_1, v_2, s_1, and s_2 are functions of T only (remember that these quantities refer to the ends of a phase transition—as along the coexistence curve in Fig. 1-12b). Therefore, Eq. 8-31 gives us

$$\left(\frac{\partial S}{\partial V}\right)_{T,n} = \frac{s_2 - s_1}{v_2 - v_1} = \frac{\Delta s}{\Delta v} = \frac{\Delta S}{\Delta V}$$

This is the slope of the linear relation S(V).

Our final result is then:

$$\frac{dp}{dT} = \frac{\Delta s}{\Delta v} = \frac{\Delta S}{\Delta V} = \frac{\Delta H}{T \, \Delta v} = \frac{\Delta H}{T \, \Delta V} = \frac{Q}{T \, \Delta V} \tag{8-32}$$

We shall refer to this as the Clausius-Clapeyron equation. It shows that there is a connection between the quantities dp/dT, ΔS, and ΔV, all referring to the same phase transition at p and T. If ΔV and Q are measured, dp/dT may be calculated. Or if dp/dT and ΔV are measured, ΔS, ΔH, and Q may be calculated without measuring a heat! This is done routinely for the liquid-gas transition where p is the vapor pressure of the liquid at T (see Section 8-3 for further details).

A qualitative connection between the slope of a two-phase line and the sign of ΔV at the phase transition was pointed out on p. 14. We can confirm this here and make the connection quantitative. Suppose, for convenience, we always consider a transition in the direction low temperature phase → high temperature phase, as indicated by the horizontal arrows in Fig. 8-3 (S → L, L → G, S → G, etc.). Then we will always have $\Delta S > 0$, because heat must be absorbed by the system ($Q > 0$) in order for the transition to take place in this direction. We see, then, from Eq. 8-32 that if the transition is taken in this direction, dp/dT and ΔV have the same sign. Examples: ordinarily $\Delta V > 0$ for S → L, and then $dp/dT > 0$ also; but for water, $\Delta V < 0$ and hence $dp/dT < 0$.

8-3 APPLICATIONS OF THE SECOND LAW

WE CONSIDER a few special topics and problems in this section. Those at the end of the section have to do with irreversible processes.

S(T)–S(0) for a pure substance. In Section 7-2, we discussed the dependence of H on T, at constant pressure, for a pure substance. We do the same thing here for the entropy. Exactly the same raw experimental data are required for S(T) as for H(T): heats of phase transitions and C_p as a function of T, both for the pressure of interest.

The way in which S increases with T for a pure substance is especially interesting because S is a measure of the amount of molecular disorder in the substance.

Equations 8-21 and 8-30 are the ones we need to apply here. Suppose, for example, as in Eq. 7-23, that we want to calculate $S(T') - S(0)$ at a temperature T' for a substance (liquid) with melting point $T_m < T'$. Then

$$S_L(T') - S_S(0) = \int_0^{T_m} \frac{C_p^S(T)}{T} dT + \frac{1}{T_m}$$

$$\times [H_L(T_m) - H_S(T_m)]$$

$$+ \int_{T_m}^{T'} \frac{C_p^L(T)}{T} dT \qquad (8-33)$$

The close resemblance to Eq. 7-23 should be noted. The first integral gives $S_S(T_m) - S_S(0)$. The next term is the entropy of fusion, Q/T_m. The second integral is equal to $S_L(T') - S_L(T_m)$. The integrals may be evaluated by measuring the area under a curve of $C_p(T)/T$ plotted against T.

As can be seen from Eq. 8-5, the second law has something to say about entropy differences or changes, but nothing to say about the absolute entropy. The same is true for the energy in the first law. This is the reason why $S_S(0)$ appears in Eq. 8-33, just as $H_S(0)$ is included in Eq. 7-23. But the third law of thermodynamics does contain information about S(0) so we shall return to this subject in the next section.

Numerical example: water. Figure 7-4 presents a plot of $H(T) - H(0)$ for pure water between T = 0 and T = 400°K, at 1 atm pressure. The same data may be used, in a very similar way, to find $s(T) - s(0)$. The first step necessary is to replot Fig. 7-3, this time as c_p/T against T. We then have to evaluate the area under this curve between 0°K and various values of T up to 400°K. At 273.1°K we add in the entropy of fusion, $\Delta s_f = \Delta H_f/T_f = 1436/273.1 = 5.3$ cal deg^{-1} mole^{-1}, and at 373.1°K we add the entropy of vaporization, $\Delta s_v = \Delta H_v/T_v = 9710/373.1 = 26.0$ cal deg^{-1} mole^{-1}. The result is shown in Fig. 8-4.

Figure 8-4 indicates how the molecular disorder in H_2O increases with temperature at 1 atm pressure. Ice, like any other substance, has its maximum order and minimum S at 0°K. As the temperature is raised above 0°K, S increases steadily because of more extensive vibrational motion of the H_2O molecules as a whole about equilibrium positions, and also because of more "rocking" of the molecules (in place of rotation). The molecules become more jittery and thus less perfectly organized, but still the long range order of the crystal does not break down until 273.1°K. Here a sudden burst of disorder is acquired (Δs_f in Fig. 8-4) as the crystal structure deteriorates leaving extensive local but no long-range organization. The molecules can now begin to rotate though rotation is considerably hindered by hydrogen bonds. There is a general loss of structure and increased violence of motion as the liquid is heated, but nothing drastically new happens until 373.1°K. Here the molecules tear apart from one another, become independent instead of entangled, and expand in volume by a factor[5] of 1620

---

[5]Incidentally, if a system of molecules with no intermolecular forces (an ideal gas) expands in volume by a factor of 1620 at constant temperature, $\Delta s = R \ln 1620 = 2.303 R \log 1620 = 14.7$ cal deg^{-1} mole^{-1}. This is more than half of Δs_v for H_2O at 1 atm. But there are clearly other very important contributions to Δs_v.

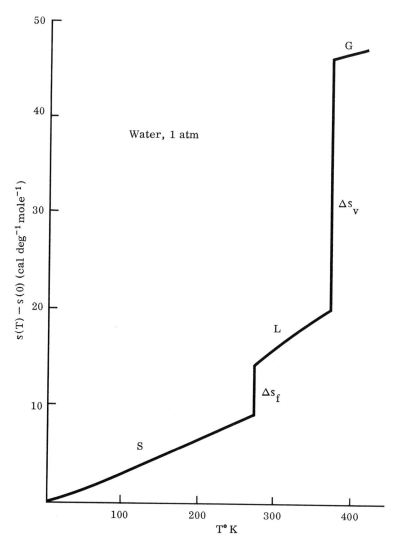

Figure 8-4
Entropy of water.

(p. 30). The disorder goes way up (Δs_V in Fig. 8-4). The molecules have exchanged the attractiveness of hydrogen bonds with neighbors for individual freedom.

Temperature dependence of liquid vapor pressure. Let us apply the Clausius-Clapeyron equation to the liquid-vapor equilibrium as a special case. Equation 8-32 becomes

$$\frac{dp}{dT} = \frac{s_G - s_L}{v_G - v_L} = \frac{H_G - H_L}{T(v_G - v_L)} \qquad (8\text{-}34)$$

where p is the vapor pressure. This is the slope of the liquid-vapor equilibrium line in Figs. 1-2 and 1-3, for example. Incidentally, as $T \to T_c$, Δs_V, ΔH_V and Δv_V all approach zero, but $\Delta s_V / \Delta v_V$, $\Delta H_V / \Delta v$, and dp/dT remain finite.

Equation 8-34 is exact and valid all along the liquid-vapor line. But this equation can be simplified considerably when it is applied at temperatures well below T_c. For in this case v_G is much larger than v_L and also the vapor pressure is small. Under these conditions: (1) we neglect v_L compared to v_G; and (2) we assume the vapor is an ideal gas $(pv_G = RT)$. Therefore

$$\frac{dp}{dT} = \frac{p(H_G - H_L)}{RT^2}$$

or

$$\frac{d \ln p}{dT} = \frac{\Delta H_V}{RT^2} \qquad (8\text{-}35)$$

Over a small temperature range (say 20° or less) the temperature dependence of ΔH_V can be neglected. Then it is easy to integrate Eq. 8-35:

$$\ln p = -\frac{\Delta H_V}{RT} + const$$

or

$$\log p = -\frac{\Delta H_V}{2.303\, RT} + const \qquad (8\text{-}36)$$

Equation 8-36 is of great practical use for it tells us that if we measure p over a small temperature range, and plot $\log p$ against $1/T$ (Fig. 8-5), then the slope of the line obtained is equal to $-\Delta H_V / 2.303\, R$. In this way we can find ΔH_V and Δs_V from vapor pressure measurements.

Numerical example: water. The vapor pressure of water at 20°C $(T_1 = 293.1\,°K)$ is $p_1 = 17.5$ mm Hg and at 30°C $(T_2 = 303.1\,°K)$ it is $p_2 = 31.8$ mm Hg. This is sufficient information to make a rather accurate calculation of ΔH_V and Δs_V (at 25°C, the mean temperature). For we have, from Eq. 8-36,

$$\log \frac{p_2}{p_1} = -\frac{\Delta H_V}{2.303\,R}\left(\frac{1}{T_2} - \frac{1}{T_1}\right) \tag{8-37}$$

and therefore

$$\Delta H_V = \frac{2.303\,RT_1\,T_2}{T_2 - T_1}\,\log\frac{p_2}{p_1}$$

$$= \frac{2.303 \times 1.987 \times 293.1 \times 303.1 \times 0.2594}{10}$$

$$= 10,550 \text{ cal mole}^{-1}$$

Also

$$\Delta s_V = \frac{\Delta H_V}{T} = \frac{10,550}{298.1} = 35.4 = \text{cal mole}^{-1}\,\text{deg}^{-1}$$

The value of ΔH_V at 100°C is 9,710 cal mole^{-1}.

Trouton's rule. The heat of vaporization ΔH_b of a liquid at the normal boiling point is approximately proportional to ϵ, the inter-molecular force parameter (see p. 113). The boiling point T_b is also approximately proportional to ϵ (see p. 54). Therefore the quotient $\Delta H_b/T_b$, which is equal to Δs_b, should be approximately independent of the strength of intermolecular forces. That is, Δs_b, the entropy of vaporization at the normal boiling point,

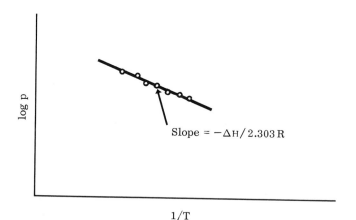

Slope $= -\Delta H/2.303\,R$

1/T

Figure 8-5
Vapor pressure—temperature plot for calculation of ΔH of vaporization.

Table 8-1
Trouton's Rule

Substance	ΔH_b (cal mole^{-1})	$T_b°K$	Δs_b (cal mole^{-1} deg^{-1})
Na	23,675	1172	20.2
Ar	1,500	87.4	17.2
Kr	2,315	121.4	19.1
N_2	1,352	77.3	17.5
I_2	10,120	457.5	22.1
HCl	3,538	189	18.7
H_2O	9,705	373.1	26.0
NH_3	5,581	239.7	23.3
C_6H_6	7,366	353.3	20.8
$n-C_8H_{18}$	8,612	398.7	21.6

should have approximately the same value for different molecules of
similar type (Trouton's rule). Table 8-1 illustrates this. This is another corresponding states effect. But it should be noted that the
normal boiling point (1 atm pressure) is not a corresponding state.
A pressure of one atmosphere may be a relatively high pressure
for one substance and a relatively low one for another. An improved
version of Trouton's rule is obtained if $s_G - s_L$ at, say, the triple
point is used rather than at the normal boiling point.

Irreversible expansion of ideal gas in isolated system. On p. 162
we described the irreversible expansion of the gas shown in Fig. 8-2a.
Let us suppose, for simplicity, that the gas is ideal. In this case the
final temperature will be the same as the initial temperature because: (a) E is independent of V for an ideal gas; (b) E increases
steadily with T (Eq. 7-16); and (c) E is necessarily constant in an
isolated system. Therefore, for the irreversible process described,

$$Q = 0, \quad W = 0, \quad \Delta E = 0, \quad \Delta T = 0, \quad \text{and} \quad \Delta S > 0$$

$$(8\text{-}38)$$

Although we know that $\Delta S > 0$, there still remains the question
as to the actual value of ΔS. To find this, we have to think up a reversible process (any one will do) that has the same initial and final
states as the irreversible process, and then apply $\Delta S = \int DQ/T$.
Suppose (in Fig. 8-2a) that the initial volume is V_1 and the final
volume is V_2. Then the initial state is characterized by n, V_1, T
and the final state by n, V_2, T. An obvious process passing from
n, V_1, T to n, V_2, T would be an isothermal expansion of the

gas. To do this reversibly, we would have to introduce a piston initially at the pressure nRT/V_1, also introduce a heat bath at T, and then slowly move the piston out keeping $p_{ex} = p = nRT/V$. The final pressure would be nRT/V_2. This type of process has already been treated in Eqs. 7-33, 7-34, 7-44 and 8-26. The value of ΔS is found to be

$$\Delta S = nR \ln \frac{V_2}{V_1} \qquad\qquad (8\text{-}39)$$

a positive quantity.

The above reversible process is the same as process A in Fig. 7-11. Equations 7-46 and 7-47 confirm that other reversible processes (for example, B + C and D + F in Fig. 7-11) may be used to calculate ΔS, and that the value found for ΔS is independent of the reversible process chosen.

Furthermore, if the expansion n, V_1, T $\rightarrow$ n, V_2, T is carried out as in the irreversible process G of p. 147, (expansion in a heat bath at T with p_{ex} = const = nRT/V_2), ΔS will also have the value given in Eq. 8-39—because S is a state function. But the value of ΔS cannot be found by measurements on this process (see Eq. 7-48).

Mixing of two ideal gases in isolated system. We now consider the spontaneous mixing of two ideal gases in an isolated system, as in Fig. 8-2c. We have n_{Ar} moles of argon, n_{Ne} moles of neon, and both gases are initially at a pressure p and temperature T. Therefore the initial volumes are $V_{Ar} = n_{Ar} RT/p$ and $V_{Ne} = n_{Ne}RT/p$. The total volume is $V_{Ar} + V_{Ne}$. The partition is removed and the gases mix irreversibly. Because the gases are ideal (negligible intermolecular forces), $\Delta T = 0$ and each gas will have its own independent properties in the final state (see Section 2-4). Thus, since argon has expanded from a volume V_{Ar} at T to a volume $V_{Ar} + V_{Ne}$ at T, the entropy of argon has increased by an amount

$$\Delta S_{Ar} = n_{Ar} R \ln \frac{V_{Ar} + V_{Ne}}{V_{Ar}}$$

Similarly,

$$\Delta S_{Ne} = n_{Ne} R \ln \frac{V_{Ar} + V_{Ne}}{V_{Ne}}$$

The total entropy change in the irreversible process is therefore

$$\Delta S = \Delta S_{Ar} + \Delta S_{Ne}$$

$$= -n_{Ar} R \ln \frac{n_{Ar}}{n_{Ar} + n_{Ne}} - n_{Ne} R \ln \frac{n_{Ne}}{n_{Ar} + n_{Ne}} \qquad (8\text{-}40)$$

This is a positive quantity called the entropy of mixing.

Incidentally, if instead of having Ar and Ne on the two sides of the partition we have Ar on both sides (at p and T), then when the partition is removed nothing happens (on the macroscopic level). Hence $\Delta S = 0$. One might wonder at what stage the positive ΔS in Eq. 8-40 becomes zero if the two atoms chosen for the experiment are gradually made to approach each other in atomic structure. This is the Gibbs paradox and it was a real problem before quantum theory was discovered. But now we know, because of the discreteness of elementary particles in atoms, that the "gradual approach" referred to above is not possible. Two atoms are either identical or they are not identical.

Irreversible heat flow in isolated system. We turn now to the process shown in Fig. 8-2b. Heat flows spontaneously from the T_2 side to the T_1 side if $T_2 > T_1$. We know this from everyday experience. We merely want to verify here that the entropy, as set up in our second law, does increase in this process as it is supposed to.

Let us consider just the very first stage in the process, in which the first batch of heat DQ (DQ > 0) passes from the T_2 side to the T_1 side. At later stages in the process the two temperatures will be nearer each other, but the same qualitative result (namely, dS > 0) will be found at every stage.

We have to think of a reversible procedure which will remove an amount of heat DQ from the T_2 side and then introduce this same amount of heat into the T_1 side. On second thought, we need not bother to specify any particular reversible process for, no matter what it is, the entropy change on the T_2 side will be $(-DQ)/T_2$ and the entropy change on the T_1 side will be DQ/T_1. The total entropy change inside the isolated system in this infinitesimal irreversible process is then

$$dS = -\frac{DQ}{T_2} + \frac{DQ}{T_1} = DQ \left(\frac{1}{T_1} - \frac{1}{T_2} \right) \qquad (8\text{-}41)$$

Since $T_2 > T_1$ and DQ > 0, dS is indeed positive.

8-4 ENTROPY, PROBABILITY, AND THE THIRD LAW OF THERMODYNAMICS

IT SHOULD already be clear that the entropy is a very important thermodynamic quantity. Thus, in an isolated system, the entropy alone determines the direction of spontaneous processes and provides the criterion for final equilibrium. Furthermore, Sections 8-5 and 8-6 will show that the entropy is also very much involved in similar questions concerning nonisolated systems—for example, systems held at constant T and V, or constant T and p. It therefore behooves us to obtain as deep an understanding of the entropy as we can. For this reason we digress in this section to examine the entropy from a nonthermodynamic point of view. But we shall return to pure thermodynamics at the end of the section where we introduce the third law of thermodynamics.

If we review the argument so far in this chapter, we see that: (a) we have used the words "entropy" and "disorder" as synonyms; (b) the entropy S, introduced via $dS = DQ_{rev}/T$, is a well-defined quantity (except for the zero of entropy); but (c) we have relied on intuition in using the term "disorder" in this way. What is missing is a precise relation between S, as defined in thermodynamics, and the behavior of the system on the molecular level. Such a relation should provide the justification for identifying "entropy" with "disorder."

This problem cannot be resolved in pure thermodynamics. In pure thermodynamics, we can define S, measure it, and manipulate it mathematically—but molecular theory does not, or need not, enter the picture at all. To reach the molecular level, we must turn to statistical mechanics.

However, we are not developing statistical mechanics in a systematic way in this book. We shall therefore have to be content with an argument based on an example.

Our procedure will be to point out first that "disorder" is closely related to the number of available molecular states for a system. We then show (using the example) that the entropy S is similarly related to the number of molecular states, and therefore conclude that S is indeed a measure of disorder.

Molecular disorder. If we look at all closely into what we mean by molecular disorder in a system, we see almost immediately a relationship between disorder and the number of possible molecular arrangements or molecular states for the system. Thus consider again (see p. 154) a barrel full of billiard balls—not a bad model for a liquid. If the billiard balls are dumped into the barrel millions of times, the exact arrangement of the balls will be somewhat different every time—and yet it is the same "liquid." Thus there are a vast number of detailed arrangements, or configurations, or complexions, or molecular states (all these terms are used) consistent with just one macroscopic state of the system— that is, consistent with, say, a certain number of billiard balls in a certain volume. This model illustrates the fact that there are an extremely large number of molecular (microscopic) states consistent with a single thermodynamic (macroscopic) state of a disordered system such as a liquid. Furthermore, if the system is held in the same thermodynamic state for, say, a second or a minute, it will pass through billions of billions of these molecular states (because of the continuous motion of the molecules).

Returning to the billiard ball analogy, the probability that the balls (when dumped into the barrel) would sometime end up in an ordered lattice arrangement is practically zero. This is because the number of arrangements of the billiard balls in a lattice ("solid") is practically negligible compared to the vast number of irregular ("liquid") arrangements possible.

Conclusion: an ordered thermodynamic state corresponds to relatively few molecular states, while a disorderd thermodynamic state corresponds to or represents a very large number of possible molecular states.

Figure 8-6 illustrates some of these ideas in a simple way. Suppose the system consists of five identical molecules placed on fifteen possible sites, not more than one molecule per site (e.g., these might be gas molecules adsorbed on the surface of a crystal). If there are no restrictions on the arrangement of the molecules, as in Fig. 8-6a, there are $15!/10!5! = 3003$ possible arrangements (only one is shown). All of these 3003 molecular states are consistent with the one thermodynamic state (specified by stating that there are 5 molecules on 15 sites). In thermodynamic equilibrium the system would pass through all of these states with equal frequency. This thermodynamic state is certainly a disordered one; no molecular structure is apparent.

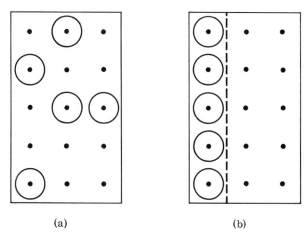

(a)   (b)

Figure 8-6
Arrangements of molecules on sites.

On the other hand, Fig. 8-6b shows an ordered thermodynamic state (5 molecules on 5 sites). There is only one possible molecular arrangement consistent with this thermodynamic state, instead of 3003.

Of course in real macroscopic systems the numbers are very much larger than in this example (see below). But still the example shows the correlation between disorder and number of molecular states.

In statistical and quantum mechanics the term "quantum state" is ordinarily used instead of "molecular state" —but this is just a change in terminology, not meaning. Quantum states are discrete or distinct and can be counted (Appendix 3 furnishes an illustration). If the molecules of a system are diatomic or polyatomic, the quantum states include not only the state of translational motion or position of the molecules but also the rotational and vibrational states. Ω is the symbol commonly used to represent the number of different quantum or molecular states corresponding to a given thermodynamic state of a macroscopic system.

Entropy and number of states. Our next task is to show that S is related to Ω. But first, let us establish a connection, which is quite simple, between Ω and probability. Suppose, in the billiard ball example, there are altogether Ω_L possible configurations of the balls that one would classify as "liquid" and Ω_S configurations that could be considered "solid" (i.e., in an ordered lattice). Then, when all configurations are possible (e.g., if the barrel is shaken up), the probability of observing the "liquid" is $P_L = \Omega_L / (\Omega_L + \Omega_S)$ and the probability of observing the "solid" is $P_S = \Omega_S / (\Omega_L + \Omega_S)$. Therefore the relative probability of solid to liquid is

$$\frac{P_S}{P_L} = \frac{\Omega_S}{\Omega_L} \qquad\qquad (8\text{-}42)$$

Similar ideas can be applied to any kind of system.

Consider, for example, N molecules of an ideal gas initially in a volume V_1, arranged as in Fig. 8-2a. After the partition is removed the volume available to the gas is V_2. That is, the gas expands from V_1 to V_2. Now we already know ΔS for this process (Eq. 8-39). What we shall do here is calculate the relative probability of initial and final states and then use Eq. 8-42 to connect Ω with S. We do not try to calculate Ω directly because this would require some knowledge of the quantum mechanics of the system. Fortunately, we need only a ratio of Ω values, not Ω itself.

When the partition is absent (the volume is V_2), the probability that any one molecule of the gas will be observed in the volume V_1

on the left side of the container is V_1/V_2. The probability that all N
molecules would be observed in V_1 is then $(V_1/V_2)^N$. But this is
just the situation of the molecules in the initial state (all in V_1). On
the other hand, when the partition is absent, the probability that all
N molecules will be observed in V_2 is $1^N = 1$, because every molecule must be somewhere in V_2 (the total volume). Therefore the
relative probability[6] of initial and final states is

$$\left(\frac{V_1}{V_2}\right)^N = \frac{P_{\text{initial}}}{P_{\text{final}}} = \frac{\Omega_{\text{initial}}}{\Omega_{\text{final}}} \qquad (8\text{-}43)$$

But we know that

$$S_{\text{final}} - S_{\text{initial}} = Nk \ln \frac{V_2}{V_1} = k \ln \left(\frac{V_2}{V_1}\right)^N$$

Comparison with Eq. 8-43 shows that, in this example at least,

$$S_f - S_i = k \ln \frac{\Omega_f}{\Omega_i} \qquad (8\text{-}44)$$

Actually, this result proves, in statistical mechanics, to be a general
relation: it applies to any thermodynamic system. It is an extremely
important equation because it establishes the connection between the
thermodynamic behavior (ΔS) of a macroscopic equilibrium system
and its molecular-mechanical behavior (Ω_f/Ω_i).

Equation 8-44 shows that S increases with increasing Ω. Since,
as we have already seen, molecular disorder also increases with Ω,
we conclude finally that it is altogether appropriate to regard S as
a measure of disorder and to use the words "entropy" and "disorder" interchangeably, as we have been doing.

Possible violation of the second law. According to the second law
of thermodynamics, a spontaneous process with $\Delta S < 0$ in an isolated system is impossible. From the molecular point of view, although this conclusion is correct for all practical purposes, it is
not exactly correct. Consider, for example, the ideal gas above.
We have in fact already calculated the probability that the gas in
V_2 will go spontaneously into the smaller volume V_1. More exactly, we have found that $(V_1/V_2)^N$ is the probability that, on

---

[6]Figure 8-6 provides another example:

$$\frac{P(a)}{P(b)} = \frac{\Omega(a)}{\Omega(b)} = 3003.$$

examining the system with volume V_2, all molecules will be observed in the volume V_1. According to the second law, this would never happen (because $\Delta S < 0$ for such a process). But the probability is not exactly zero. For example, if $V_1 = \frac{1}{2}V_2$, the probability is $1/2^N$. Since N is usually about 10^{23}, the probability is about $1/10^{10^{22}}$. If one observed the system once every second for a million years, the probability of seeing this violation of the second law at least once would be only $10^{13}/10^{10^{22}}$, which is still equal to about $1/10^{10^{22}}$. Such a small probability can be safely ignored!

Third law of thermodynamics. For our purposes the third law is much less important than the first two laws, so we shall not say a great deal about it.

The third law brings together in a single statement a large number of experimental observations about the behavior of S at extremely low temperatures. Since no exceptions to the third law have been noted, it is presumably a general law of nature. What has been observed (and this is our statement of the third law[7]) is the following: if for any isothermal process involving only pure substances (e.g., changes in V, p, magnetic field, phase transitions, chemical reactions), ΔS for the process is measured at lower and lower temperatures, the value of ΔS approaches zero as T approaches zero. This is new information about S, not contained in the second law.

For example, let A and B be two different crystalline forms of the same pure substance. Let the isothermal process be A → B, at constant pressure. Then the third law states that at T = 0,

$$\Delta S = S_B(0) - S_A(0) = 0$$

or

$$S_A(0) = S_B(0)$$

The third law is concerned, strictly, with entropy differences at T = 0 and not with individual values of S(0). In fact, the actual numerical values chosen for S(0) for the various pure substances have no physical significance (i.e., they cannot be measured). Yet it is very useful to have some convention about individual values of S(0). Whatever the convention is, it must be consistent with $\Delta S(0) = 0$ for all possible isothermal processes. The one convention universally

---

[7]An alternative statement, which can be proved to be equivalent to that above, is: it is impossible by any process to bring any thermodynamic system to the absolute zero of temperature in a finite number of operations. This is sometimes referred to as the principle of the unattainability of the absolute zero.

adopted is to choose $S(0) = 0$ for all pure substances. This choice is obviously consistent with the third law and is simpler than any other. Also, it is rather natural to assign the value zero to the state of minimum disorder (maximum order)—which is reached at $T = 0$. So-called tables or values of "absolute entropies" often encountered are based on this convention. Thus, in Fig. 8-4, we put $s(0) = 0$ and say, for example, that the entropy of water is $s = 16.72$ cal deg^{-1} mole^{-1} at 1 atm and 25°C.

In statistical mechanics, the general expression for the entropy of a pure substance is

$$S = k \ln \Omega + \text{const} \tag{8-45}$$

where the arbitrary constant is independent of the thermodynamic state of the substance. This relation is consistent with Eq. 8-44 because the constant always cancels on taking differences.

It is found in the quantum mechanics of systems of atoms and molecules that at $T = 0$ any system is in its lowest possible energy state (except for helium, this would be a crystal with zero-point vibrational energy) and that this state has $\Omega = 1$. The system runs out of "choices" as $T \rightarrow 0°K$; there is only one quantum state available (compare Fig. 8-6b).

Therefore, at $T = 0$, Eq. 8-45 becomes $S(0) = \text{const}$. Hence

$$S = k \ln \Omega + S(0)$$

With the convention $S(0) = 0$, we have finally

$$S = k \ln \Omega \tag{8-46}$$

This is the Boltzmann equation. It is possibly the best known equation in statistical mechanics. It tells us that the entropy (or disorder) is related in a very simple way to the number of quantum states. The more quantum (or molecular) states available to a thermodynamic system, the larger the entropy.

The reason that S depends on $\ln \Omega$ rather than on Ω itself is easy to understand. Suppose we have two different thermodynamic ststems, at the same temperature, with S_1, Ω_1 and S_2, Ω_2, respectively. We then combine the two systems, as in Fig. 8-7, to form a new system (the wall between 1 and 2 is not removed). The entropy S of the new system will be $S = S_1 + S_2$, because $DQ = DQ_1 + DQ_2$ in Eq. 8-5. Also, the number of quantum states Ω of the new system will be $\Omega = \Omega_1 \Omega_2$, because for each quantum state of system 1, system 2 can be in Ω_2 different states. Hence the total number of possibilities is $\Omega_1 \Omega_2$. The fact that Ω is a product while S is a sum necessitates a logarithmic dependence of S on Ω (log of a product = sum of logs):

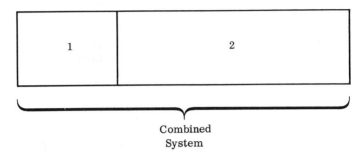

Figure 8-7
Two thermodynamic systems, and the combined system.

$$S_1 = k \ln \Omega_1, \qquad S_2 = k \ln \Omega_2 \qquad \text{(separate systems)}$$

$$S_1 + S_2 = k \, (\ln \Omega_1 + \ln \Omega_2) = k \ln (\Omega_1 \Omega_2)$$

$$S = k \ln \Omega \qquad \text{(combined system)}$$

Even without knowing any quantum mechanics, we can get an idea of the magnitude of Ω in typical cases by using Eq. 8-46 together with experimental values of S. Figure 8-4 (see also Table 10-1) shows that a typical value for the entropy of one mole of a pure substance is, say, $10 R$. Then

$$S = 10R = 10N_0 k = k \ln \Omega$$

and

$$\Omega = e^{10N_0} \cong e^{6 \times 10^{24}} \cong 10^{10^{24}}$$

This is a LARGE number! By comparison, the number of atoms on the earth is something like only 10^{50}.

From the molecular point of view, a spontaneous process in an isolated system becomes possible when a new group of quantum states is made available or accessible to the system (e.g., by removal of a partition, introduction of a catalyst, etc.). If the initial thermodynamic state has Ω_i quantum states, and the number of additional quantum states that become available is $\Omega_f - \Omega_i$, then the total number of quantum states in the final thermodynamic state is Ω_f. The entropy change in the spontaneous process is then given by Eq. 8-44. ΔS is necessarily positive because $\Omega_f > \Omega_i$.

8-5   FREE ENERGY FUNCTIONS

IN SECTION 8-1 a need was demonstrated for a disorder state function (the entropy) to supplement the energy function. Sections 8-2 through 8-4 have been devoted to the formal introduction of the entropy into thermodynamics. In particular, we have seen that the condition for equilibrium and for the approach thereto in an isolated system can be expressed in terms of the entropy alone: $dS \geq 0$.

But in practical thermodynamics we are usually not concerned with isolated systems. More often we are interested in systems with T and V held constant, and still more often in systems with T and p constant.

If a spontaneous process occurs in a system with T and V constant, what criterion replaces $dS \geq 0$? We consider this and the analogous question for p and T constant in the next two subsections.

Helmholtz free energy. If we introduce $TdS \geq DQ$ (Eq. 8-7) into

$$dE = DQ - p \, dV$$

we obtain

$$dE \leq T \, dS - p \, dV \tag{8-47}$$

where the equality holds for a reversible process and the inequality for an irreversible process. This is a quite general equation. Thus, if E and V are constant (isolated system), we get $dS \geq 0$ (Eq. 8-11). But if T and V are constant,

$$dE - T \, dS = d(E - TS) \leq 0 \qquad (T, V \text{ const})$$

or

$$dA \leq 0 \qquad (T, V \text{ const}) \tag{8-48}$$

where we have defined $A \equiv E - TS$. A is called the Helmholtz free energy.

If T and p are constant in Eq. 8-47,

$$dE - T \, dS + p \, dV = d(E - TS + pV) \leq 0 \qquad (T, p \text{ const})$$

or

$$dG \leq 0 \qquad (T, p \text{ const}) \tag{8-49}$$

where $G \equiv E - TS + pV$. G is the Gibbs free energy.[8] Note

[8]In some books the symbol F is used in place of G, and in others F is used in place of A!

also that $G = H - TS$, and that A and G are both state functions.

All three of the above special cases of Eq. 8-47 (and others as well) can be summarized in the one statement

$$(dS)_{int} \geq 0 \qquad\qquad (8\text{-}50)$$

which we have already encountered in Eqs. 8-9 and 8-10. But this statement is a little too general for our purposes, and it is not expressed in terms of a state function, so we return to Eqs. 8-48 and 8-49.

We see above that the combined function $E - TS$ arises in the important case of T and V const. Strictly, the analogue of $dS \geq 0$ (isolated system) is $d[S - (E/T)] \geq 0$. But this is equivalent to $d(E - TS) \leq 0$. The significant point is that <u>both</u> S and E are involved in governing the approach to equilibrium. We could go on writing the combination $E - TS$, but for brevity we have introduced the new symbol A.

The physical significance of Eq. 8-48 is the following (compare the discussion of Eq. 8-11). If spontaneous processes are possible in a system that occupies a fixed volume V and is in a constant temperature bath at T, the Helmholtz free energy $E - TS$ of the system decreases during such processes and at equilibrium $E - TS$ has its minimum possible value: $A \rightarrow$ minimum. This is illustrated schematically in Fig. 8-8 (compare Fig. 8-1).

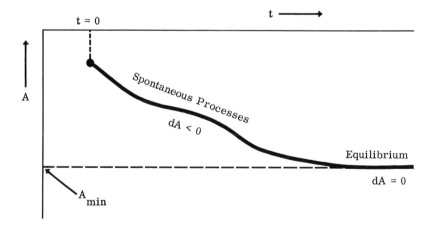

Figure 8-8
Schematic representation of Helmholtz free energy decrease in a closed system with constant V and T .

In a spontaneous process in an isolated system, S can increase but E is forced to stay constant. However, in a constant T, V system, not only can S increase but also E can decrease (these are the natural tendencies). Both of these would contribute to a decreasing value of A. But ordinarily an increase in S and a decrease in E are incompatible because some degree of order is required for low E. The usual situation is that, in a spontaneous T, V process, E and S both increase or they both decrease. In either case A decreases (or the process would not occur), and the final equilibrium state is a compromise state with E not so low as it might be and with S not so high as it might be, but yet with A at the lowest possible value consistent with the way in which the system was originally prepared.

Example. Take as the initial state of a system a sample of gaseous hydrogen atoms at V and T. The possible spontaneous process is H + H → H_2. At equilibrium, the gas will be a mixture of H and H_2. The extent to which the reaction takes place depends on T. Hydrogen atoms have a higher entropy and a higher energy than hydrogen molecules. Therefore, in this spontaneous process, S and E both decrease. Of course A also decreases (Fig. 8-9) and has, at

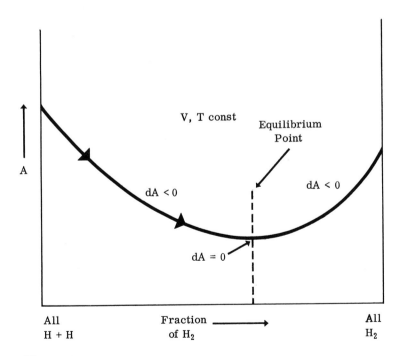

Figure 8-9
Minimum Helmholtz free energy at chemical equilibrium (schematic).

equilibrium, its lowest possible value consistent with V, T, and the amount of hydrogen in the container.

If the initial state is H_2 gas instead of H gas, with the same V, T and mass of hydrogen as above, the spontaneous process will be $H_2 \rightarrow H + H$. Both E and S increase in this case, but again A must decrease (Fig. 8-9). The equilibrium state is the same as above: the mixture of H and H_2 is the same, as are also the final values of E, S, and A.

Gibbs free energy. There is more that could be said about A, but let us save these comments, or analogous ones, for G because G is the more important of the two free energy functions.

Equation 8-49 shows that when a system held at constant p and T (as in Fig. 1-7) approaches equilibrium, the combination of variables that determines the direction of approach and also determines the final equilibrium state is $E - TS + pV$. This is certainly too long an expression to rewrite many times so we use the symbol G to represent it. The term pV may be thought of as a correction, added on to $E - TS$, and made necessary by the constancy of p rather than V (the term p dV in Eq. 8-47 no longer drops out). Usually the pV term is not very important.

As a matter of fact, the $-TS$ term may also be thought of as a ''correction'' to E, although E and $-TS$ are often of equal importance. The idea here is that in purely mechanical systems (billiard balls, wheels, pulleys, weights, etc.), $E \rightarrow$ minimum determines the equilibrium or stable state.[9] But when a system is placed in a constant temperature bath, we have seen that a term $-TS$ must be added to E to obtain the correct equilibrium condition.

This is an appropriate place to explain the origin of the term ''free'' energy, because the explanation is related to the above comments. In a reversible (frictionless) process carried out by a purely mechanical system, $DW = -dE$ (there is no heat bath). The system can do work on the outside at the expense of its own energy. But for any isothermal system (i.e., in a heat bath), the corresponding expression is

$$DW = -dE + T \, dS = -dA \qquad (T \text{ const}) \qquad (8\text{-}51)$$

We see here that the work which the system can do is related to $E - TS$ rather than to E as above: the ''energy'' that is free to be used as work by an isothermal system is $E - TS$, not E.

In many important cases (e.g., in a chemical battery that furnishes electrical work) the p dV work is not useful or available but another kind of work is (electrical, contractile, etc.). Then we break up DW into two parts,

---

[9]Of course, in order for $E \rightarrow$ minimum, the system must be able to transfer some of its energy to its surroundings (e.g., by friction).

$$DW = p \, dV + DW_{available}$$

and find

$$DW_{available} = -dE + T \, dS - p \, dV$$

$$= -dG \qquad (T, \, p \text{ const}) \qquad (8\text{-}52)$$

Thus, in a reversible constant T, p process, the amount of <u>available</u> (non pV) work that a system can do is determined not by the decrease in E or A, but by the decrease in G. So G is another kind of free "energy."

But let us come back now to the most important property of G. Namely, Eq. 8-49 shows that G decreases during spontaneous processes in systems at constant p and T and reaches a minimum value at equilibrium: G → minimum. Figure 8-8 applies to this situation if we replace V by p and A by G.

A reversible process at constant T and p is characterized by dG = 0, or G = const. We pointed out on p. 161 that reversible processes in isolated systems are virtually nonexistent because there is no way to control what happens in an isolated system. But this is not the case in a constant p, T system; it is easy to conceive of reversible processes. Examples are phase transitions and chemical reactions that proceed <u>at</u> equilibrium. In all such systems ΔG = 0.

The next section and the next two chapters will be concerned largely with applications of the principle that G attains its minimum value at equilibrium. But let us mention very briefly here a few examples of spontaneous processes occurring at constant p and T, and in which, therefore, G → minimum. (a) Ice at 1 atm and 10°C melts to form liquid water. (b) Some solid NaCl dissolves in water at 1 atm and 25°C. (c) Gaseous H atoms form an equilibrium mixture of H and H_2 in a container held at constant T and p (if V is held constant, A → minimum; but here G → minimum). (d) Liquid water and alcohol mix to form a solution at 1 atm and 25°C. (e) "Dry ice" evaporates under room conditions. (f) Ag^+ and Cl^- form a precipitate of solid AgCl when aqueous solutions of $AgNO_3$ and NaCl are mixed under room conditions. (g) A fluid, held at constant p and T but not yet at equilibrium, adjusts its radial distribution function until that distribution is attained which minimizes G for the fluid.

In all of these cases we can be sure that G in the final state is less than G in the initial state—or the process would not have taken place. The breakdown of the negative quantity ΔG for such processes into the separate contributions ΔE, −T ΔS, and p ΔV is often informative. The usual situation is that p ΔV is small or negligible, and that ΔE and ΔS have the same sign (see the discussion of A in the preceding subsection). Alternatively, pV may be combined with E and ΔG separated into ΔH and $-T\,\Delta S$. For example: in (a) above, ΔH and ΔS are both positive; in (c), ΔH and ΔS are both negative; and, in (e), ΔH and ΔS are both positive.

If we consider a spontaneous constant p, T process at a very low temperature, T and ΔS are both small (third law) and hence $\Delta G \cong \Delta H$. Thus, the equilibrium criterion becomes, in effect, H → minimum. It is this criterion that a solid uses (at low temperatures) when it "decides" which particular crystal structure and which intermolecular distances to adopt. Because pV is very small for a condensed phase, the criterion is, to a good approximation, E → minimum.

On the other hand, at <u>very</u> high temperatures, because TS increases faster[10] with temperature than H, the term $-T\,\Delta S$ dominates in ΔG. Thus, in constant p, T processes occurring at very high temperatures, S → maximum is the effective equilibrium condition.

The above two paragraphs can be summarized by saying that low energy is determinate at low temperatures while high entropy or disorder is determinate at high temperatures. At intermediate temperatures, the tendencies H → minimum and S → maximum usually work in opposite directions, and then the equilibrium state involves a compromise.

An example: the H, H_2 mixture referred to above will be almost all H_2 at low temperatures (because the chemical bond gives a low E) and almost all H at very high temperatures (H gas is more disordered than H_2 gas). We shall encounter a number of other examples in the following section and chapters.

We have made some of these comments about the competing roles of energy and disorder, in determining equilibrium, earlier in the book but here we are in a position to base our remarks on a firm thermodynamic foundation rather than on intuition.

Calculation of free energy changes. It should be obvious by now that the state functions $E - TS$ and $E - TS + pV$ play significant roles in thermodynamics. It is therefore important to be able to calculate values of ΔA and ΔG for various processes, or, in other words, to be able to calculate changes in A and G. We came to the same conclusion with respect to the entropy in Section 8-2.

As a matter of fact, other motivation has already led us on pp. 167 and 168 to the fundamental free energy equations for reversible processes:

$$dA = -S\,dT - p\,dV \qquad (8-53)$$

[10]E and H become proportional to T as T → ∞, but S also increases with T.

$$\left(\frac{\partial A}{\partial T}\right)_V = -S, \qquad \left(\frac{\partial A}{\partial V}\right)_T = -p \tag{8-54}$$

and

$$dG = -S \, dT + V \, dp \tag{8-55}$$

$$\left(\frac{\partial G}{\partial T}\right)_p = -S, \qquad \left(\frac{\partial G}{\partial p}\right)_T = V \tag{8-56}$$

These equations show how A changes with T and V, and how G changes with T and p.

Let us apply Eq. 8-56b to two simple cases that we shall need in the next section.

Ideal gas. In order to integrate Eq. 8-56b (when applied to any system), V must be known as a function of p (at constant T). If the substance is an ideal gas,[11] this relation is simply $V = nRT/p$. Therefore

$$G(p_2) - G(p_1) = nRT \ln \frac{p_2}{p_1} \tag{8-57}$$

For one mole,

$$G(p_2) - G(p_1) = RT \ln \frac{p_2}{p_1} \tag{8-58}$$

It is often convenient to compare the free energy[12] of a substance at an arbitrary pressure p with its free energy at some standard or reference pressure, usually chosen as 1 atm. For this purpose we put $p_2 = p$ atm and $p_1 = 1$ atm in Eq. 8-58. Then

$$G(p,T) = G^0(T) + RT \ln p \text{ (atm)} \tag{8-59}$$

In this equation we have introduced the symbol G^0 (called the standard free energy) to mean G (1 atm). As indicated in the notation, G^0 depends on T (see Eq. 8-56a). Equation 8-59 shows how to calculate G at any p (provided the gas is still ideal) if G^0 is known at the same temperature.

Of course there is no true absolute free energy, but if some convention is adopted about the zero of free energy, then tables of G^0 values for various gases can be prepared. This is discussed in Chapter 10.

---

[11]For a slightly imperfect gas, we would obtain V(p) from Eq. 4-5.
[12]From here on, "free energy" by itself will mean "Gibbs free energy."

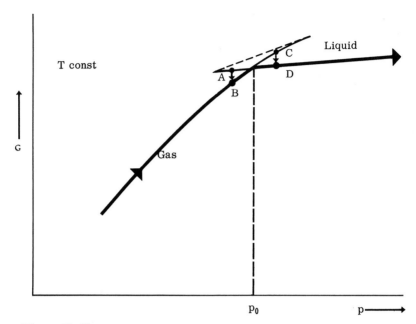

Figure 8-10
Gibbs free energy near a gas-liquid phase transition (schematic).

According to Eq. 8-59, G increases logarithmically with p (Fig. 8-10). Incidentally, since V is a positive quantity for any kind of substance, Eq. 8-56b shows that G always increases, in one way or another, with p.

To understand the logarithmic pressure dependence of G for an ideal gas, we go back to Eq. 8-57. We have

$$\Delta G = \Delta(E - TS + pV) = \Delta E - T\,\Delta S + \Delta(pV)$$

$$= nRT \ln \frac{p_2}{p_1}$$

The process implied here is a reversible isothermal expansion or compression of the gas. Since T is constant and the gas is ideal, $\Delta E = 0$ and $\Delta(pV) = 0$. Therefore $\Delta G = -T\,\Delta S$. The free energy change is thus entirely an entropy effect in this case, and in fact we note that Eq. 8-57 is consistent with Eq. 8-29. As the pressure increases (volume decreases), the entropy decreases; hence the free energy increases.

Because G is a composite function, $E - TS + pV$, we are almost always forced to decompose it into separate terms, as above, in order to comprehend free energy changes.

Incompressible Solid or Liquid. Compared to a gas, solids and liquids (not near the critical point) are practically incompressible. As a first approximation, let us assume that V is independent of p for such a substance. Then integration of Eq. 8-56b leads to

$$G(p_2) - G(p_1) = V(p_2 - p_1)$$

or

$$G(p_2) - G(p_1) = v(p_2 - p_1)$$

We again put $p_2 = p$ atm, $p_1 = 1$ atm, and $G(1 \text{ atm}) = G^0$. Then

$$G(p, T) = G^0(T) + v(p - 1) \qquad (8\text{-}60)$$

where p is in atmospheres. The molar volume v depends slightly on temperature. Here we find that G increases linearly with p (Fig. 8-10). But actually v is very small (condensed phase) and hence the slope of the G-p line is almost zero. For most practical purposes, the free energy of a solid or liquid (not near the critical point) can be taken as independent of pressure: $G \cong G^0(T)$.

The reader may wish to find $G(p,T)$ for a solid or liquid in the next higher approximation: instead of assuming v is independent of p, use

$$v(p,T) = v_0(T)[1 - \beta(T)(p - 1)] \qquad (8\text{-}61)$$

where β is the compressibility (Eq. 5-3) and v_0 is the molar volume at p = 1 atm.

8-6 GIBBS FREE ENERGY, PHASE TRANSITIONS, AND PHASE DIAGRAMS

THIS SECTION is devoted to a discussion of the role played by the free energy G in phase transitions and phase diagrams. As will be seen, G is the key function in a thermodynamic analysis of this subject.

G(T) − H(0) for a pure substance. Beginning on pp. 131 and 172, we indicated how to calculate $H(T) - H(0)$ and $S(T) - S(0)$, respectively, for a pure substance. Figures 7-4 and 8-4 illustrate such a calculation for water at 1 atm pressure. For completelness, we do the same thing here for the free energy.

We could integrate Eq. 8-56a to find the temperature dependence

of G. But it is easier to use the relation $G = H - TS$, as we already
have $H(T)$ and $S(T)$. On introducing the usual convention $S(0) = 0$,
the required relation for practical calculations is

$$G(T) - G(0) = G(T) - H(0)$$

$$= [H(T) - H(0)] - TS(T) \qquad (8\text{-}62)$$

Thus, for water at 1 atm, at each value of T we multiply the
ordinate in Fig. 8-4 (change cal to kcal) by T, and subtract this
from the ordinate in Fig. 7-4 to obtain the ordinate in Fig. 8-11
(at T).

There are two points in particular to notice about Fig. 8-11. One
is that the slope of the curve is negative and becomes progressively
more negative as T increases. This is because $(\partial G / \partial T)_p = -S \leq 0$
and S increases with T (Fig. 8-4). The other point is that there is
no discontinuity in $G(T) - H(0)$ at a phase transition, as there is in
$H(T) - H(0)$ and in $S(T)$. There is, however, a discontinuity in the
<u>slope</u> of $G(T) - H(0)$. In fact, the discontinuities in Figs. 7-4 and
8-4 exactly cancel each other when these two figures are put together to produce Fig. 8-11. This is a consequence of Eq. 8-30.
At a phase transition (p and T const),

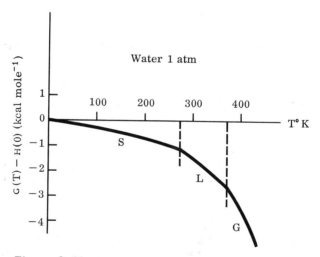

Figure 8-11
Gibbs free energy of water.

$$\Delta G = \Delta (H - TS) = \Delta H - T \, \Delta S$$

But $\Delta H = T \, \Delta S$. Therefore

$$\Delta G = 0 \qquad\qquad\qquad (8\text{-}63)$$

That is, the two phases in a phase equilibrium have the same value of G. Thus, in Fig. 8-11,

$$G_S (273.1\,°K, \; 1 \; atm) = G_L (273.1\,°K, \; 1 \; atm)$$

and

$$G_L (373.1\,°K, \; 1 \; atm) = G_G (373.1\,°K, \; 1 \; atm)$$

Equation 8-63 also follows directly from the fact that $dG = 0$ for any reversible, constant p, T process.

Figure 8-11 shows how $G(T) - H(0)$ changes along a horizontal line (p = 1 atm), from left to right, in the phase diagram, Fig. 1-3. In the next two subsections we investigate the way in which G varies along vertical lines in such a diagram. That is, we consider the pressure dependence of G at constant T.

Gas-liquid transition. Before considering the full phase diagram, let us look at a two phase situation for simplicity. Suppose we start with a very dilute gas and increase the pressure at a constant temperature well below T_c, as in Fig. 1-8b. The G → L phase transition begins when p reaches the vapor pressure, which we denote here by p_0. When $p > p_0$, only the liquid phase remains.

The heavy solid line in Fig. 8-10 shows how the free energy G changes during this process. The curve labeled "Gas" gives $G(p)$ according to Eq. 8-59, while the "Liquid" curve follows Eq. 8-60. The gas is assumed ideal and the liquid is assumed incompressible over the pressure ranges shown. The two curves cross at $p = p_0$, and at this pressure the free energy "switches" from the gas branch to the liquid branch. In accordance with Eq. 8-63, there is no discontinuity in free energy at $p = p_0$: $G_G(p_0) = G_L(p_0)$. While the system passes from point 2 to 2′ in Fig. 1-8b (i.e., while both phases are present and gas is compressed into liquid), the system remains at the intersection point ($p = p_0$) in Fig. 8-10. That is, $G = $ constant ($dG = 0$) during the phase transition.

The light solid curves in Fig. 8-10 represent metastable states. For example, if, when the pressure is increased, the liquid phase does not appear at $p = p_0$ as it should, the gas becomes super-saturated as at point C. The gas at C is metastable relative to the liquid at D. Figure 8-10 makes this quite clear because the liquid at D has a lower free energy than the gas at C: at the same p and T, the state with the lowest possible free energy is the stable or equilibrium state. The spontaneous, constant p, T process C → D may be expected (especially if dust particles or other foreign nuclei are present to start the condensation); in this process $\Delta c < 0$ and c → minimum.

Completely analogous comments may be made about the process liquid at A → gas at B. In fact, one can see at a glance that the heavy solid lines represent the stable behavior of the system while the light solid lines represent metastable behavior, because the heavy lines correspond to the lowest possible free energy at each p (T is constant in the whole diagram)—the heavy lines lie below the light lines.

The dashed curve connecting the two metastable branches in Fig. 8-10 is equivalent to the unstable path BC in Fig. 4-9. The dashed curve would be found from van der Waals equation, or other similar equations, but not from any experimental system.

The fact that a phase transition starts suddenly at a sharply defined point, such as point 2 in Fig. 1-8b, may seem puzzling. A chemical reaction, for example in a gas, does not behave in this way—it starts and proceeds gradually, as outside conditions such as pressure or temperature are changed. Figure 8-10 helps to clarify this situation in a "geometrical" way because the figure shows that $c_L(p)$ and $c_G(p)$ have different slopes and hence intersect in a sharply defined point—the point at which the transition occurs. The molar free energy of the equilibrium system is $c = c_G(p)$ for $p \leq p_0$ and $c = c_L(p)$ for $p \geq p_0$.

From a molecular point of view, the essential difference between a phase transition and a chemical reaction is that there is a cooperative aspect to a phase transition that is missing in a chemical reaction. Thus, in a dilute gas chemical reaction A ⇌ B, the probability that any given molecule is in state A (or state B) is independent of the state of the other molecules in the gas. But, in a phase transition (such as gas ⇌ liquid), if A = molecule in the gas phase and B = molecule in the liquid phase, there is a tendency for a large number of molecules to switch as a group from state A to state B because the molecules in state B can stabilize each other (hence the term "cooperative") through intermolecular attractions. Unlike the chemical reaction case, the tendency for the conversion of a particular A into a B is not independent of the state of the other molecules; rather, the conversion is aided by the presence of other B molecules. Hence a phase transition resembles a landslide or autocatalytic process.

Free energy and phase diagrams. Let us now look into the relation between the free energy function and phase diagrams. Figure 8-12 presents a typical such diagram. At any point (p, T) in the region

marked S, the solid state is the stable or observed state. The
equivalent statement in terms of the free energy is that at such a
point the free energy of the solid is lower than the free energy of
liquid or gas (or any other possible solid state). Thus, a phase
diagram shows the region of the p-T plane in which the indicated
phase (S, L, G, etc.) has a free energy lower than the free energy of any other possible phase. Along a two-phase line, the two
phases involved have equal free energies. At the triple point, gas,
liquid, and solid all have the same value of the free energy.
    The above remarks are brought out in more detail in Fig. 8-13

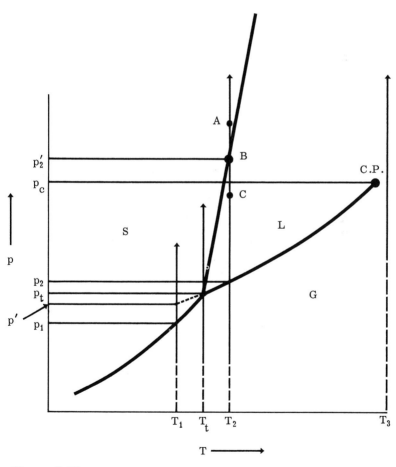

Figure 8-12
Typical phase diagram.

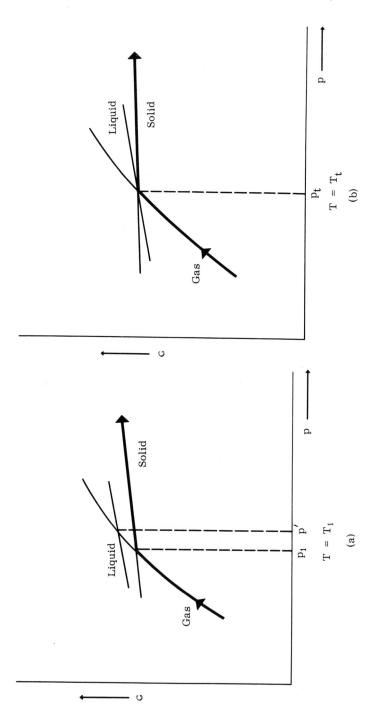

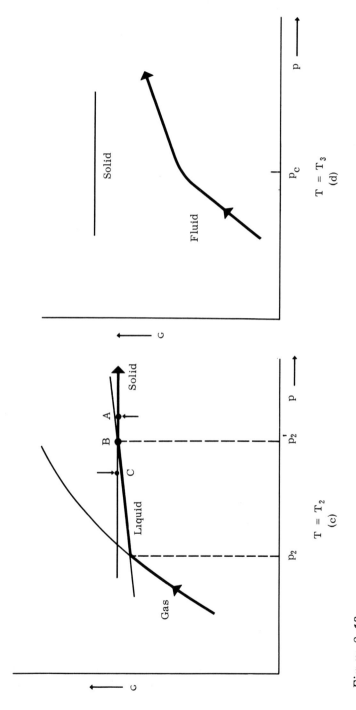

Figure 8-13
Gibbs free energy curves at different temperatures.

(schematic), which is closely related to Fig. 8-12. Figure 8-13a
presents plots of $c_S(p)$, $c_L(p)$ and $c_G(p)$ at a temperature T_1 below the triple point temperature T_t. These curves show how the
free energies of the three phases change as the system moves up
the vertical line (p increases) at $T = T_1$ in Fig. 8-12. In Fig. 8-12,
the S-L line tilts to the right; therefore $v_L > v_S$. This is reflected
in Fig. 8-13 by the fact that the slope of the liquid curve is greater
than the slope of the solid curve (because $\partial c/\partial p = v$). Both slopes
are exaggerated for clarity. At pressures below p_1, the gas has the
lowest free energy in Fig. 8-13a and is therefore the indicated stable
phase in Fig. 8-12. But when $p > p_1$, the solid has the lowest free
energy and is the stable phase. There is no pressure at which the
liquid has the lowest free energy; this is shown in Fig. 8-12 by the
fact that the vertical line at $T = T_1$ does not pass through the liquid
region.

The pressure p_1 is the vapor pressure of the solid at $T = T_1$. At
this pressure, gas and solid are in equilibrium ($c_G = c_S$). The heavy
solid line in Fig. 8-13a represents the stable behavior of the system,
as the pressure is increased at $T = T_1$. The light lines represent
metastable behavior. From the figure it appears possible, incidentally, that if the gas (on being compressed) fails to form solid at
$p = p_1$, it might form liquid (metastable) at a slightly higher pressure (p' in Figs. 8-12 and 8-13a).

Figures 8-13b and 8-13c are very similar diagrams for slightly
higher temperatures, T_t and $T_2 > T_t$, respectively. The liquid
phase makes its appearance when $T \geq T_t$, and these free energy
diagrams give some insight into how this comes about. The essential feature is that the liquid curve moves downward, relative to the
gas and solid curves, as the temperature rises. At a temperature
such as $T_2 > T_t$, there is a pressure range ($p_2 < p < p_2'$) in which
the liquid has the lowest free energy and is therefore the stable
phase. The question of why the liquid curve moves downward, as
mentioned above, is a difficult problem in statistical mechanics.

As $T \to T_c$, the slopes of the gas and liquid c vs p curves, at
their intersection point (two phase equilibrium), become closer to
each other. This is because v_G and v_L approach each other as
$T \to T_c$. When $T \geq T_c$, there is no longer a discontinuity in slope
at all—the curve is smooth as in Fig. 8-13d ($T_3 > T_c$).

Consider the process Solid → Liquid at points A, B, and C in
Figs. 8-12 and 8-13c. At point A, the free energy change for this
process is positive: $\Delta c > 0$. Therefore the process cannot occur
spontaneously. The solid is stable relative to liquid and will not
melt. At point B, $\Delta c = 0$. Solid and liquid phases are equally stable

and in equilibrium with each other. The process can be carried out reversibly by slowly increasing the volume at constant pressure. At point C, $\Delta G < 0$. Solid will melt spontaneously to form liquid, which is the stable phase at this p and T.

Comparison of states of matter. We have already discussed (p. 106) the different stabilizing tendencies at work in the three states of matter. But having in the meantime acquired some background in thermodynamics, we are now in a position to make our remarks more explicit. Let us therefore review the situation in thermodynamic terms.

The free energy is $G = E - TS + pV$. We can ignore pV in a qualitative discussion such as the present one. At low temperatures, G is approximately equal to E for any state of matter because of the factor T in TS (in the solid, $S \rightarrow 0$ as well). Since the solid has the lowest E of the three states (because of optimal intermolecular attractions), it has the lowest G and is therefore the stable state at low temperatures. At high temperatures the term $-TS$ is dominant in G (see the footnote on p. 192). The gas state has the largest entropy of the three states, and hence the lowest G. Therefore the gas state is stable at high temperatures.

When gas and solid are in equilibrium with each other, as on the solid-gas line below T_t, the two phases have the <u>same</u> G. How is this possible at a fairly low temperature where the solid is supposed to be more stable? It can happen because the entropy per mole of gas can be made as high as one pleases by <u>reducing</u> the <u>pressure</u> of the gas (Eq. 8-29)—that is, by making it more dilute. Therefore the contribution of the low energy of the solid to the free energy of the solid can be matched by the contribution of the high entropy of the gas to the free energy of the gas. Of course the lower the energy of the solid, the lower the necessary gas pressure to make $G_S = G_G$. In other words, the stronger the attractive forces in a solid, the lower its vapor pressure—which is just what we should expect.

To recapitulate: at low temperatures and <u>ordinary</u> pressures the solid state has the lowest G; but if the pressure is reduced sufficiently, eventually $G_S = G_G$; indeed, if the pressure is reduced even more, the gas has the lowest G. This is confirmed by inspection of a phase diagram. Even very near T = 0, the gas phase is the stable phase <u>if</u> the pressure is low enough.

The liquid state is as usual difficult to discuss because of its intermediate position. The liquid has both energy and entropy values in between those of solid and gas—but the liquid is nearer to the solid than to the gas in these respects (see Figs. 7-4 and 8-4, for example). In the liquid-solid equilibrium, the solid is favored (G_S is lowered) by a lower energy but the liquid is favored (G_L is lowered) by a higher entropy. In the liquid-gas equilibrium, the liquid has the lower energy and the gas the higher entropy. Again the molar entropy of the gas can be increased as much as necessary to achieve equilibrium, $c_L = c_G$, by a lowering of the gas (vapor) pressure.

The attainment of an equilibrium (equality of free energy) between a lower energy state and a higher entropy state is one of the most common phenomena in thermodynamics. It must necessarily occur in a phase equilibrium (because ΔH and Δs have the same sign), but chemical reactions provide many additional examples (Chapter 10).

Maxwell's equal area theorem. Van der Waals equation (and others like it) gives a loop instead of a horizontal line at a phase transition in a p-v diagram (see p. 69 and Fig. 4-8). We want to show here that the horizontal line which must be inserted to indicate the "experimental" behavior of the system should be located so that the two areas cut out of the loop (Fig. 4-8) by the line are equal.

This is an application of Eq. 8-56, which we rewrite here as

$$\left(\frac{\partial c}{\partial p}\right)_T = v \qquad\qquad (8\text{-}64)$$

Figure 8-14 gives v plotted against p (instead of the more customary p versus v), and exhibits a loop. The line AD is drawn in such a way that the two shaded areas are equal. In the phase transition, gas at A is supposed to be in equilibrium with liquid at D. We know that $c_G = c_L$ at equilibrium. In order to prove that the line is located correctly we have to show, then, that $c_A = c_D$.

Let us start with the fluid at A and move reversibly along the v-p curve to point B (T remains constant). Then

$$c_B - c_A = \int_A^B v\ dp = I + II + III$$

where I, II, and III are the areas indicated in the figure. Next, let us go from B to C (p decreases in this process):

$$c_C - c_B = \int_B^C v\ dp = -\int_C^B v\ dp = -(II + III + IV + V)$$

Finally, we pass from C to D:

$$c_D - c_C = \int_C^D v\ dp = V$$

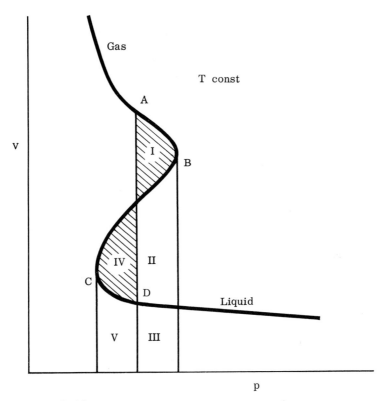

Figure 8-14
Equal area theorem.

We add these three integrals together and find

$$G_D - G_A = I - IV$$

But the line was drawn to make $I = IV$. Therefore $G_D = G_A$, as was to be proved.

PROBLEMS

8-1. Calculate ΔS in cal mole^{-1} deg^{-1} for the process: one mole ideal gas at 200°C, V = 20 liters → same gas at 200°C and V = 40 liters.

8-2. The vapor pressure of liquid water at 25°C is 23.8 mm Hg. Assume that the Gibbs free energy of liquid water is independent of pressure. Calculate ΔG in calories for the process:

one mole H_2O →   one mole H_2O
(liquid, 25°C, 1 atm)   (gas, 25°C, 1 atm)

8-3. The melting point of a solid (which we call X) at 1 atm pressure is 27.0°C and the heat of fusion is 60 cal g^{-1}. The molecular weight of X is 40 g $mole^{-1}$. The density of solid X at the melting point is 1.60 g cm^{-3}, and the density of liquid X at the melting point is 1.25 cm^{-3}. For the reversible process,

one mole of solid X   →   one mole of liquid X
at 1 atm and 27.0°C   at 1 atm and 27.0°C

calculate: (a) Q in cal; (b) ΔH in cal; (c) ΔS in cal deg^{-1} (d) ΔG in cal; (e) Δp in atm; (f) ΔV in cm^3; (g) W in liter-atm; (h) W in cal; (i) Δ(pV) in liter-atm; (j) ΔE in cal.

8-4. The triple point of water is at 273°K and 4.58 mm Hg. At the triple point, the heat of fusion is 79.8 cal g^{-1} and the heat of vaporization is 596 cal g^{-1}. Calculate ΔH, ΔE, ΔS and ΔG for each of the following processes: (a) melting of one mole of ice; (b) vaporization of one mole of liquid water; and (c) sublimation of one mole of ice, all at 273°K and 4.58 mm Hg. Make an "energy level" diagram showing the relative energies of one mole of solid, liquid and gas at the triple point. Do the same for the entropy.
One mole of ice contains two moles of hydrogen bonds. If we make the approximation that ΔE of sublimation is entirely due to breaking all the hydrogen bonds in ice, what is the hydrogen bond energy in ice, per mole? If we make the further approximation that ΔE of melting of ice is entirely due to the breakage of a fraction of the hydrogen bonds in ice, calculate this fraction.

8-5. Calculate ΔS when 0.5 mole of liquid water at 0°C is mixed with 0.5 mole of liquid water at 100°C, in an isolated system. Assume c_V = 18 cal deg^{-1} $mole^{-1}$ over the whole range of temperature.

8-6. Assuming that the density of liquid mercury stays constant at 13.5 g cm^{-3}, calculate ΔG for the process:

one mole Hg (liquid)   →   one mole Hg (liquid)
at 25°C and 1 atm   at 25°C and 101 atm

8-7. One mole of an ideal gas is heated at constant pressure from 25°C to 300°C. Calculate ΔS for the process. Assume c_V = 3R/2.

8-8. Consider the process

one gram liquid H_2O →   one gram solid H_2O
at −5°C and 1 atm   at −5°C and 1 atm

What is the sign of ΔH for this process, of ΔS, of ΔG? Does ΔH = TΔS?

8-9. Consider the process

> 11 g of CO$_2$ gas (ideal)   →   11 g of CO$_2$ gas (ideal)
> at 300°K and 1 atm   at 400°K and 1 atm

Take c_p for CO$_2$ gas as constant and equal to 9.2 cal deg^{-1} mole^{-1}. If the process is carried out reversibly, at constant pressure, by gradual heating, calculate, or give the value of: (a) Δp in atm; (b) ΔT in °K; (c) ΔV in liters; (d) W in cal; (e) Q in cal; (f) ΔH in cal; (g) $\Delta(pV)$ in cal; (h) ΔE in cal; (i) ΔS in cal deg^{-1}.

If the process is carried out irreversibly by a sudden change in heat bath temperature, calculate or give the value for the irreversible process of: (j) ΔE in cal; (k) ΔS in cal deg^{-1}.

8-10. A pure substance exists in two crystalline forms A and B which are in equilibrium with each other at 500°K and 100 atm pressure. Under these conditions, v_A = 30 cm^3 mole^{-1} and v_B = 24 cm^3 mole^{-1}. For the reversible process

> one mole of A at   →   one mole of B at
> 500°K and 100 atm   500°K and 100 atm,

the heat Q = -1200 cal. For the above process calculate or give the value of: (a) ΔH in cal; (b) ΔS in cal deg^{-1}; (c) ΔG in cal; and (d) W in cal.

Assuming incompressibility of A and B, calculate (e) ΔG in cal for the process

> one mole of A at   →   one mole of B at
> 500°K and 300 atm   500°K and 300 atm

(f) Is A or B more stable at 500°K and 300 atm? (g) Is A or B more stable at 450°K and 100 atm? (h) Show roughly how the A-B equilibrium line looks on a p-T (phase) diagram for this substance. Label the point p = 100 atm and T = 500°K.

CHAPTER 9

BINARY
LIQUID SOLUTIONS

IN THIS chapter we apply some of the background acquired in earlier chapters, especially in Chapter 8, to a few important topics concerning binary (two component) solutions. For definiteness, we shall have in mind liquid solutions, but solid solutions (e.g., alloys) can be treated in much the same way. Gaseous solutions, on the other hand, present a rather special case that is considerably easier to understand than liquid or solid solutions, particularly if the gas mixture is very dilute (see Section 2-4 and p. 178, for example). The only gaseous solutions that will enter into our considerations here will be of this simple type.

In order to make the thermodynamic parts of this chapter logical, calculus will have to be used in several derivations. Some readers may prefer to omit the details of these derivations and note the results only.

9-1   BINARY SOLUTIONS WITH BOTH COMPONENTS VOLATILE

IN THIS section we treat a binary liquid solution which is in equilibrium with a vapor phase containing both components; that is, both components in the liquid phase are volatile. Examples are a solution of acetic acid in water (vinegar), or a solution of ethyl alcohol in water. Sections 9-2 and 9-3 will then be concerned with liquid solutions in which one component is volatile and one nonvolatile (or virtually so). For example: salt in water; or sugar in water.

Chemical potentials. First we must make a digression to introduce some new and rather general ideas that are indispensable in the thermodynamic discussion of a system in which two solutions are in equilibrium with each other. In this section, for example, we study a liquid solution in equilibrium with a gaseous solution. The Gibbs free energy of the entire system is

$$G = G_G + G_L$$

where G = gas and L = liquid. Actually, the argument we are about to give applies to any two kinds of phases, not just gas and liquid. We label the components 1, 2, ..., c (in a binary system, c = 2). Now consider the following process: dn_i moles of any one component i are transferred from the liquid phase to the gaseous phase, with p and T held constant. According to Eq. 8-49, if this process takes place with the two phases in equilibrium with each other, $dG = 0$. But if it is a spontaneous process which occurs as the two phases approach equilibrium with each other, $dG < 0$.

Each phase has its own set of mole numbers: n_1^G, n_2^G, ... and n_1^L, n_2^L, ..., where the subscripts refer to the different components. If dn_i moles of component i are transferred from liquid to gas, $dn_i^G = dn_i$ and $dn_i^L = -dn_i$. The change in G in the process is then

$$dG = dG_G + dG_L = \frac{\partial G_G}{\partial n_i^G} dn_i^G + \frac{\partial G_L}{\partial n_i^L} dn_i^L$$

$$= \left(\frac{\partial G_G}{\partial n_i^G} - \frac{\partial G_L}{\partial n_i^L}\right) dn_i \qquad (9-1)$$

where, in the partial derivatives, the quantities held constant are p, T, and all the other mole numbers. These derivatives prove to be so important they are given the special symbol μ and called chemical potentials. There is a chemical potential for each component in each phase. Using this new notation, Eq. 9-1 becomes

$$dG = \left(\mu_i^G - \mu_i^L\right) dn_i \qquad (9-2)$$

If the process occurs at equilibrium, $dG = 0$ and $dn_i > 0$; hence we must have $\mu_i^G = \mu_i^L$. Since this argument can be applied to any component and to any pair of phases in equilibrium (even if there are more than two phases present in the system), we come to the following quite general and very important conclusion: whenever two or more phases are in equilibrium with each other, <u>the chemical potential of each component must have the same value in each phase in which the component appears</u> (it may not be present in every phase).

If the process described occurs spontaneously, $dG < 0$ and $dn_i > 0$; therefore $\mu_i^L > \mu_i^G$. We note here that molecules of component i diffuse spontaneously from the high μ_i phase (L) to the low μ_i phase (G). By the same token, if we had $\mu_i^G > \mu_i^L$, the direction of diffusion would be G → L. This resembles the spontaneous flow of heat from a high temperature region to a low temperature region (see p. 179). As a matter of fact, the chemical potentials have the same significance for the direction of flow of the different components in nonequilibrium systems (and for the condition of final equilibrium) as the temperature has for the flow of heat: the temperature is a "thermal potential." Similarly, the pressure can easily be shown to be a "volume potential." Thus we see that the chemical potentials join a select class of important thermodynamic variables.

Because molecules diffuse in the direction from high chemical potential to low, the chemical potential in any region may be regarded as a measure of the "escaping tendency" of the molecules in the region. The higher the escaping tendency or chemical potential, the less stable the molecules.

What is the status of the chemical potential when we have a two-phase equilibrium with only one component in the system? The argument above is applicable for any number of components, including c = 1. Therefore, in a one-component two-phase equilibrium such as <u>liquid ⇌ gas</u>,

$$\mu_G = \mu_L$$

where

$$\mu_G \equiv \left(\frac{\partial G_G}{\partial n_G}\right)_{p,T} \quad \text{and} \quad \mu_L \equiv \left(\frac{\partial G_L}{\partial n_L}\right)_{p,T}$$

Now these derivatives take a simple form in this case of a one-component system. For in any one-phase, one-component system of n moles at p and T, each of the n moles has a Gibbs free energy $c(p,T)$ which is a function of p and T only (Eqs. 8-59 and 8-60 are examples), and G for the entire system is given by $G = nc(p,T)$. In other words, G is proportional to the size of the system. Therefore

$$\mu = \left(\frac{\partial G}{\partial n}\right)_{p,T} = c = \frac{G}{n} \qquad (9\text{-}3)$$

Thus, in a one-component system, μ is the same quantity as the molar Gibbs free energy. The equality of μ between two phases in equilibrium is then seen to be identical with the similar equality of c already noted in Eq. 8-63.

Although the principle of equality of chemical potential for each component in each phase turns out to be nothing new as far as one-component systems are concerned, it is something new for solutions. For the principle shows how to generalize the one-component result (equality of c) to systems with any number of components.

An important consequence of the above principle concerning chemical potentials is the following. If a liquid solution is in equilibrium with its vapor, the chemical potential μ_i^G of any component i in the gas phase can be used as a measure of μ_i^L in the liquid phase. The former quantity is usually much easier to study experimentally than the latter. Thus the gas phase in equilibrium with a liquid solution serves as an indirect source of information about properties of the liquid. If the vapor is sufficiently dilute to be treated as an ideal gas mixture, the situation is especially simple. For in this case each component in the gas behaves just as if the other components were absent (see Section 2-4). That is, each component in the gas may be regarded, by itself, as a one-component gas. But $\mu = c$ for a one-component gas, and c is given by Eq. 8-59. Therefore, in this case, we have

$$\mu_i^L = \mu_i^G = c_i^0(T) + RT \ln p_i \qquad (9\text{-}4)$$

where p_i is the partial pressure of component i in the gas phase and $c_i^0(T)$ is the standard free energy of gaseous component i.

In the remainder of this section Eq. 9-4 is exploited. By use of this equation, experimental measurements on the partial pressures of the two gaseous components give thermodynamic information about the binary liquid solution.

There is a more general form of Eq. 9-4 that can be employed for the same purpose if the gas phase is not ideal, that is, if the partial pressures are quite high. But for simplicity we shall confine ourselves here to Eq. 9-4.

Ideal liquid solutions. Consider a binary liquid solution made up of n_1 moles of component 1 and n_2 moles of component 2. The (relative) composition of the solution is conveniently expressed by the mole fractions:

$$x_1 = \frac{n_1}{n_1 + n_2}, \qquad x_2 = \frac{n_2}{n_1 + n_2}$$

Because of the relation $x_1 + x_2 = 1$, one of the mole fractions is not an independent variable. We shall generally use x_2 as the independent composition variable.

The liquid solution, at temperature T, is in equilibrium with its vapor, with partial pressures p_1 and p_2. If the temperature is held constant, but the composition x_2 of the solution is varied, the two partial pressures will also vary. One can then plot p_1 and p_2 as functions of x_2, with T constant. There are three kinds of plot observed, depending on the molecules chosen and the temperature. The simplest type is considered in this subsection; the other two cases are treated in the following subsections.

Experimental partial pressures for a liquid mixture of ethylene bromide ($C_2H_4Br_2$; component 1) and propylene bromide ($C_3H_6Br_2$; component 2) at 85°C are shown in Fig. 9-1, as functions of x_2. The partial pressure curves are found to be straight lines in this case. This is quite unusual. Ordinarily, as we shall see, the p_i curves are more complicated. But when this straight-line behavior is observed, the liquid solution is called <u>ideal</u>. Such a solution is, however, not to be confused with an ideal gas mixture. In an ideal gas the molecules are far apart and intermolecular interactions are negligible; in an ideal liquid solution, on the other hand, the molecules are densely packed—as they are in any liquid phase. Hence the intermolecular potential energy of such a solution is by no means a small quantity. But we shall have more to say on this subject below.

A few other examples of solutions observed to be ideal are: n-hexane and n-heptane at 30°C; ethyl bromide and ethyl iodide at 30°C; and n-butyl chloride and n-butyl bromide at 50°C.

For any ideal binary liquid solution, the two partial pressures are given by the linear equations

$$p_1 = (1 - x_2)p_1^0 = x_1 p_1^0; \qquad p_2 = x_2 p_2^0 \qquad\qquad (9\text{-}5)$$

where p_i^0 (see Fig. 9-1) is the vapor pressure of pure liquid component i at the same temperature as the solution. The partial pressure equation $p_i = x_i p_i^0$ is known as <u>Raoult's law</u>.

Aside from linear partial pressure curves (Raoult's law), ideal

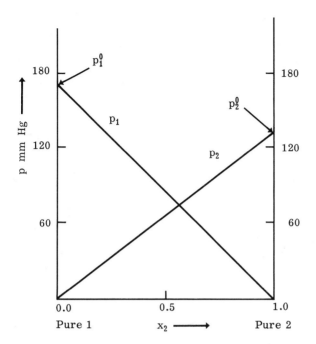

Figure 9-1
Vapor pressure curves in ideal binary solution.

solutions have some other simple properties which are thermodynamic consequences of (i.e., which can be derived from) the partial pressure behavior; these additional properties may be verified
experimentally. Let us deduce the most important of these. First,
we consider the so-called free energy of mixing, ΔG_{mix}. This is
the change in G for the following process:

n_1 moles of pure liquid 1 at T

+ n_2 moles of pure liquid 2 at T

→ liquid solution of 1 and 2 with n_1, n_2, T   (9-6)

Therefore

$$\Delta G_{mix} = G_{final\ state} - G_{initial\ state}$$

$$= G(n_1, n_2\ solution) - n_1\ G_1 - n_2\ G_2 \qquad (9-7)$$

where G_1 and G_2 refer to the pure liquids. In order to calculate the
quantity 9-7, let us start with n_2 moles of pure liquid 2 and gradually

add, at constant temperature, n_1 moles of component 1. For each small addition of dn_1 moles, the change in G will be

$$dG = \mu_1 \, dn_1 \qquad (n_2 \text{ const}) \qquad\qquad (9\text{-}8)$$

since $\mu_1 \equiv (\partial G/\partial n_1)_{n_2}$. On integrating Eq. 9-8, we have

$$\int_{n_1=0}^{n_1} dG = G(n_1, n_2) - G(0, n_2) = \int_0^{n_1} \mu_1 \, dn_1 \, (n_2 \text{ const}) \qquad (9\text{-}9)$$

where $G(0, n_2)$ is the Gibbs free energy of n_2 moles of pure 2. This quantity is equal to $n_2 G_2$. To evaluate the integral on the right, we use Eqs. 9-4 and 9-5:

$$\mu_1 \text{ (solution)} = \mu_1 \text{ (vapor)} = G_1^0(T) + RT \ln p_1$$

$$= G_1^0(T) + RT \ln p_1^0 + RT \ln \frac{n_1}{n_1 + n_2}$$

$$= G_1 \text{ (pure liquid 1)} + RT \ln \frac{n_1}{n_1 + n_2} \qquad (9\text{-}10)$$

This is the integrand in the above integral. We note that G_1 and n_2 are constant in the integration and that we need the integrals

$$\int \ln x \, dx = x \ln x - x$$

and

$$\int \ln (x + a) \, dx = \int \ln (x + a) \, d(x + a)$$

$$= (x + a) \ln (x + a) - (x + a)$$

where $x = n_1$ and $a = n_2$. Equation 9-9 becomes, then,

$$G(n_1, n_2) - n_2 G_2 = n_1 G_1 + RT \left[n_1 \ln n_1 + n_2 \ln n_2 \right.$$

$$\left. - (n_1 + n_2) \ln (n_1 + n_2) \right]$$

Therefore, from Eq. 9-7,

$$\Delta G_{mix} = RT \, (n_1 \ln x_1 + n_2 \ln x_2) \qquad\qquad (9\text{-}11)$$

This quantity is always negative, as we should expect (spontaneous mixing). Nonideal solutions have additional terms in the equation

for ΔG_{mix}. The simple terms above are characteristic of ideality.

The physical implications of Eq. 9-11 become apparent if we
carry the argument a little further. We differentiate both sides of
the equation

$$G(n_1, n_2) - n_1 G_1 - n_2 G_2 = RT\left(n_1 \ln \frac{n_1}{n_1 + n_2} + n_2 \ln \frac{n_2}{n_1 + n_2}\right)$$

$$(9\text{-}12)$$

with respect to pressure, holting T, n_1, and n_2 constant. Using Eq.
8-56b, the result is

$$V(n_1, n_2) - n_1 v_1 \text{ (pure 1)} - n_2 v_2 \text{ (pure 2)} = 0 \qquad (9\text{-}13)$$

because all quantities on the right-hand side of Eq. 9-12 are held
constant in the differentiation. But the left-hand side of Eq. 9-13 is
just the volume change in the process 9-6. Therefore $\Delta V_{mix} = 0$.
This means that when the two pure liquids are mixed to form the
solution, there is no expansion or contraction: the final volume is
exactly the sum of the initial volumes of the pure liquids. Furthermore, this is true for any choice of n_1 and n_2. The fact that
$\Delta V_{mix} = 0$ has been confirmed experimentally for ideal solutions,
but of course for most solutions it is found that $\Delta V_{mix} \neq 0$.

If we differentiate both sides of Eq. 9-12 with respect to T,
holding p, n_1, and n_2 constant we obtain, with the aid of Eq. 8-56a,

$$\Delta S_{mix} = -R(n_1 \ln x_1 + n_2 \ln x_2) \qquad (9\text{-}14)$$

a positive quantity. Then, from Eq. 9-11 and the relation $\Delta G =
\Delta H - T \Delta S$, which holds for any isothermal process,

$$\Delta H_{mix} = \Delta G_{mix} + T \Delta S_{mix} = 0 \qquad (9\text{-}15)$$

Because this is a constant pressure process,[1] ΔH_{mix} is the heat of
the process, Q_{mix}. Hence no heat is evolved or absorbed when the
two constituents of an ideal solution are mixed. This is confirmed

---

[1] The vapor is very dilute (ideal gas) and hence its total pressure $(p_1 + p_2)$
cannot be large (a few atmospheres at most). Since only condensed phases
are involved in the process 9-6, a pressure of this magnitude is for practical
purposes p = 0 = const. See, for example, Eq. 8-60.

experimentally. Most solutions (nonideal) <u>do</u> exhibit a heat effect on mixing.

In view of

$$\Delta E_{mix} = \Delta H_{mix} - p \, \Delta V_{mix}$$

we also have $\Delta E_{mix} = 0$ for an ideal solution. The temperature and kinetic energy are constant in the process under discussion so this relation gives us information about the potential energy. The potential energy of pure liquid 1 is due to 1-1 interactions while in pure liquid 2 there are 2-2 interactions. When the pure liquids are mixed, the resulting solution has 1-1, 2-2, and 1-2 interactions. Thus, on forming the solution, some 1-1 and 2-2 interactions are replaced by 1-2 interactions. Hence, the fact that $\Delta E_{mix} = 0$ implies that the three types of interaction are interchangeable or equivalent. But according to Eq. 3-16, this would be the case if $r_1^* = r_2^*$ and $\epsilon_1 = \epsilon_2$. Consequently, we expect binary solutions to have "ideal" properties when the two components are isotopes of each other, or are at least very closely related in atomic constitution and in molecular structure and size (see the examples listed above).

We emphasized earlier that an ideal gas mixture and an ideal liquid solution are quite different systems. Yet it is interesting that they both have the same entropy of mixing: compare Eqs. 8-40 and 9-14. The basic reason for this is that, in both cases, the potential energy does not perturb the random mixing of molecules (this is true despite the fact that the potential energy is zero in the former case but not in the latter).

Nonideal liquid solutions. Ideal solutions are rare. Figures 9-2, 9-3, and 9-4 show more typical behavior. The most common kind of deviation from Raoult's law is that exhibited in Fig. 9-2; this is known as <u>positive</u> deviation from ideality. Figure 9-3 shows <u>negative</u> deviation from ideality.

Partial pressures above the Raoult's law lines (positive deviation) signify, according to Eq. 9-4, that the escaping tendencies of the two components are larger in the actual solution than they would be if the solution were ideal. This in turn means that each kind of molecule "prefers" its own company to the company of the other component. This preference may result from an energy or an entropy effect, or both. In the former case, 1-1 and 2-2 interactions have a lower potential energy (are more stable) than 1-2 interactions. Entropy effects can arise, for example, with molecules that differ greatly in size.

In Fig. 9-4 (aqueous alcohol solutions), positive deviations from ideality increase with the size of the hydrocarbon part of the alcohol molecule for two reasons. First, hydrocarbon-hydrocarbon and

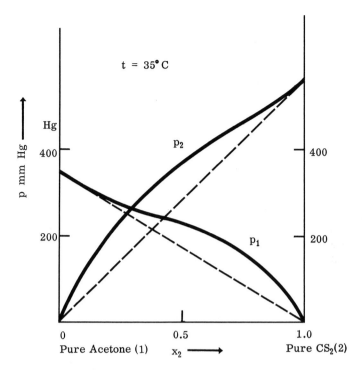

Figure 9-2
Vapor pressure curves in acetone-CS_2 solution.

water-water interactions are more favorable than hydrocarbon-water interactions. The longer alcohol molecules introduce, per molecule, more "undesirable" contact between hydrocarbon and water. This is an energy effect. The second reason for the increasing deviation is the entropy effect mentioned above (i.e., an increasing difference between the two molecular sizes).

Negative deviations from ideality may generally be attributed to unusually strong 1-2 attractive interactions, such as hydrogen bonds. An interaction of this type lowers the escaping tendency of both components.

It will be noted in Figs 9-2, 9-3, and 9-4 that, when the solution is very dilute in component 2 ($x_2 \rightarrow 0$), the partial pressure p_2 is linear in x_2 with a proportionality constant that differs from the Raoult's law value p_2^0. That is, we observe near $x_2 = 0$ that $p_2 = k_2 x_2$ rather than $p_2 = p_2^0 x_2$. The equation $p_2 = k_2' x_2$ is called Henry's <u>law</u> and $k_2(T)$ is the Henry's law constant. In the special case of an ideal solution $k_2 = p_2^0$, but ordinarily $k_2 \neq p_2^0$. At higher values of x_2, nonlinear correction terms must be added to take care

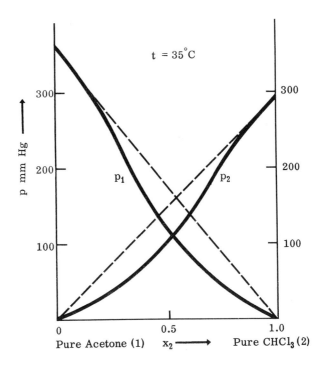

Figure 9-3
Vapor pressure curves in acetone-CHCl₃ solution.

of the curvature in the function $p_2(x_2)$ (just as in the virial expansion for an imperfect gas):

$$p_2 = k_2 x_2 + a x_2^2 + b x_2^3 + \cdots$$

Since Henry's law applies to extremely dilute solutions only, k_2 is a property of individual component 2 molecules completely surrounded by component 1 molecules. On the other hand, in pure liquid 2, each component 2 molecule is in an environment of other component 2 molecules only. If we had a solution made up of component 2 and an isotope of component 2 (in place of component 1), we would observe Raoult's law $p_2 = p_2^0 x_2$ over the whole range of x_2 values. Near $x_2 = 0$, each type 2 molecule would be surrounded by isotope molecules—which are the same as type 2 molecules as far as intermolecular forces are concerned. Therefore, if we compare $p_2 = k_2 x_2$ with $p_2 = p_2^0 x_2$ (near $x_2 = 0$), we conclude that the difference between k_2 and p_2^0 must be attributed, on the molecular level, to the difference between a type 2 molecule surrounded by type 1

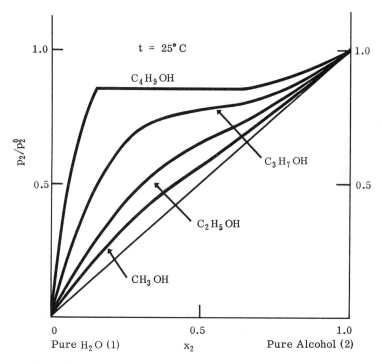

Figure 9-4
Vapor pressure curves in water-alcohol solutions.

molecules and a type 2 molecule surrounded by type 2 molecules.

If molecules 1 and 2 are similar in size, we can explain any deviation from ideality, that is, any difference between k_2 and p_2^0, as an energy effect. Let us derive a simple and approximate equation for this effect. Let z be the mean number of nearest neighbors[2] in liquid 1, liquid 2, and in the solution (use of the same z is reasonable because the molecular sizes are assumed to be about equal). A typical value might be $z \cong 10$ (Chapter 6). Let $-\epsilon_2$ be the nearest neighbor interaction energy between two type 2 molecules, and let $-\epsilon_{12}$ be the corresponding energy for a 1-2 interaction (Chapter 3). Now according to Eq. 9-4,

$$\mu_2\binom{\text{actual}}{\text{solution}} = c_2^0(T) + RT \ln k_2 + RT \ln x_2 \qquad (9\text{-}16)$$

---

[2] In Chapter 5 and Chapter 6 we used n_1 for this quantity but here we must avoid confusion with the number of moles, n_1.

$$\mu_2 \left(\begin{array}{c}\text{isotope}\\ \text{solution}\end{array}\right) = G_2^0(T) + RT \ln p_2^0 + RT \ln x_2 \qquad (9\text{-}17)$$

We are going to assume, in effect, that the two chemical potentials differ only through potential energy terms (recall that $G = E - TS + pV$ and that $\mu_2 = \partial G/\partial n_2$). Now ∂ (potential energy)$/\partial n_2$ is equal to the change in potential energy on adding a single type 2 molecule to the system. Therefore, if we subtract Eq. 9-17 from Eq. 9-16, we get

$$(-z\epsilon_{12}) - (-z\epsilon_2) = RT \ln k_2 - RT \ln p_2^0$$

or

$$\frac{k_2}{p_2^0} = e^{z(\epsilon_2 - \epsilon_{12})/RT} \qquad (9\text{-}18)$$

This is the desired result. If 2-2 attractions are stronger than 1-2 attractions ($\epsilon_2 > \epsilon_{12}$), then $k_2 > p_2^0$ as expected (positive deviation). On the other hand, if $\epsilon_{12} > \epsilon_2$, then $k_2 < p_2^0$ (negative deviation). Note that, when $k_2 > p_2^0$, k_2/p_2^0 increases as the temperature is lowered. We shall return to this point in the next subsection.

In the above discussion of Henry's law, we have chosen 2 as the dilute component ($x_2 \rightarrow 0$) and 1 as the concentrated component. But the two components have equivalent status in these solutions so we could have made the opposite choice. Near $x_2 = 1$, component 1 obeys Henry's law:

$$p_1 = k_1 x_1 = k_1 (1 - x_2) \qquad (x_1 \rightarrow 0 \quad \text{or} \quad x_2 \rightarrow 1)$$

where k_1 is the Henry's law constant for component 1.

There is nothing unique or very striking about Henry's law behavior because any positive value of the Henry's law constant might be observed, depending on the choice of molecules for the solution. But it is surprising, offhand, to notice in Figs. 9-2, 9-3 and 9-4 that, for any nonideal solution, Raoult's law is obeyed by the concentrated component while the dilute component is following Henry's law. That is,

$$p_2 = k_2 x_2 \quad \text{and} \quad p_1 = p_1^0 x_1 = p_1^0 (1 - x_2) \qquad \text{near } x_2 = 0$$

and

$$(9\text{-}19)$$

$$p_1 = k_1 x_1 = k_1 (1 - x_2) \quad \text{and} \quad p_2 = p_2^0 x_2 \qquad \text{near } x_2 = 1$$

However, as we shall now show, the Raoult's law behavior of the concentrated component is a necessary thermodynamic consequence of the Henry's law behavior of the dilute component.

We are given that $p_2 = k_2 x_2$ near $x_2 = 0$ and we want to prove that $p_1 = p_1^0(1 - x_2)$ also near $x_2 = 0$. From Eq. 9-4,

$$\mu_2(\text{solution}) = c_2^0(T) + RT \ln k_2(T) + RT \ln \frac{n_2}{n_1 + n_2} \qquad (9\text{-}20)$$

We shall make use of the mathematical relation

$$\frac{\partial^2 G}{\partial n_1 \partial n_2} = \left(\frac{\partial \mu_1}{\partial n_2}\right)_{n_1} = \left(\frac{\partial \mu_2}{\partial n_1}\right)_{n_2} \qquad (9\text{-}21)$$

We have, from Eqs. 9-20 and 9-21,

$$d\mu_1 = \left(\frac{\partial \mu_2}{\partial n_1}\right)_{n_2} dn_2 = -\frac{RT \, dn_2}{n_1 + n_2} \qquad (n_1 \text{ const})$$

Next, we integrate this equation from $n_2 = 0$ to n_2 (we have to stay within the Henry's law composition range), holding n_1 constant:

$$\mu_1(n_1, n_2) - \mu_1(n_1, 0) = -RT \ln \frac{n_1 + n_2}{n_1} \qquad (9\text{-}22)$$

Since

$$\mu_1(n_1, 0) = c_1 = c_1^0 + RT \ln p_1^0$$

Eq. 9-22 becomes

$$\mu_1(\text{solution}) = c_1^0 + RT \ln p_1^0 + RT \ln (1 - x_2) \qquad (9\text{-}23)$$

Comparison of this relation with Eq. 9-4 gives the required result, $p_1 = p_1^0(1 - x_2)$.

It should be noticed that the above derivation also proves that if one component (say 2) obeys Raoult's law over the whole compostion range (ideal solution), then the other component (1) also necessarily does the same. For in this case we put $k_2 = p_2^0$ (which does not affect the derivation), and we can carry out the integration from $n_2 = 0$ to arbitrary n_2.

As a matter of fact, for any binary solution, if one partial pressure curve (say p_2) is measured, as in Fig. 9-4, the other partial pressure curve (p_1) can be calculated (it need not be measured) using Eq. 9-21 —provided we know the value of p_1^0.

Immiscibility. This subsection is concerned entirely with positive deviations from ideality. Our object is to see what happens when the extent of deviation becomes quite large.

Even though Eq. 9-18 is very approximate and somewhat limited in applicability it does suggest two ways in which the extent of positive deviation (as measured by the value of k_2/p_2^0, for example) can be increased. One way is to lower the temperature; the other is to increase $\epsilon_2 - \epsilon_{12}$ (at constant temperature) by choosing a suitable series of related molecules for component 2 (or for component 1). In either case, the exponent in Eq. 9-18 and hence k_2/p_2^0 is increased.

Figure 9-4 illustrates the second method mentioned above, while Fig. 9-5a shows a typical example of the first method. As we might expect from the preceding paragraph, the families of curves in Figs. 9-4 and 9-5a are very similar. Because of this, we confine our attention below to Fig. 9-5a.

Figure 9-5a refers to solutions of the same two components at a series of different temperatures, $T_3 > T_C > T_2 > T_1$. As the

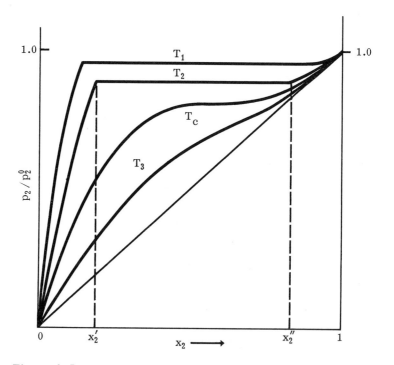

Figure 9-5a

Vapor pressure curves for the same solution at different temperatures, showing critical behavior (schematic).

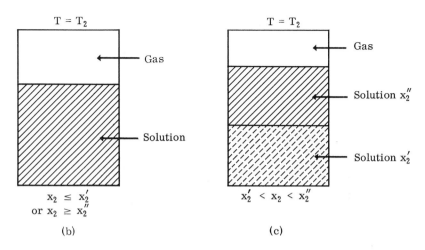

$T = T_2$ $T = T_2$

Gas

Gas

Solution x_2''

Solution

Solution x_2'

$x_2 \leq x_2'$ $x_2' < x_2 < x_2''$
or $x_2 \geq x_2''$

(b)   (c)

Figure 9-5b, c
Phase separation (immiscibility) for $T_2 < T_c$.

temperature is lowered, starting with $T = T_3$, k_2/p_2^0 increases. When $T = T_c$ is reached, a critical curve is obtained ($\partial p_2/\partial x_2 = \partial^2 p_2/\partial x_2^2 = 0$ at the critical point). The p_2 curve has a flat portion for temperatures (such as T_1 and T_2) less than T_c. This behavior is very reminiscent of that shown in Fig. 1-12b for the one-component gas-liquid phase transition. This resemblance is important in the general theory of phase transitions, but we shall not pursue it much further here.

To see the physical significance of the flat parts of the p_2 curves, consider the following experiment at temperature T_2. We start with pure component 1 ($x_2 = 0$) and gradually add component 2. We measure p_1 and p_2 after each addition of component 2. The system appears at first as in Fig. 9-5b. When enough component 2 has been added to reach the composition $x_2 = x_2'$, we notice that a second liquid layer begins to form. A sample of this second layer shows it to have the composition x_2''. If we now continue to add component 2, it is found that the two partial pressures stay constant and also that each of the two liquid layers (Fig. 9-5c) maintains constant composition, but that the relative amount of the second layer (richer in component 2 than the first layer) increases. In the range $x_2' < x_2 < x_2''$, the mole fraction x_2, which appears as abscissa in Fig. 9-5a, is the over-all mole fraction of the two liquid phases. That is, x_2 refers to all of the liquid present. When x_2 reaches the value x_2'' the liquid layer with composition x_2' disappears. Then for $x_2 > x_2''$, the system appears again as in Fig. 9-5b—there is only one liquid phase.

Figure 9-5a concerns component 2, but the situation with respect

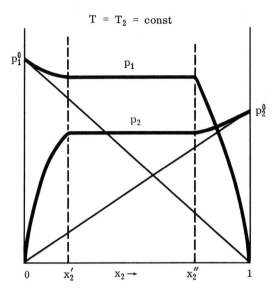

Figure 9-6
Vapor pressure curves with phase separation.

to component 1 is similar. This is illustrated in Fig. 9-6 which
shows both partial pressures at the temperature T_2.

The phase transition in this system appears, then, as a separation of one liquid phase into two liquid phases, over part of the
composition range, if $T < T_c$. This is analogous to a one-component system ''separating'' into gas and liquid phases, over a
range in densities, below T_c. Incidentally, it was mentioned at
the end of Chapter 1 that a one-component fluid is opalescent at
the critical point. The same is true of a two-component solution
at its critical point, and for essentially the same reason: large
fluctuations in composition cause extensive scattering of light.

The two components of the solution are said to be ''miscible
in all proportions'' (i.e., for all values of x_2) if the above phase
separation does <u>not</u> occur—as, for example, at $T = T_3$ in Fig.
9-5a. When phase separation does occur, the two components are
said to be <u>immiscible</u> over a certain composition range (x_2' to x_2''
in Fig. 9-5a or 9-6).

The phenomenon we are discussing is undoubtedly familiar to
the reader. There are many everyday examples of two liquids exhibiting immiscibility: gasoline + water; oil + water; etc. Oil
and water are immiscible over almost the whole composition range
at room temperature. There is very little water in the oil layer and
very little oil in the water layer (x_2' is near zero; x_2'' is near unity).

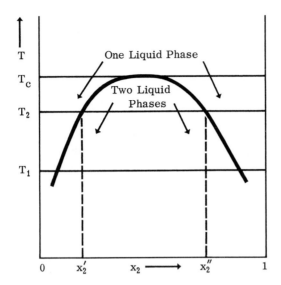

Figure 9-7
Coexistence curve for a binary solution.

It is clear from Fig. 9-5 that the range of immiscibility increases as the temperature decreases. This range is zero at $T = T_c$, it extends from x_2' to x_2'' at $T = T_2$, etc. Figure 9-7 is a plot of the range of immiscibility against temperature. The resulting curve is called a coexistence curve, just as in Fig. 1-12b. For points x_2, T inside the coexistence curve in Fig. 9-7, two liquid phases are present; at any point outside the coexistence curve, only one liquid phase exists.

Although Fig. 9-7 represents typical behavior, there are more complicated cases which the interested reader will find discussed in physical chemistry textbooks.

Phase separation is an excellent example of energy-entropy competition. When two pure liquids are brought into contact, the entropy favors complete mixing (miscibility) because the mixture (solution) is a more disordered state than the two pure liquids. On the other hand, if 1-1 and 2-2 interactions are more favorable (lower potential energy) than 1-2 interactions, the energy opposes mixing because the pure liquids have 1-1 and 2-2 interactions only. At high temperatures $(T > T_c)$ the entropy dominates, as usual, and the two liquids are miscible in all proportions. At low temperatures $(T < T_c)$, miscibility occurs over only part of the composition range. When two liquid phases are present below T_c, neither liquid is pure. Some mixing takes place within each liquid phase even though the liquids have not mixed completely with each other. Thus a compromise is reached between energy and entropy. In every case, the equilibrium state of the solution minimizes the free energy for the given n_1, n_2, and T.

9-2   COLLIGATIVE PROPERTIES OF DILUTE SOLUTIONS

IN THIS section we shall be concerned with four properties of very dilute binary liquid solutions. The dilute component, 2, is called the solute and the concentrated component, 1, the solvent. This terminology was not introduced in Section 9-1 because the two components had equivalent status there. More specifically, we shall consider a dilute solution in equilibrium with another phase that contains the solvent only. The second phase may be gas, solid, or liquid. The four properties we shall study are vapor pressure lowering, boiling point elevation, freezing point lowering, and osmotic pressure. In the first two of these properties the second phase mentioned above is a gas; in the third it is a solid; and in the fourth it is a liquid.

These four properties have in common the fact that they are all "solute particle counters." That is, the measured property depends only on the number of solute particles in the dilute solution and not on the nature of the particles (be they small molecules, large molecules, ions, etc.). Properties of this type are called colligative properties. Among other things, colligative properties are useful for molecular weight determinations, because the molecular weight may be calculated if the weight of solute is known and the number of solute molecules (or moles) is measured.

Incidentally, the pressure of a dilute gas is a very similar "particle counting" property (see Eq. 2-4). In this case the gas molecules are the "solute" and the "solvent" is the vacuum in which the gas molecules move.

If the binary solution is not very dilute, intermolecular forces between solute molecules affect the colligative properties. These properties then depend on the nature of the particular solute as well as on the number of solute molecules. They are thus no longer strictly "colligative." In this section we consider very dilute solutions only. More concentrated solutions are discussed briefly in the next section.

Vapor pressure lowering. We found in Eq. 9-23 that when a binary solution is dilute in solute, the solvent vapor obeys Raoult's law, $p_1 = p_1^0(1 - x_2)$. This result does not depend on the value of p_2^0; it is valid even for very small values of p_2^0. Therefore the solvent vapor in equilibrium with a very dilute solution of nonvolatile ($p_2^0 \rightarrow 0$) solute obeys Raoult's law. Examples of nonvolatile solutes are sucrose in water, NaCl in water, etc.

Addition of a small amount of nonvolatile solute to the pure solvent lowers the vapor pressure of the solvent from p_1^0 to p_1, where

$$p_1^0 - p_1 = p_1^0 x_2 \qquad (9\text{-}24)$$

The amount of vapor pressure lowering is seen from this equation to depend on the number of moles of solute (n_2) in the solution but not on the particular solute molecule used. Solvent vapor pressure lowering is therefore a colligative property, and a particularly simple and obvious one.

Equation 9-24 holds only if x_2 is small ($n_2 \ll n_1$). In this case $x_2 \to n_2/n_1$ so we can also write

$$p_1^0 - p_1 = p_1^0 n_2/n_1 \qquad (9\text{-}25)$$

This is the limiting law ($x_2 \to 0$) for vapor pressure lowering, in the same sense that the ideal gas equation is the limiting law ($n/V \to 0$) for the gas pressure. Note in particular that $p_1^0 - p_1$ is simply proportional to the number of moles of solute, n_2. If n_2 is doubled, $p_1^0 - p_1$ is doubled, etc. Also, if each molecule of solute dissociates into ν particles (e.g., $\nu = 2$ for NaCl in water), $p_1^0 - p_1$ is ν times as large as would otherwise be the case, because the vapor pressure lowering depends only on the number of solute particles of whatever type (e.g., each Na^+ and Cl^- in an NaCl solution makes the same contribution to $p_1^0 - p_1$). Therefore,

$$p_1^0 - p_1 = p_1^0 n_2 \nu/n_1 \qquad (9\text{-}26)$$

for a solution that contains n_2 moles of a solute each molecule of which dissociates into ν particles. Similarly, if the molecules of an ideal gas (n moles) each dissociate into ν particles (e.g., at very high temperatures), $pV = n\nu RT$.

If there is partial dissociation only, as for example in a weak electrolyte, ν is the average number of particles per molecule.

The physical implications of vapor pressure lowering are emphasized in Fig. 9-8. If pure solvent and solution (with nonvolatile solute) are both present as shown in the figure, liquid level A will be observed to drop slowly while level B rises. Solvent is transported from pure solvent to solution, via the vapor phase, because the vapor pressure (or escaping tendency) of pure solvent is larger than the vapor pressure of solvent with solute. The fact that solvent molecules move spontaneously from pure solvent to solution means that the solvent molecules are more stable (have a lower chemical potential) in the solution than in the pure solvent. This is confirmed by Eq. 9-23:

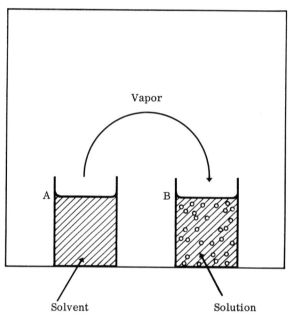

Figure 9-8
Spontaneous transfer of solvent.

$$\mu_1 \text{ (solution)} = G_1 \text{ (pure solvent)} + RT \ln (1 - x_2)$$

$$= G_1 \text{ (pure solvent)} - \frac{RTn_2}{n_1} \qquad (9\text{-}27)$$

The last line follows because

$$\ln (1 - x_2) \rightarrow -x_2 \rightarrow -n_2/n_1 \qquad \text{as} \qquad x_2 \rightarrow 0$$

Addition of a little solute to solvent stabilizes the solvent (lowers μ_1)—but what is the physical explanation of this? It is purely an entropy of mixing effect and has nothing to do with the specific interaction between a solute molecule and its surrounding solvent molecules (this is apparent from the nonspecific term $-RTn_2/n_1$ in Eq. 9-27). When solute molecules are added to the solvent, the resulting solution has an extra entropy (of mixing) not present in the initial state (pure solvent + pure solute). This extra entropy lowers the Gibbs free energy and hence contributes to the stability of the solution and the components in it. For a very dilute solution, the effect is the same whether the solution is nonideal or ideal (compare Eqs. 9-10 and 9-27).

Boiling point elevation. We have seen above that a nonvolatile solute lowers the vapor pressure of the solvent. One consequence of this is that the solution has a higher normal boiling point than the pure solvent: a higher temperature is required to cause the vapor pressure of the solvent in the solution to reach 1 atm.

Figure 9-9 is a schematic ("blown up") plot of the vapor pressure of pure solvent and the vapor pressure of solvent in a dilute solution, as a function of temperature, in the neighborhood of the normal boiling point T_b. The figure may also be viewed as part of the liquid-gas region of the phase diagram. The liquid-gas equilibrium line is seen to be lowered by the addition of solute to the liquid solvent. The amount of lowering is given by Eq. 9-25. Consequently, the solution requires a temperature $T_b + \Delta T_b$ to restore the solvent vapor pressure to p_1^0. ΔT_b is the boiling point elevation, a positive quantity. Now we already know from Eq. 8-35 that the slope of the vapor pressure curve at the boiling point is $p_1^0 \Delta H_b / RT_b^2$, where ΔH_b is the molar heat of vaporization of the solvent at the normal

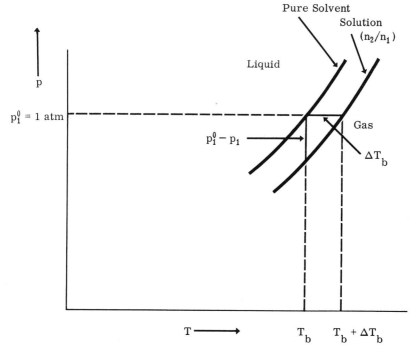

Figure 9-9
Calculation of boiling point elevation.

boiling point. From the figure, another expression for the same slope is

$$\frac{p_1^0 - p_1}{\Delta T_b} \quad \text{or} \quad \frac{p_1^0 n_2}{n_1 \, \Delta T_b}$$

When we equate the two expressions for the slope and solve for ΔT_b, we find

$$\Delta T_b = \frac{RT_b^2 \, n_2}{n_1 \, \Delta H_b} \tag{9-28}$$

This quantity is a colligative property because no property of the solute, other than n_2, enters into Eq. 9-28. ΔT_b is proportional to n_2. The coefficient of n_2, $RT_b^2 / n_1 \, \Delta H_b$, has to do with solvent, not solute.

The molality m of a solution is defined as the number of moles of solute per 1000 g of solvent. Therefore

$$m = \frac{1000 \, n_2}{n_1 \, M_1}$$

where M_1 is the molecular weight of the solvent. Equation 9-28 is often written in the form

$$\Delta T_b = C_b \, m \tag{9-29}$$

where

$$C_b = \frac{RT_b^2 \, M_1}{1000 \, \Delta H_b} \tag{9-30}$$

C_b is called the boiling point constant. It depends on the solvent, not the solute. For water, C_b = 0.514 deg per molality unit; for benzene, C_b = 2.64 deg per molality unit; etc. The reader should verify these values, using Eq. 9-30.

If the solute dissociates into ν particles, $\Delta T_b = C_b \, \nu m$.

Freezing point lowering. Here we investigate the effect a small amount of solute added to a liquid solvent has on the liquid-solid (freezing) equilibrium of the solvent. We consider only those cases in which the solute is virtually absent (insoluble) in the solid phase. This is analogous to nonvolatility of solute in the liquid-gas equilibrium. As we shall see, the normal freezing point T_f of the solvent

is lowered by solute. Our object is to calculate the extent of lowering and see that it is a colligative property. We shall give two different derivations because they are both instructive.

The first method of calculation is basically the same as that used
for the elevation of the boiling point (Fig. 9-9). However, in the
present case we do not know in advance the pressure change analogous to $p_1^0 - p_1$ in Fig. 9-9. Hence we must first make a separate
calculation of the pressure change.

In Fig. 9-10a, pure liquid and solid have the same chemical potential and hence are in equilibrium with each other at $T = T_f$,
$p = p' = 1$ atm. If solute is added to liquid solvent while the temperature is held fixed at T_f, the chemical potential of the solvent is
lowered, as we have seen in Eq. 9-27. Hence, in Fig. 9-10a, the μ_1
curve for the solution is below μ_1 for the pure solvent. Therefore
the μ_1 curve for the solution intersects the μ_1 curve for the solid
at a higher pressure than p', call it p''. That is, at $T = T_f$, the
solution freezes at a pressure p'' rather than p'. In the figure, the
slope of the μ_1 (solid) line is

$$\frac{a}{c} = \frac{a}{p'' - p'} = v_s$$

where v_s is the molar volume of the solid (see Eq. 8-56b). Similarly,
the slope of the dilute solution line is

$$\frac{a + b}{c} = \frac{a + b}{p'' - p'} = v_L$$

Also, from Eq. 9-27, the lowering of μ_1 is $b = RT_f n_2 / n_1$. By
combining these relations we find

$$p'' - p' = \frac{RT_f n_2}{(v_L - v_s) n_1} \tag{9-31}$$

Now we can proceed as with Fig. 9-9. Figure 9-10b shows an expanded version of part of the solid-liquid equilibrium region of the
phase diagram. The liquid-solid equilibrium line is shifted upward,
when solute is present in the solvent, by an amount given in Eq. 9-31.
Hence, as is clear from the figure, the freezing point of the solution
at p' is lowered from T_f to $T_f + \Delta T_f$, where ΔT_f is a negative
quantity. We can find ΔT_f by equating the two available expressions for the slope of the liquid-solid equilibrium line at the freezing point:

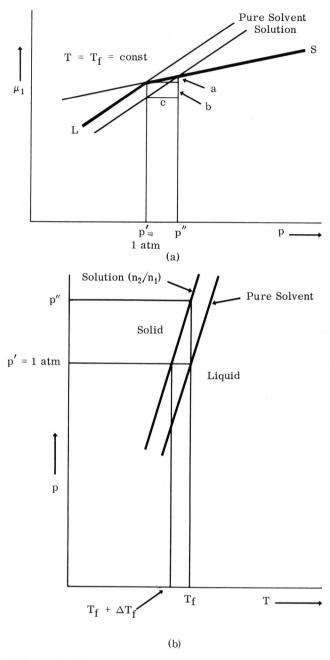

Figure 9-10
Calculation of freezing point lowering.

$$\frac{\Delta H_f}{T_f(v_L - v_S)} = \frac{p'' - p'}{-\Delta T_f}$$

where ΔH_f is the molar heat of fusion at the normal freezing point, a positive quantity. Then, using Eq. 9-31,

$$\Delta T_f = -\frac{RT_f^2 n_2}{n_1 \Delta H_f} \tag{9-32}$$

This result is very similar to Eq. 9-28.

It is left to the reader to verify that Eq. 9-32 is still obtained for a solvent such as water for which $v_S > v_L$ (Figs. 9-10a and 9-10b assume that $v_L > v_S$).

We now turn to the second (and shorter) proof of Eq. 9-32. In Fig. 9-11 we plot μ_1 against T at constant pressure (1 atm). For pure solid and liquid, this is essentially the same as Fig. 8-11. The μ_1 (solution) curve is again of course below the μ_1 (pure solvent) curve. The freezing point of the solution is at $T_f + \Delta T_f$, where the μ_1 (solid) and μ_1 (solution) curves cross. The slope of the μ_1 (solid) curve is, according to Eq. 8-56a, $-s_S$. This slope is also equal to $-a/c$ in the figure. The slope of the μ_1 (liquid) curve is $-s_L$, or $-(a + b)/c$ in the figure. Thus we have that

$$s_S = \frac{a}{c}, \qquad s_L = \frac{a + b}{c}, \qquad c = -\Delta T_f, \qquad b = \frac{n_2 RT_f}{n_1}$$

From $a = s_S c = s_L c - b$, we find

$$\Delta T_f = -\frac{RT_f n_2}{n_1 \Delta s_f} = -\frac{RT_f^2 n_2}{n_1 \Delta H_f}$$

which is the same as Eq. 9-32.

In terms of the molality,

$$\Delta T_f = -C_f m, \qquad C_f = \frac{RT_f^2 M_1}{1000 \, \Delta H_f} \tag{9-33}$$

If there is dissociation, $\Delta T_f = -C_f \nu m$. For water, the freezing point constant $C_f = 1.86$ deg per molality unit; for benzene ($T_f = 5.5°C$), $C_f = 5.1°$ per molality unit; etc.

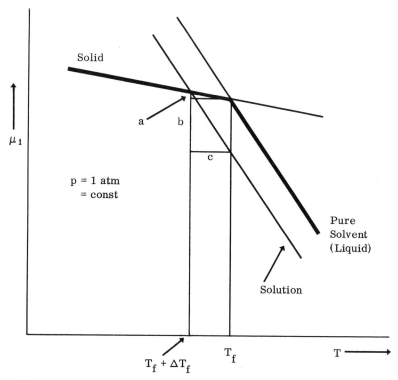

Figure 9-11
Calculation of freezing point lowering.

The lowering of the freezing point by a solute is of course the principle involved in the use of antifreeze in automobile radiators. However, the freezing point of a concentrated solution such as one might use in practice could not be calculated accurately from Eq. 9-32 because this equation is a limiting law—it applies to very dilute solutions only.

It was pointed out in connection with Fig. 9-8 and Eq. 9-27 that addition of solute to liquid solvent contributes additional stability to this phase (μ_1 is lowered). This can also be seen by viewing Figs. 9-9 and 9-10b as parts of the complete phase diagram. A phase diagram shows the regions of the p-T plane in which each of the possible phases is most stable. We see from Figs. 9-9 and 9-10b that addition of solute to the liquid phase causes the liquid region of the p-T plane to <u>expand</u> at the expense of the gas and solid regions.

Osmotic pressure. Figure 9-12a represents, schematically, an osmotic pressure experiment. Two portions of liquid solvent are separated by a semi-permeable membrane that allows passage of solvent molecules (1) but <u>not</u> solute molecules (2). In many experiments, the solute molecules are large and are simply blocked by small pores in the membrane. Suppose we start with pure solvent, at pressure p and temperature T, on both sides of the membrane. We then add a little solute to the right-hand side of the system, keeping p and T constant. The result of this is that solvent (1) will begin to flow spontaneously through the membrane from left to right, because the chemical potential μ_1 of the solvent on the right has been lowered by the solute. In Fig. 9-12b, both left and right-hand sides of the system start at point A, but the right-hand side drops to point B when solute is added to it. Equilibrium can be restored (and the net transport of solvent stopped) by increasing the pressure on the right-hand side sufficiently to bring μ_1 (right) back up to its original value. The temperature is held constant. Thus, in this new equilibrium state, the left-hand side is still at point A in Fig. 9-12b but the right-hand side is at point C ($\mu_1^A = \mu_1^C$). The increase in pressure, Π, necessary to restore equilibrium with respect to solvent flow, is called the <u>osmotic</u> <u>pressure</u>.

The slope of the lines in Fig. 9-12b is equal to v_L and is also equal to

$$\frac{\overline{AB}}{\overline{AC}} = \frac{n_2 RT/n_1}{\Pi}$$

Therefore

$$\Pi v_L n_1 = n_2 RT$$

or

$$\Pi V = n_2 RT \qquad (9\text{-}34)$$

where n_2 is the number of moles of solute on the right-hand side of the system and V is the volume of the right-hand side of the system (remember that we are interested in the limit of very small n_2/n_1; hence $V = n_1 v_L$).

The osmotic pressure limiting law is the same as the dilute gas limiting law for p, pV = nRT! The ideal gas may be thought of as a limiting form of osmotic system in which the "solvent" is a vacuum (in Fig. 9-12a, p = 0 and $\Pi = p_{gas}$). But the kinetic interpretation of ideal gas pressure (Appendix 4) applies only to this limiting case and cannot be extended to true osmotic systems.

The osmotic pressure obviously provides a particle counting

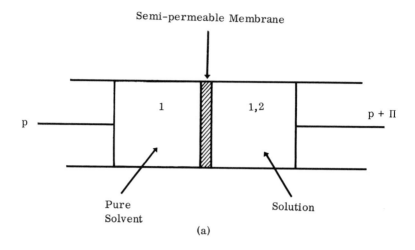

(a)

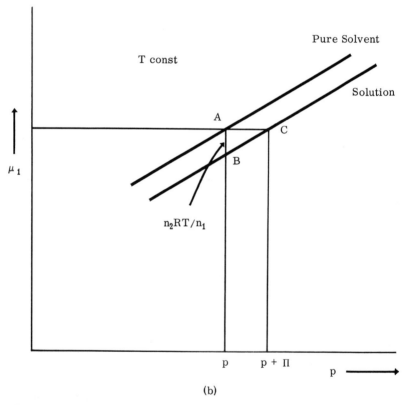

(b)

Figure 9-12
Osmotic pressure.

method. It has proved especially useful as a method for the determination of the molecular weights of macromolecules such as proteins.

As a numerical example, let us calculate the osmotic pressure of an aqueous solution of volume 100 cm^3 and temperature 25°C that contains 0.20 g of a protein of molecular weight 69,000. Then

$$\Pi = \frac{n_2 RT}{V} = \frac{(0.20/69,000) \times 0.082 \times 298.1}{0.100}$$

$$= 7.1 \times 10^{-4} \text{ atm} = 0.54 \text{ mm Hg} = 7.3 \text{ mm H}_2\text{O}$$

A column of solvent, rather than mercury, is ordinarily used to measure Π.

9-3 DEVIATIONS FROM DILUTE SOLUTION BEHAVIOR

IN THE preceding section we discussed four limiting laws for very dilute solutions. These are analogues of the ideal gas law for a very dilute gas. The purpose of this section is to indicate very briefly how the dilute solution limiting laws may be extended into the range of more concentrated solutions — just as, in Chapter 4, we introduced the virial expansion to take care of deviations from ideality in gases.

The four colligative properties are obviously not independent of each other. In fact, they all follow from Eq. 9-27 for the chemical potential of the solvent. This equation, in turn, is a consequence of Henry's law for the solute. Because of the interconnection between the four properties, for brevity we discuss only one of them here. We choose the osmotic pressure because of the thermodynamic similarity between osmotic pressure and the pressure of an imperfect gas (Chapter 4).

There are two main classes of solute, nonelectrolyte and electrolyte. Separate discussions are required for these two cases.

The solute is a nonelectrolyte. A nonelectrolytic solute is one that does not ionize when dissolved in the solvent. A typical example is sucrose (table sugar), $C_{12}H_{22}O_{11}$, in water.

The solute molecules are independent of each other when the solution is very dilute. Each solute molecule moves around in the solution, completely surrounded by solvent molecules. The interaction between a solute molecule and its neighboring shell of solvent molecules may be simple or complex — but the nature of this interaction has no effect on the colligative properties discussed in the preceding section. These properties depend merely on the number of solute molecules. For example,

$$\Pi = \frac{n_2}{V} RT = cRT, \qquad c = \frac{n_2}{V}$$

where c is often expressed in moles of solute per liter of solution (molar concentration).

If the concentration of solute is increased above the "very dilute" range, interactions between pairs of solute molecules have to be taken into account first, then interactions between solute triplets, etc. The pair interaction is, however, more complex than in the case of two gas molecules. When two solute molecules, in a solvent, are near each other, there is not only the direct solute-solute interaction to consider but there is also an effect, which may be important, owing to the perturbation of the solvent shell around each solute molecule by the presence of the other solute molecule and shell.

As the reader has probably anticipated by this time, these solute interactions are taken care of thermodynamically by the introduction of a virial expansion which is completely analogous to that in Eq. 4-3:

$$\frac{\Pi}{cRT} = 1 + B(T, \mu_1)c + C(T, \mu_1)c^2 + \cdots \qquad (9\text{-}35)$$

where B, C, ... are the virial coefficients. These coefficients depend not only on the temperature (as in Eq. 4-3) but also on the choice of solvent and on either μ_1 or p for the pure solvent (see Fig. 9-12b).

A common method for finding B from experimental data is to plot Π/cRT against c. The limiting slope of the curve, as c $\rightarrow$ 0, is B.

It will be recalled that B(T) for a gas is related by Eq. 4-6 to u(r) — the negative of the work necessary to pull apart two gas molecules in a vacuum from an initial separation r to r = ∞. It can be shown in statistical mechanics that Eq. 4-6 also applies to B in Eq. 9-35 provided that we now interpret u(r) in Eq. 4-6 as being the negative of the work necessary to pull apart two solute molecules in the pure solvent (rather than in a vacuum).

Finally, we consider a numerical example. For sucrose in water at 25°C and p = 1 atm, it has been found experimentally that the second and third osmotic pressure virial coefficients are

$$B = 305 \text{ cm}^3 \text{ mole}^{-1} \qquad \text{and} \qquad C = 88 \times 10^3 \text{ cm}^6 \text{ mole}^{-2}$$

Let us calculate Π for a sucrose solution with c = 0.50 moles liter^{-1}. We have

$$\Pi = cRT(1 + Bc + Cc^2 + \cdots)$$

$$= 0.50 \times 0.0821 \times 298.1$$

$$\times \left[1 + 0.305 \times 0.50 + 88 \times 10^{-3} \times 0.25\right]$$

$$= 12.2 \text{ atm} \times (1.00 + 0.15 + 0.02) = 14.3 \text{ atm}$$

Incidentally, we might note for comparison that an ideal gas (STP) at $0°C$ with $c = 1/22.41 = 0.0446$ moles liter^{-1} has $p = 1$ atm.

The solute is an electrolyte. First we consider <u>strong</u> electrolytes, that is, solute molecules that, in solution, dissociate completely into ions (e.g., NaCl in water, $Ba(NO_3)_2$ in water, etc.).

For concreteness, let us begin by discussing an aqueous solution of NaCl. The solvent is water and the solute consists of equal numbers of Na^+ ions and Cl^- ions. If the solution is very dilute, the usual colligative properties are found, as was mentioned in the preceding section. The number of particles counted by these properties is the <u>total</u> number of ions of both types. In a very dilute solution, each ion is essentially independent of the other ions and has an environment of oriented H_2O dipoles. The ion-H_2O and H_2O-H_2O interactions determine all the properties of the solution.

Now if we increase the NaCl concentration above the "very dilute" range, it would be natural to expect that a virial expansion type of correction to various properties, as in Eq. 9-35 for example, would be appropriate. Unfortunately, this is not the case, for the following reason. As has been mentioned in connection with both Eqs. 4-3 and 9-35, the second virial term is related to solute-solute pair interactions, the third virial term to solute triplet interactions, etc. Implicit in this statement is the assumption that the solute intermolecular forces are of short range. For we are assuming that a solute molecule in a dilute (but not very dilute) solution interacts with zero, one or at most a small number of other solute molecules at a time. But in an NaCl solution, the solute interactions are of the types Na^+-Na^+, Na^+-Cl^-, and Cl^--Cl^-. All of these are coulombic, with potential energy falling off as $1/r$. As is shown in Fig. 3-5, this is a long-range interaction—not short range. The first departures from very dilute solution behavior in NaCl are due, therefore, not simply to pair interactions but to "many-body" or "collective" interactions between numerous ions at relatively large distances from each other. That some new feature is involved is suggested by the experimental fact that, unlike Eq. 9-35, the first correction term for the osmotic pressure of an NaCl solution is found to be proportional to $c^{1/2}$, not c. Furthermore, from the theoretical point of view, if we try to calculate a second virial coefficient B from Eq. 4-6, using a coulombic potential and $e^{-u/kT} = 1 - (u/kT)$ as in Eq. 4-25, we get a divergent or infinite integral (in fact, even if $u \sim 1/r^2$ or $1/r^3$, the integral diverges). This shows that the virial expansion method breaks down for electrolyte solutions.

The conclusion we reach, then, is that a completely new approach is required in the theoretical investigation of the departures of electrolyte solutions from the laws of very dilute solutions.

A satisfactory method for attacking this problem was first found by Debye and Hückel in 1923. It has been applied in recent years not only to ions in a solvent (electrolyte solutions) but also to ions in a vacuum—that is, to an ionized gas or plasma. The Debye-Hückel theory, and extensions of it, are too mathematical to discuss here in any detail. We shall merely give a little further background, and a few results.

Although there is a coulombic interaction between ions in a solvent, as mentioned above, the interaction does differ in one important respect from Eq. 3-4. Instead of that equation we have

$$u(r) = \frac{q_1 q_2}{Dr} \tag{9-36}$$

where D is a property of the solvent used, and of p and T. D is called the dielectric constant; it is a dimensionless quantity that can be measured experimentally. $D = 1$ for a vacuum, but $D > 1$ for any solvent. For water at $25°C$, $D = 78.5$. Thus the work necessary to separate an Na^+ ion from a Cl^- ion in pure water is about 80 times less than in a vacuum. The bare charge-charge interaction is, so to speak, "shielded" or "diluted down" by the presence of the solvent. The forces involved in determining the work of separation in a solvent, referred to above, are quite complicated. The solvent dipoles are oriented somewhat by the two charges, and the charges induce further dipoles, so that we have to take into account not only the ion-ion interaction (as in a vacuum) but also ion-dipole and dipole-dipole interactions. The net effect is contained in the dielectric constant introduced in Eq. 9-36. The quantitative theory of the dielectric constant of a dilute gas is relatively simple, but such a theory for a complex liquid like water is extremely difficult—in fact, a satisfactory theory is not available yet.

In the Debye-Hückel theory of, say, NaCl in water, we have, in effect, a system containing two kinds of particle, Na^+ and Cl^- (the solvent is taken care of implicitly by the introduction of D in Eq. 9-36). There are three kinds of interaction: Na^+-Na^+, Na^+-Cl^-, and Cl^--Cl^-. For each of these there are two contributions: the coulombic part in Eq. 9-36, and a Lennard-Jones part as in Chapter 3. We are interested here in the first correction term to the ideal osmotic pressure law. Thus, we are concerned with an

electrolyte solution that is dilute, though not "very dilute." Because
of the diluteness of the solution and of the long range of the coulombic
part of the interaction potential, the Lennard-Jones potential, which
is short-ranged, makes no contribution to the first osmotic correction
term. The coulombic interactions are responsible for the whole effect. This is in distinct contrast to Eq. 9-35, for a nonelectrolyte
solution, where potentials of the Lennard-Jones type determine the
virial coefficients.

The properties of a dilute electrolyte solution reflect a compromise between two opposing tendencies. The coulombic interactions
(potential energy) tend to organize the ions with each Na^+ surrounded
by Cl^- and each Cl^- surrounded by Na^+, but this tendency is re-
sisted by the entropy which favors a random arrangement of ions.
The result is that the ions are not in a lattice but move more or less
haphazardly through the solvent. But an instantaneous photograph
would show a certain amount of statistical ordering: on the average
there will be more Na^+ ions than Cl^- ions near a given Cl^-, and
vice versa.

We now state the Debye-Hückel result for Π. Suppose we have an
electrolyte solution consisting of a solvent and various ionic species
$i = 1, 2, \ldots, c$. The volume of the solution is V and N_i is the number of ions of type i. The charge on an ion of type i is $\lambda_i e$, where e
is the charge on a proton. For example, $\lambda = +1$ for Na^+, $\lambda = -2$
for $SO_4^=$, etc. Then the osmotic pressure is given by

$$\frac{\Pi}{kT} = \sum_{i=1}^{c} \frac{N_i}{V} - \frac{\kappa^3}{24\pi} \tag{9-37}$$

where κ is defined by

$$\kappa^2 \equiv \frac{4\pi e^2}{DkT} \sum_{i=1}^{c} \left(\frac{N_i}{V} \cdot \lambda_i^2 \right)$$

In a plasma, $D = 1$. The dimensions of κ are $(length)^{-1}$. In the expression for κ^2, the concentration N_i/V of each ion is multiplied
by the square of its charge number λ_i, and then a summation over
all ion types is carried out. Because of the factor λ_i^2, ions such as
Ca^{++}, $SO_4^=$, etc., with multiple charge make especially large contributions to κ^2.

The sum $\Sigma_i (N_i/V)$ in Eq. 9-37 is of course just the "very dilute" solution term. The correction term owing to the coulombic
interactions between the ions is $-\kappa^3/24\pi$. This term is negative
because the net ionic interaction is attractive (see p. 60): negative
ions have more positive ion neighbors then negative ion neighbors,

etc. The osmotic effect (i.e., the contribution to Π) of the ions is reduced somewhat by this net attraction. Before the theory of electrolyte solutions was developed, this reduction in Π was incorrectly attributed to incomplete dissociation of the salt molecules in solution.

To get some idea of the numerical magnitudes involved, let us rewrite Eq. 9-37 for an important special case. Consider an electrolyte solution of the NaCl or 1–1 type (λ_1 = +1, λ_2 = −1) with water as solvent, p = 1 atm, and t = 25°C. If the molar concentration (moles liter^{-1}) of the salt is c, then

$$\frac{\Pi}{RT} = 2c - 0.781c^{3/2} \tag{9-38}$$

or

$$\Pi = 2cRT\,(1 - 0.390c^{1/2})$$

For example, if c = 0.01 mole liter^{-1},

$$\frac{\Pi}{RT} = 0.02 - 0.00078 = 0.0192, \qquad \Pi = 0.47 \text{ atm}$$

The correction term is about 4% of the leading term at this concentration. If c = 10^{-4} mole liter^{-1},

$$\frac{\Pi}{RT} = 2 \times 10^{-4} - 0.78 \times 10^{-6}, \qquad \Pi = 3.7 \text{ mm Hg}$$

In this case the correction term is 0.4% of the leading term, and about negligible. Thus the solution may be considered "very dilute" for c < 10^{-4} mole liter^{-1}, but the Debye-Hückel correction term is needed for c between 10^{-4} and 10^{-2} mole liter^{-1}. If c is much larger than 10^{-2} mole liter^{-1}, additional correction terms — which we shall not discuss — should be added to Eq. 9-38.

Perhaps the most important qualitative conclusion that can be drawn from this numerical example is that ionic interactions in electrolyte solutions are important at very low concentrations compared to nonionic solute-solute interactions (see the discussion of Eq. 9-35). Of course the reason for this is simply that the coulombic interaction has a very long range.

Weak electrolytes. There are many acids, bases, and even a few salts that dissociate partially but not completely into ions. For example, if HA represents such an acid and is the solute in a solution, the solute particles present in the solution would be HA, H^+ and A^-, a mixture of ionic and nonionic species. The extent of dissociation is governed by the laws of chemical equilibrium, which we shall study in the next chapter. At that time we shall discuss a numerical example which combines the Debye-Hückel theory with the ideas of chemical equilibrium.

9-4 SOLUBILITY

THE EXTENT to which gas molecules dissolve in a liquid solvent, or the extent to which a solid dissolves in a liquid solvent, is determined by relative energy and entropy considerations such as those mentioned on p. 203. We give a very brief and rather qualitative discussion of this subject in this section.

Solubility of a gas in a liquid. Let us consider the solubility of gaseous component 2 in liquid component 1 (the solvent). If component 2 has a partial pressure p_2 in the gas phase (assumed throughout this section to be ideal), how much of this component will dissolve in the solvent? We recognize immediately that this is the same system discussed at length in Section 9-1. For small enough p_2, Henry's law is obeyed and the amount of gas dissolved (as measured by its mole fraction in the solution) is proportional to p_2: $x_2 = p_2/k_2$.

From the thermodynamic point of view, component 2 in the gas at p_2 has a certain chemical potential μ_2; molecules of component 2 from the gas will dissolve in the solvent until the chemical potential in the liquid solution reaches the value μ_2. At equilibrium, μ_2 (gas) = μ_2 (sol), where sol = solution.

Component 2 molecules in the solution are part of a liquid phase and have a liquid-like energy and entropy, except for the fact that the entropy of component 2 in the solution has an important concentration dependent term that would not be present in pure liquid component 2. For example, if the solution is ideal (see Eq. 9-14),

$$S \text{ (sol)} = n_1[s_1 \text{ (pure 1)} - R \ln x_1] + n_2[s_2 \text{ (pure 2)} - R \ln x_2]$$

where the term referred to above is $-R \ln x_2$. This term makes a contribution $RT \ln x_2$ to μ_2 in the solution. As component 2 molecules dissolve in the solvent, $RT \ln x_2$ increases in value until finally $\mu_2(\text{sol}) = \mu_2(\text{gas})$.

This situation is quite similar to the vaporization of pure solid or liquid discussed on p. 203. The molar entropy of a dilute gas has a term $-R \ln p$ and the molar Gibbs free energy has a corresponding term $RT \ln p$ which adjusts its value (through increasing or decreasing the vapor pressure p) until G(solid or liquid) = G(gas). The pressure p, like x_2 in the preceding paragraph, is a measure of concentration: $p = cRT$, where $c = n/V$ = concentration.

Because molecules of component 2 in the solution are liquid-like (surrounded by semiorganized close neighbors), they have a much lower potential energy than in the gas state. In order to achieve $\mu_2(\text{gas}) = \mu_2(\text{sol})$, these molecules must then have a lower entropy in the solution than in the gas. Therefore we expect that, for any p_2 in the gas, the concentration of component 2 in the solution will be larger than in the gas because a lower entropy is associated with a higher concentration (see the terms $-R \ln x_2$ and $-R \ln p$ mentioned above).

A less formal way to say the same thing is that because component 2 molecules are attracted by solvent molecules, component 2 will have a higher concentration in the solution than in the gas phase. But there is a limit to how high this concentration will be — because the molar entropy of component 2 in the solution goes down as its concentration goes up.

This difference in concentrations (between gas and solution) is especially obvious in the case that component 2 is an isotope of component 1. For then the distribution of component 2 between gas and liquid solution will be the same as for component 1. Therefore $c_2(\text{sol})/c_2(\text{gas})$ has the same value as $c_1(\text{pure liquid})/c_1(\text{pure vapor})$. This ratio is equal to $v_1(\text{pure vapor})/v_1(\text{pure liquid})$, and is usually a large number.

For any very dilute solution,

$$\frac{c_2(\text{sol})}{c_2(\text{gas})} = \frac{n_2/n_1 \, v_1(\text{solvent})}{p_2/RT} = \frac{x_2/v_1}{k_2 x_2/RT} = \frac{RT}{k_2 v_1} \qquad (9\text{-}39)$$

Of course k_2 often has the same order of magnitude as p_2^0 and p_1^0 ($k_2 = p_2^0$ if the solution is ideal) so the ratio 9-39 ordinarily has the order of magnitude $RT/p_1^0 v_1 = v_1(\text{vapor})/v_1(\text{liquid})$, as in the isotope case above (for which $k_2 = p_2^0 = p_1^0$).

A numerical example: it is found experimentally that the concentration ratio in Eq. 9-39 for CO_2 gas at $-59\,^\circ\text{C}$ has the value 42.3 when the solvent is methyl alcohol, 66.4 when it is acetone, and 74.5 when it is methyl acetate.

Solubility of a solid in a liquid. Imagine first a pure solid (component 2) in equilibrium with its vapor. Both phases have the same molar Gibbs free energy or chemical potential μ_2. The solid has a lower potential energy and a lower entropy than the gas. The molar entropy of the gas includes a term $-R \ln p_2$, or $-R \ln c_2$ as we prefer to write it here (another term, $-R \ln RT$, arising from the relation $p_2 = c_2 RT$, is constant in the following argument). This contributes $RT \ln c_2$ to the chemical potential μ_2.

Now suppose we "flood" the gas phase with a liquid solvent, component 1 (at the same temperature). How is the above equilibrium in component 2 shifted? The solid phase, and its chemical potential, is unaffected so we concentrate on what happens to the gas molecules.

Each "gas" molecule is now surrounded by liquid component 1 molecules. Thus the component 2 molecules become liquid-like. The main thermodynamic effect is that the potential energy of type 2 molecules is lowered considerably by close neighbor interactions with type 1 molecules. This in turn lowers the chemical potential of component 2 in the solution (formerly gas) and hence causes more molecules of solid to dissolve in the solvent [because μ_2(solid) $>$ μ_2(sol)]. This process will continue until the term RT ln c_2 in μ_2(sol) becomes large enough to bring the value of μ_2(sol) into equality with μ_2(solid).

At the outset of our hypothetical experiment, the concentration of vapor, c_2(gas), above the solid provides a measure of the "solubility" of the solid in a vacuum. The final concentration c_2(sol) measures the solubility of the same solid in the solvent. Since gas and solution are in equilibrium with the same solid, they would be in equilibrium with each other if the experiment were arranged suitably (all three phases present). Hence Eq. 9-39 applies to the ratio c_2(sol)/c_2(gas) of the two solubilities referred to above. Conclusion: the solid is generally much more soluble in the solvent than in the vacuum. Of course this is not to say that the solid is necessarily very soluble in the solvent. Although the entropy of component 2 molecules is higher in the solvent than in the solid, the potential energy of these molecules may be much lower in the solid, which would lead to a very small solubility. A wide range in solubilities is encountered experimentally—depending on the choice of solid, solvent, and temperature. Each case or type of case requires careful discussion in order to understand the balance of energy and entropy in solid and in solvent, so we shall leave the subject at this point.

Distribution of solute between two solvents. If two practically immiscible solvents are in contact, a solute (component 2) will adjust its distribution between the solvents until, at equilibrium, μ_2 (solvent 1) = μ_2 (solvent 1'). When the solutions are dilute in component 2, the ratio c_2 (solvent 1)/c_2 (solvent 1') is called the distribution coefficient, a function of temperature (not concentration). For example, at 25°C,

$$\frac{c_{Br_2} \text{ (in } CCl_4)}{c_{Br_2} \text{ (in } H_2O)} = 22.7, \qquad \frac{c_{I_2} \text{ (in } CHCl_3)}{c_{I_2} \text{ (in } H_2O)} = 131$$

We leave it as an exercise for the reader to discuss this kind of system from the point of view of energy-entropy balance or competition.

PROBLEMS

9-1. A dilute binary solution is made by adding W_2 g of solute (molecular weight M_2) to W_1 g of solvent (molecular weight M_1). The volume of the solution is V liters. Obtain an algebraic expression for each of the following properties of the solution in terms of W_1, W_2, M_1, M_2, and V. (a) Density of solution in g cm^{-3}; (b) number of moles of solute; (c) weight percent of solute; (d) mole fraction of solvent; (e) molarity of solute; (f) molality of solute.

9-2. Calculate the molecular weight of a solute (in a liquid solvent) 1.00 g of which in 112 cm^3 of solution gives an osmotic pressure of 1.00 atm at 0°C.

9-3. Calculate the vapor pressure (in mm Hg) of an aqueous NaCl solution at 80°C, given that the vapor pressure of pure water at 80°C is 355 mm Hg and the mole fraction of NaCl is 0.050.

9-4. It is suspected that a protein molecule of molecular weight 20,000 dissociates into two smaller molecules, each of molecular weight 10,000, when the protein is dissolved in water. To check this point, 1.0 g of protein is dissolved in enough water to form 100 cm^3 of solution at 7.0°C. The osmotic pressure is measured and found to be 8.7 mm Hg. Does the protein dissociate, or not?

9-5. An ideal liquid solution has a composition x_2 = 0.30. The vapor pressures of the pure liquids are p_1^0 = 200 mm Hg and p_2^0 = 400 mm Hg. (a) Calculate the partial pressures p_1 and p_2 (in mm Hg) in the equilibrium (ideal) vapor. (b) Calculate the mole fractions x_1 and x_2 in the vapor phase.

9-6. A solution is prepared by dissolving 2.00 g of a nonvolatile solid of molecular weight 80 in 100 g of a liquid solvent of molecular weight 60. (a) Calculate the mole fraction of solute in the solution (the solute does not dissociate). (b) Calculate the molality of solute in the solution. (c) The density of the pure solvent is 0.75 g cm^{-3}. Calculate the osmotic pressure of the solution in mm Hg. The temperature is 0° C.

9-7. Calculate C_b and C_f for water as solvent.

CHAPTER 10

CHEMICAL
EQUILIBRIUM

WE have discussed phase transitions at some length in earlier chapters. Phase transitions are a consequence of intermolecular forces. Chemical reactions are basically rather similar to phase transitions but they involve intermolecular (interatomic) forces rather than intermolecular forces. In a phase transition there is an equilibrium between two condensed or aggregated states (molecules held together by intermolecular forces) or between one aggregated state and one nonaggregated state (gas). Similarly, chemical reactions may involve different aggregated states (atoms held together in different ways by interatomic forces), as in

$$B—B + C—C \rightleftarrows 2B—C \tag{10-1}$$

or

$$\triangle \rightleftarrows \triangle \tag{10-2}$$

or an aggregated and a nonaggregated state, as in

$$A—A \rightleftharpoons 2A \tag{10-3}$$

The essential difference between a phase transition and a chemical reaction is that in the former case the number of particles participating in the state change is huge, whereas this number is very small in a chemical reaction. For example, a crystal-vapor equilibrium may be written

$$A_n \rightleftharpoons nA \tag{10-4}$$

(crystal)   (vapor)

where n is of the order of, say, 10^{22} whereas a typical chemical reaction would be

$$A_2 \rightleftharpoons 2A \tag{10-5}$$

There are intermediate cases (e.g., the aggregation of soap molecules in aqueous solution) in which n is in the range 10 to 100 or more, but such cases are not very common.

The cooperative aspect of a phase transition, a feature not present in a chemical reaction (see p. 198), is due to the large value of n.

Of course an important quantitative difference between most phase transitions and chemical reactions is that intermolecular forces are much weaker than interatomic (chemical bond) forces. Again, there are intermediate cases (see p. 46).

This chapter is devoted largely to chemical equilibria occurring in an ideal gas mixture (Section 10-1)—this being the simplest case. But we shall also discuss briefly reactions in solution (Section 10-2) and so-called heterogeneous equilibria (Section 10-3). Section 10-4 is concerned with the use of chemical thermodynamic tables. Most of the examples will be taken up in this last section; the earlier sections provide the necessary general theory.

There is one very basic point that should be emphasized at the outset. The methods of this chapter are applicable to questions of equilibrium and of relative stability of different states in chemically reacting systems. But thermodynamics can tell us nothing about rates of chemical reactions; about catalysts to use to speed the approach to equilibrium; etc. We have to ignore here the question of how a system gets to equilibrium; we simply study the equilibrium state itself.

10-1 CHEMICAL REACTIONS IN AN IDEAL GAS MIXTURE

Isomeric equilibrium. We begin with the least complicated case, the equilibrium between two isomers (different molecules that contain the same atoms). Equation 10-2 provides an example. Other examples are 10-I to 10-IV:

$$
\begin{matrix}
\text{H} & \text{H} & \text{H} & \text{H} \\
| & | & | & | \\
\text{H}-\text{C}-\text{C}-\text{C}-\text{C}-\text{H} \\
| & | & | & | \\
\text{H} & \text{H} & \text{H} & \text{H}
\end{matrix}
\;\rightleftharpoons\;
\begin{matrix}
\text{H} & \text{H} & \text{H} \\
| & | & | \\
\text{H}-\text{C}-\text{C}-\text{C}-\text{H} \\
| & | & | \\
\text{H} & \text{H} & \text{H} \\
& \text{H}-\text{C}-\text{H} \\
& | \\
& \text{H}
\end{matrix}
$$

n-butane   isobutane

(10-I)   (10-II)

$$
\underset{\text{Cl}}{\overset{\text{H}}{\diagdown}}\text{C}=\text{C}\underset{\text{Cl}}{\overset{\text{H}}{\diagup}}
\;\rightleftharpoons\;
\underset{\text{Cl}}{\overset{\text{H}}{\diagdown}}\text{C}=\text{C}\underset{\text{H}}{\overset{\text{Cl}}{\diagup}}
$$

cis 1,2-dichloroethylene   trans 1,2-dichloroethylene

(10-III)   (10-IV)

The gas mixture here consists of two kinds of molecules which are interconvertible. Or another way to put this is that there are two different states (structures) available to each molecule, and transitions between these two states occur. Because the gas is ideal (very dilute), a transition in any one molecule is independent of what is going on in the other molecules. At equilibrium, a certain fraction (depending on the particular case) of the molecules is in each of the two states; also each molecule spends these same fractions of its time in the two states.

In the example 10-2, if the chemical bonds have approximately the same energy (which might or might not be the case), the triangular molecule would be favored, at equilibrium, by a lower energy (three bonds vs two) but the "open" molecule has the advantage of a higher entropy (the X atoms have more vibrational and rotational freedom). The equilibrium distribution between these two different structures will depend on temperature. The triangular form will predominate at low temperatures but the open form will win the competition at high temperatures. Thus we see that energy and entropy are involved in a chemical equilibrium in much the same way as in a phase equilibrium.

Let us turn now to a systematic thermodynamic analysis of an isomeric ideal gas reaction, which we shall write $A \rightleftharpoons B$. Suppose that we have a mixture of n_A moles of A and n_B moles of B in a volume V at T. The system is closed, and at equilibrium with respect

to all processes (thermal diffusion, molecular diffusion, etc.) except
the chemical equilibrium. The partial pressures are $p_A = n_A RT/V$
and $p_B = n_B RT/V$, and the total pressure is $p = p_A + p_B$. Now let
the chemical reaction occur spontaneously (a catalyst may be needed
to make the rate appreciable), with p and T held constant (in this
reaction, because the total number of molecules stays constant, V
will be constant also). The Gibbs free energy of the system decreases
as the reaction proceeds and reaches its minimum possible value at
reaction equilibrium. We use this fact to find what the equilibrium
state is.

Because the gas is ideal, the two components are independent of
each other (except for the chemical reaction). Hence the Gibbs free
energy of the system G is the sum of G_A and G_B. We choose as independent variables n ($= n_A + n_B$), p, T, and $x_B = n_B/(n_A + n_B)$.
As the reaction takes place, n, p, and T remain constant (closed
system at p and T), but x_B changes because of the interconversion
of A and B molecules. In order to find the equilibrium point, we
shall therefore minimize G with respect to x_B holding n, p, and
T constant.

The expression for $G(n, p, T, x_B)$ is

$$G = G_A + G_B = n_A c_A + n_B c_B$$

$$= n_A \left[c_A^0(T) + RT \ln p_A \right] + n_B \left[c_B^0(T) + RT \ln p_B \right]$$

$$= (1 - x_B) n \left[c_A^0(T) + RT \ln(1 - x_B)p \right]$$

$$+ x_B n \left[c_B^0(T) + RT \ln x_B p \right] \tag{10-6}$$

where c_A^0 and c_B^0 are standard molar Gibbs free energies. The
function G in Eq. 10-6 is plotted against x_B in Fig. 10-1 for a typical
case. Equilibrium occurs at $x_B = x_B^e$, where G is a minimum. If the
system starts at any composition other than x_B^e, G decreases spontaneously ($dG < 0$) until equilibrium is reached. Then $dG = 0$. The
partial pressures at equilibrium, in terms of x_B^e, are $p_A^e = (1 - x_B^e)p$
and $p_B^e = x_B^e p$.

But let us find the value of x_B^e. To do this we use Eq. 10-6 and
set $\partial G/\partial x_B = 0$:

$$\frac{\partial G}{\partial x_B} = 0 = -nRT - nc_A + nRT + nc_B = n(c_B - c_A)$$

Thus, at equilibrium,

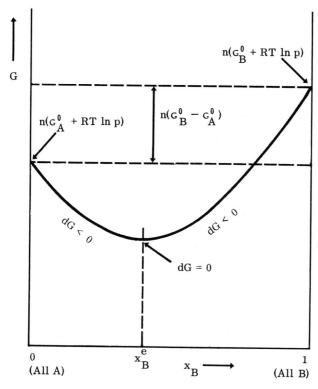

Figure 10-1
Minimum Gibbs free energy at isomeric chemical
equilibrium (schematic).

$$G_A = G_B \tag{10-7}$$

or

$$G_A^0(T) + RT \ln p_A^e = G_B^0(T) + RT \ln p_B^e \tag{10-8}$$

or

$$G_A^0(T) + RT \ln (1 - x_B^e)p = G_B^0(T) + RT \ln x_B^e p \tag{10-9}$$

The result 10-7 is what we might have guessed by analogy with a
phase equilibrium. In view of Eq. 10-9, the value of x_B^e may be found
from the relation

$$- RT \ln \frac{x_B^e}{1-x_B^e} = - RT \ln \frac{x_B^e}{x_A^e} = G_B^0(T) - G_A^0(T)$$

$$= \Delta G^0(T) \tag{10-10}$$

An equivalent equation is

$$- RT \ln \frac{p_B^e}{p_A^e} = G_B^0(T) - G_A^0(T) = \Delta G^0(T) \tag{10-11}$$

Thus the value of the standard free energy change determines the ratio of the numbers of B to A molecules at equilibrium. This is a reasonable result because the standard free energy difference makes a "fair" comparison between the free energies of A and B molecules: both kinds of molecules are taken at the same partial pressure (1 atm) and temperature (T), and therefore at the same concentration (c = p/RT). If A molecules are more stable than B molecules (both at 1 atm partial pressure, and T) because of a lower energy (e.g., stronger chemical bonds) or higher entropy (e.g., more internal rotational and vibrational freedom), or both, we will have $G_A^0 < G_B^0$ and $\Delta G^0 > 0$. Then, from Eqs. 10-10 and 10-11, we would find $x_A^e > x_B^e$ or $p_A^e > p_B^e$. In other words, there will be more A molecules than B molecules at equilibrium, as expected. Figure 10-1 illustrates this case ($G_A^0 < G_B^0$). Of course the situation is just reversed if B molecules are more stable than A molecules.

An alternative and simpler derivation of Eqs. 10-7 to 10-9 is the following. Suppose we have an infinitely large system of A and B molecules at equilibrium. If we convert one mole of A into one mole of B, at equilibrium, holding total p and T constant, the process is reversible and therefore $\Delta G = 0$. We imagine the use of an infinite system here so that the concentrations of A and B remain effectively constant during the process mentioned. Explicitly, the process is

$$\text{one mole of A} \atop \text{at } p_A^e \text{ and T} \quad \rightarrow \quad \text{one mole of B} \atop \text{at } p_B^e \text{ and T} \tag{10-12}$$

For this process,

$$\Delta G = 0 = G_{final} - G_{initial} = G_B(p_B^e, T) - G_A(p_A^e, T)$$

This result is identical with Eqs. 10-7 to 10-9.

For the process 10-12, $\Delta G = 0$. Another important process is

$$\text{one mole of A} \atop \text{at 1 atm and T} \quad \rightarrow \quad \text{one mole of B} \atop \text{at 1 atm and T} \tag{10-13}$$

For this process $\Delta G = \Delta G^0$ since here the two substances are in their standard states. If $G_A^0 > G_B^0$ (i.e., if ΔG^0 is negative), the process 10-13 will occur spontaneously. If $G_B^0 > G_A^0$ (i.e., if ΔG^0 is positive), the process would take place spontaneously in the opposite direction. Of course process 10-12 does not go spontaneously in either direction: there is no driving force toward equilibrium because equilibrium has already been reached.

The equilibrium point is located in Fig. 10-1 by noting the composition x_B^e that minimizes G, the total free energy of the system. An alternative but equivalent procedure is to plot $G_A(p_A)$ and $G_B(p_B)$ separately, and find x_B^e as that value of x_B at which the two curves intersect ($G_A = G_B$). This method is shown in Fig. 10-2 for the same case as in Fig. 10-1. The two functions used are

$$G_A = G_A^0 + RT \ln p + RT \ln (1 - x_B)$$

$$G_B = G_B^0 + RT \ln p + RT \ln x_B \tag{10-14}$$

Let us return now to Eq. 10-11, which is a very important result. Since ΔG^0 is a function of temperature only, it must be that p_B^e/p_A^e is also a function of temperature only. The implication of this is that, for any given temperature, regardless of the amounts[1] of the two gases started with, when equilibrium is finally reached the __ratio__ p_B^e/p_A^e will always have the same value (the separate partial pressures p_A^e and p_B^e will generally have different values in different cases). For this reason, the value of the ratio is called a constant, the __equilibrium constant__ (though it depends on T), and the notation used is

$$K_p(T) \equiv p_B^e/p_A^e \tag{10-15}$$

Therefore, the relation between $K_p(T)$ and ΔG^0 is

$$\Delta G^0(T) = - RT \ln K_p(T) \tag{10-16}$$

If ΔG^0 is known, K_p may be calculated, and vice versa. We shall see below that both of these last two equations can be generalized to apply to more complicated chemical equilibria.

A numerical example: in Figs. 10-1 and 10-2,

$$K_p(T) = \frac{x_B^e}{1 - x_B^e} = \frac{0.4}{0.6} = 0.667$$

If, say, $T = 298.1°K$, then

---

[1] The gas mixture must be ideal.

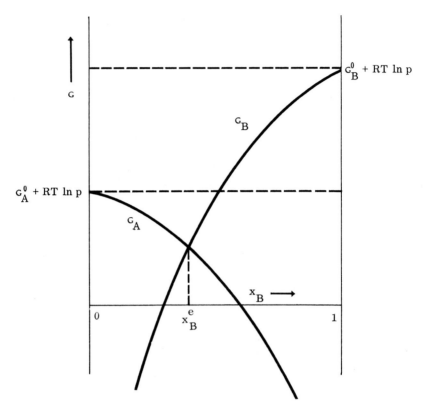

Figure 10-2
Equality of chemical potentials at isomeric chemical equilibrium
(schematic).

$$\Delta G^0 = G^0_B - G^0_A = -1.987 \times 298.1 \times 2.303 \log 0.667$$
$$= 240 \text{ cal}$$

An actual example of an isomeric reaction will be analyzed in Section
10-4.

In every case, three properties are interrelated: if A molecules
are more stable than B molecules under standard conditions, $\Delta G^0 >$
0 and $K_p < 1$; if B molecules are more stable than A molecules,
$\Delta G^0 < 0$ and $K_p > 1$.

Consider the quite arbitrary process

$$\begin{array}{cc} \text{one mole of A} & \rightarrow & \text{one mole of B} \\ \text{at } p_A \text{ and T} & & \text{at } p_B \text{ and T} \end{array} \qquad (10\text{-}17)$$

where in general p_A and p_B correspond neither to chemical equilibrium nor to standard states. For this process,

$$\Delta G = G_B(p_B) - G_A(p_A) = (G^0_B + RT \ln p_B)$$

$$- (G^0_A + RT \ln p_A)$$

$$= \Delta G^0 + RT \ln \frac{p_B}{p_A} = - RT \ln K_p + RT \ln \frac{p_B}{p_A} \qquad (10\text{-}18)$$

The processes 10-12 and 10-13 are special cases of 10-17. In the first case (equilibrium), $p_A = p_A^e$, $p_B = p_B^e$, and $\Delta G = 0$. In the second case (standard states), $p_A = p_B = 1$ atm and $\Delta G = \Delta G^0$.

In summary: of two molecules in an isomeric chemical equilibrium, the more stable one will have the lower standard Gibbs free energy, G^0, and will predominate in the equilibrium mixture; the partial pressure ratio at equilibrium is a function of T only and is determined by the values of $\Delta G^0(T)$ and T, through Eq. 10-16.

Arbitrary ideal gas reaction. The above considerations can be extended to reactions of any degree of complexity. Let us choose as a sufficiently complicated prototype the reaction

$$\nu_A A + \nu_B B \rightleftharpoons \nu_C C \qquad (10\text{-}19)$$

An example would be

$$N_2 + 3H_2 \rightleftharpoons 2NH_3$$

where $\nu_A = 1$, $\nu_B = 3$, and $\nu_C = 2$. Suppose we have an infinitely large closed system containing A molecules at p_A, B molecules at p_B, and C molecules at p_C. The temperature is T and total pressure is p. Now consider the constant p, T process

$$\begin{array}{ccccc} \nu_A \text{ moles of A} & + & \nu_B \text{ moles of B} & \rightarrow & \nu_C \text{ moles of C} \\ \text{at } p_A \text{ and } T & & \text{at } p_B \text{ and } T & & \text{at } p_C \text{ and } T \end{array} \qquad (10\text{-}20)$$

Of course, unless ν_C happens to be equal to $\nu_A + \nu_B$, the total number of molecules in the closed system will change in this process and hence V will change. The Gibbs free energy change is

$$\Delta G = G_{final} - G_{initial}$$

$$= \nu_C {}^G C(p_C, T) - \nu_A {}^G A(p_A, T) - \nu_B {}^G B(p_B, T)$$

$$= \nu_C \left[{}^G_C{}^0(T) + RT \ln p_C \right] - \nu_A \left[{}^G_A{}^0(T) + RT \ln p_A \right]$$

$$- \nu_B \left[{}^G_B{}^0(T) + RT \ln p_B \right]$$

$$= \Delta {}^G{}^0(T) + RT \ln \frac{p_C^\nu C}{p_A^{\nu_A} p_B^{\nu_B}} \qquad (10\text{-}21)$$

where

$$\Delta {}^G{}^0(T) = \nu_C {}^G_C{}^0(T) - \nu_A {}^G_A{}^0(T) - \nu_B {}^G_B{}^0(T) \qquad (10\text{-}22)$$

If the process occurs <u>at</u> equilibrium, Eq. 10-21 becomes

$$\Delta G = 0 = \Delta {}^G{}^0(T) + RT \ln \frac{\left(p_C^e\right)^{\nu_C}}{\left(p_A^e\right)^{\nu_A} \left(p_B^e\right)^{\nu_B}}$$

From this equation we see that the equilibrium partial pressure quotient must be a function of T only, which we denote by $K_p(T)$:

$$K_p(T) = \frac{\left(p_C^e\right)^{\nu_C}}{\left(p_A^e\right)^{\nu_A} \left(p_B^e\right)^{\nu_B}} \qquad (10\text{-}23)$$

$$\Delta {}^G{}^0(T) = - RT \ln K_p(T) \qquad (10\text{-}24)$$

Thus, regardless of the amounts of gases A, B, and C started with, provided the mixture is ideal, when the reaction 10-19 has reached equilibrium, the quotient of partial pressures in Eq. 10-23 will always have the same value at the same temperature, though the individual partial pressures at equilibrium will generally depend on the starting conditions. This is a very important result which could hardly have been anticipated on intuitive grounds.

The partial pressures in Eqs. 10-21 and 10-23 should be expressed in atm. The units of K_p are then atm to the power $\nu_C - \nu_A - \nu_B$.

The equilibrium condition $\Delta G = 0$ can be written

$$\nu_A {}^G A + \nu_B {}^G B = \nu_C {}^G C \qquad (10\text{-}25)$$

This is the generalization of Eq. 10-7.

The free energy change for the process

$$\begin{array}{ccc} \nu_A \text{ moles of } A & \nu_B \text{ moles of } B & \nu_C \text{ moles of } C \\ \text{at 1 atm and } T & + \text{ at 1 atm and } T & \to \text{ at 1 atm and } T \end{array} \qquad (10\text{-}26)$$

is ΔG^0 as given in Eq. 10-22. This quantity determines the value of K_p (or vice versa), through Eq. 10-24. Of course ΔG^0 can again (as in Eq. 10-11) be interpreted in terms of the relative energies and entropies of the reactants and products in the reaction, but this is not always easy in the case of complicated reactions. Some simple examples are treated in Section 10-4.

If the products in the process 10-26 are more stable than the reactants, $\Delta G^0 < 0$ and $K_p > 1$. The process would then occur spontaneously from left to right, as written. If, on the other hand, the reactants are more stable than the products, $\Delta G^0 > 0$ and $K_p < 1$. The process 10-26 would then take place spontaneously from right to left.

We have stressed the importance of the fact that the quotient of partial pressures at equilibrium is a function of temperature only. It is easy to see that the quotient of concentrations at equilibrium is also a function of temperature only. For we have

$$p_A^e = c_A^e \, RT, \quad p_b^e = c_B^e \, RT, \quad p_C^e = c_C^e \, RT$$

and hence Eq. 10-23 can be written

$$K_p(T) = \frac{\left(c_C^e\right)^{\nu_C} \left(RT\right)^{\nu_C - \nu_A - \nu_B}}{\left(c_A^e\right)^{\nu_A} \left(c_B^e\right)^{\nu_B}}$$

Therefore

$$\frac{\left(c_C^e\right)^{\nu_C}}{\left(c_A^e\right)^{\nu_A} \left(c_B^e\right)^{\nu_B}} = K_c(T) \qquad (10\text{-}27)$$

where K_c is a <u>concentration equilibrium constant</u>, related to K_p by

$$K_c(T) = K_p(T) (RT)^{\nu_A + \nu_B - \nu_C} \qquad (10\text{-}28)$$

Since K_p is a function of temperature only, so too is K_c. The usual concentration unit is moles liter^{-1}. Then the units of K_c are (moles liter^{-1})$^{\nu_C - \nu_A - \nu_B}$.

From the relations

$$G = G^0(T) + RT \ln p$$

and $p = cRT$ for each participant in a gaseous chemical reaction, it is clear that we can also write

$$G = G^*(T) + RT \ln c \qquad (10\text{-}29)$$

where $G^*(T)$ ($= G^0 + RT \ln RT$) is the value of G when $c = 1$ mole liter^{-1}. This is a different choice of standard state, common for reactions in solution but not for gaseous reactions. It follows from Eq. 10-29 that

$$\Delta G^*(T) = -RT \ln K_c(T) \qquad (10\text{-}30)$$

where ΔG^* is the value of ΔG for the ideal gas process

$$\nu_A \text{ moles of } A \atop \text{at 1 mole liter}^{-1} \text{ and } T \quad + \quad \nu_B \text{ moles of } B \atop \text{at 1 mole liter}^{-1} \text{ and } T$$

$$\rightarrow \nu_C \text{ moles of } C \atop \text{at 1 mole liter}^{-1} \text{ and } T \qquad (10\text{-}31)$$

Returning now to $K_p(T)$, the temperature dependence of this quantity is of considerable interest. We can derive an expression for $d\ln K_p/dT$ as follows. We first differentiate Eq. 10-24 with respect to T:

$$\frac{d\Delta G^0}{dT} = \nu_C \frac{dG_C^0}{dT} - \nu_A \frac{dG_A^0}{dT} - \nu_B \frac{dG_B^0}{dT}$$

$$= - R \ln K_p - RT \frac{d\ln K_p}{dT} \qquad (10\text{-}32)$$

But, from Eq. 8-56a,

$$\frac{dG_A^0}{dT} = \left(\frac{\partial G_A}{\partial T}\right)_{p=1 \text{ atm}} = -s_A(1 \text{ atm}) = -s_A^0(T)$$

and

$$- R \ln K_p = \Delta G^0/T$$

Therefore Eq. 10-32 becomes

$$-\nu_C s_C^0 + \nu_A s_A^0 + \nu_B s_B^0 = -\Delta s^0 = \frac{\Delta G^0}{T} - RT \frac{d\ln K_p}{dT}$$

or

$$\frac{d \ln K_p}{dT} = \frac{\Delta G^0 + T\Delta s^0}{RT^2} = \frac{\Delta H^0(T)}{RT^2} \qquad (10\text{-}33)$$

where $\Delta s^0(T)$ and $\Delta H^0(T)$ are the entropy and heat content changes in the "standard" process 10-26. Since

$$\frac{d \log K_p}{d(1/T)} = -\frac{\Delta H^0}{2.303R} \qquad (10\text{-}34)$$

if K_p is measured experimentally over a small temperature range and $\log K_p$ is plotted against $1/T$, the slope of the resulting line is $-\Delta H^0/2.303\,R$. Then ΔH^0 is easy to calculate from the slope. The same method is used in connection with the vapor pressure equation, 8-36. Thus, if K_p (at T) and $d\log K_p/dT$ (in the neighborhood of T) are both measured, we can calculate ΔG^0 from K_p and ΔH^0 from the temperature dependence. Then Δs^0 is also available from $\Delta G^0 = \Delta H^0 - T\Delta s^0$. The separation in this way of ΔG^0 into an energy part and an entropy part is of course very helpful, in fact, essential for an interpretation of ΔG^0, for any reaction, on the molecular level. We shall have more to say about ΔH^0 and Δs^0 in Section 10-4.

The connection between ΔH^0 and ΔE^0 is

$$\Delta H^0 = \Delta E^0 + \Delta(pV) = \Delta E^0 + RT \, \Delta n$$

$$= \Delta E^0 + RT \, (\nu_C - \nu_A - \nu_B) \qquad (10\text{-}35)$$

Usually the last term is not very important.

Because this is an ideal gas reaction, ΔH^0 and ΔE^0 are independent of the partial pressures used in the process 10-20 (see pp. 168 and 169). If the reaction takes place at constant total pressure, ΔH^0 is equal to the heat of the reaction, Q (heat absorbed by the system from the surroundings). But if the reaction occurs at constant volume, $\Delta E^0 = Q$. If ΔH^0 is positive (reactants have lower energy than products), heat is absorbed by the system and the reaction is called endothermic. If ΔH^0 is negative (products have lower energy than reactants) heat is evolved by the system and the reaction is called exothermic.

Imperfect gas reactions. If the mixture of reactant and product gases is not dilute, a more general thermodynamic treatment of this problem is required. We shall merely state the result: Eqs. 10-23 and 10-24 are still applicable but the partial pressures must be corrected for gas imperfections.

10-2 CHEMICAL REACTIONS IN VERY DILUTE SOLUTION

IN THIS section we discuss chemical reactions between very dilute solutes in a liquid solvent. We might expect intuitively that replacing a vacuum as background for the reaction (Section 10-1) by a solvent as background (as in this section) ought not to change the basic results found above. This turns out to be the case.

Let us again use Eq. 10-19 as the prototype reaction. We shall prove below that Eqs. 10-27 and 10-30 apply to the present system as well as to dilute gases. The equilibrium constant $K_c(T)$ is also a function of the pressure p put on the solution, but this is a very small effect (the solution is a condensed phase) which we shall ignore. Of course the value of K_c depends on the choice of solvent. Another complication is that the standard process 10-31 is outside the "very dilute" concentration range (see Section 9-3). ΔG^* therefore refers to a hypothetical solution in which the Henry's law behavior of each solute is extrapolated to the concentration c = 1 mole liter^{-1}.

Equilibrium constant calculations, based on Eq. 10-27, can be made for solutions that are not "very dilute." Such calculations will, however, be approximate unless the concentrations appearing in Eq. 10-27 are suitably corrected (by methods we shall not discuss).

We turn now to a proof of Eqs. 10-27 and 10-30 for reactions in solution. Suppose we have an infinitely large solution of solutes A, B, and C in solvent 1. Consider the constant p,T process

$$\nu_A \text{ moles of A} + \nu_B \text{ moles of B} \rightarrow \nu_C \text{ moles of C} \qquad (10\text{-}36)$$
$$\text{at } c_A \qquad\qquad \text{at } c_B \qquad\qquad \text{at } c_C$$

The Gibbs free energy change in this process is

$$\Delta G = \frac{\partial G}{\partial n_A}\Delta n_A + \frac{\partial G}{\partial n_B}\Delta n_B + \frac{\partial G}{\partial n_C}\Delta n_C$$

$$= -(\nu_A \mu_A + \nu_B \mu_B) + \nu_C \mu_C$$

since

$$\Delta n_A = -\nu_A, \quad \Delta n_B = -\nu_B, \quad \text{and} \quad \Delta n_C = \nu_C$$

If the process occurs at equilibrium, $\Delta G = 0$ and

$$\nu_A \mu_A + \nu_B \mu_B = \nu_C \mu_C . \qquad (10\text{-}37)$$

This is the analogue of Eq. 10-25 for a gas reaction.

Because the solution is very dilute in all solutes, each solute behaves independently of the others (except for the reaction). Therefore, from Eq. 9-16, for any solute, say, A,

$$\mu_A = G_A^0 + RT \ln k_A + RT \ln \frac{nA}{n_1}$$

$$= G_A^0 + RT \ln k_A v_1 + RT \ln \frac{nA}{n_1 v_1}$$

$$= G_A^* + RT \ln c_A \qquad\qquad (10\text{-}38)$$

where we have defined

$$G_A^*(T) \equiv G_A^0(T) + RT \ln k_A(T) v_1(T)$$

(k_A and v_1 also depend slightly on p). We see from Eq. 10-38 that G_A^* is the value of μ_A at $c_A = 1$ mole liter^{-1} (extrapolating Henry's law to this concentration). We obtain in the same way analogous expressions for μ_B and μ_C. On substitution of these and Eq. 10-38 into Eq. 10-37, we again deduce Eqs. 10-27 and 10-30, though the meaning of ΔG^* is different here.

We now consider two examples.

Weak acid HA. Let us calculate the osmotic pressure of an aqueous solution of a weak acid HA of concentration 0.06 mole liter^{-1}, at 25°C. The dissociation constant for the reaction

$$HA \rightleftharpoons H^+ + A^-$$

at this temperature is given as $K_c = 2.0 \times 10^{-3}$. We shall use Eq. 10-27 to find the concentrations of HA, H$^+$, and A$^-$ at equilibrium. We shall then employ the Debye-Hückel correction, as in Eq. 9-38, to find Π (of course all three kinds of particles, HA, H$^+$, and A$^-$, contribute to Π).

Let $c_{H^+}^e = c_{A^-}^e = y$. Then $c_{HA}^e = 0.06 - y$. Thus

$$K_c = 2.0 \times 10^{-3} = \frac{y^2}{0.06 - y}$$

The solution of this quadratic equation is y = 0.01. Therefore

$$c_{H^+}^e = c_{A^-}^e = 0.01 \text{ mole liter}^{-1} \quad \text{and} \quad c_{HA}^e = 0.05 \text{ mole liter}^{-1}.$$

For the calculation of Π, we note that the total concentration of particles is 0.07 mole liter^{-1}. The Debye-Hückel correction is the same as that for a strong 1-1 electrolyte of concentration 0.01 mole liter^{-1}. Therefore, from Eq. 9-38,

$$\frac{\Pi}{RT} = 0.07 - 0.00078 = 0.0692, \quad \Pi = 1.69 \text{ atm.}$$

Incidentally, the value of ΔG^* for this reaction is

$$\Delta G^* = -RT \ln K_C = -1.987 \times 298.1 \times 2.303 \log 0.0020$$

$$= 3680 \text{ cal.}$$

Symmetrical dibasic acid H_2A. In a symmetrical acid such as

$$HOOC-(CH_2)_n-COOH$$

where n is as large as 5 or 10, the two COOH groups dissociate practically independently of each other (if n is small, say, $n = 0$, 1, or 2, one group affects the other through electrostatic interaction). This independence leads to a simple relation, which we now derive, between the two successive dissociation constants of the acid.

Let us denote the acid by HAH. Then there are three forms of A to consider, at equilibrium:

HAH	HA$^-$ or AH$^-$	A$^=$
c_0^e	c_1^e	c_2^e

The first dissociation constant, K_1, for the reaction

$$HAH \rightleftharpoons H^+ + (HA^- \quad \text{or} \quad AH^-)$$

is

$$K_1 = c_{H^+}^e \, c_1^e / c_0^e$$

The second constant, K_2, for

$$(HA^- \quad \text{or} \quad AH^-) \rightleftharpoons H^+ + A^=$$

is

$$K_2 = c_{H^+}^e \, c_2^e / c_1^e$$

The ratio of K_1 to K_2 is then

$$\frac{K_1}{K_2} = \frac{(c_1^e)^2}{c_0^e \, c_2^e} \tag{10-39}$$

Let P be the probability that a particular COOH group has an undissociated H^+ at equilibrium. Then $1 - P$ is the probability that the H^+ is dissociated. Since the two COOH groups are equivalent and independent of each other, the concentration ratios are related to P in a simple way:

$$c_0^e : c_1^e : c_2^e = P^2 : 2P(1 - P) : (1 - P)^2$$

Therefore

$$\frac{K_1}{K_2} = \frac{[2P(1 - P)]^2}{P^2(1 - P)^2} = 4$$

Thus we have the rather interesting result that K_1/K_2 can be calculated without knowing K_1 or K_2. In other words, $K_1/K_2 = 4$ for all symmetrical long chain dibasic acids. Of course, if the chain is not long enough, K_1/K_2 will deviate some from the limiting value 4.

It is easy to see that the above result is an entropy effect. From Eq. 10-39, the reaction

$$HAH + A^= \rightleftharpoons 2(HA^- \quad \text{or} \quad AH^-) \tag{10-40}$$

has the equilibrium constant $K_C = 4$. Therefore

$$\Delta G^* = -RT \ln 4 = -2RT \ln 2$$

But

$$\Delta G^* = \Delta H^* - T\Delta S^*$$

and, in this case, $\Delta H^* = 0$ because reactants and products have the same types and numbers of chemical bonds. Therefore

$$-T\Delta S^* = -2RT \ln 2,$$

or

$$\Delta S^* = 2R \ln 2 = 2k \ln 2^{N_0}$$

This entropy change, for the reaction 10-40, arises from the fact that the singly dissociated species on the right side of 10-40 has two possible configurations, HA^- and AH^-, whereas each of the reactant species on the left side has only one configuration. This is a simple and direct application of Eq. 8-44.

10-3 HETEROGENEOUS CHEMICAL EQUILIBRIA

A CHEMICAL reaction that involves more than one phase is called heterogeneous. Because of the wide variety of possibilities for reactions of this type, it is not very convenient to give a general treatment of the problem. We therefore confine ourselves to two typical examples.

Dissociation of solid CaCO$_3$. Consider the chemical equilibrium

$$CaCO_3(s) \rightleftharpoons CaO(s) + CO_2(G) \qquad\qquad (10\text{-}41)$$

where s = solid, G = gas. The system contains three phases. The pressure on the system is that of the gaseous CO$_2$ (assumed ideal), p_{CO_2}. ΔG for the constant p,T process

$$\begin{array}{ccc}
\text{1 mole of} & \quad \text{1 mole of} & \quad \text{1 mole at} \\
\text{CaCO}_3 \text{ at p,T} & \xrightarrow{\quad} \quad \text{CaO at p,T} & + \quad \text{CO}_2 \text{ at p,T}
\end{array}$$

is given by

$$\Delta G = {}^{G}C_{aO} + {}^{G}CO_2 - {}^{G}CaCO_3$$

where, from Eq. 8-60,

$$^{G}C_{aO} = {}^{G}\overset{0}{C}_{aO}(T) + {}^{V}C_{aO}(p - 1)$$

$$^{G}CaCO_3 = {}^{G}\overset{0}{C}aCO_3(T) + {}^{V}CaCO_3(p - 1)$$

$$^{G}CO_2 = {}^{G}\overset{0}{C}O_2(T) + RT \ln p$$

For the low pressures we are interested in here, the terms in $^{V}C_{aO}$ and $^{V}CaCO_3$ are very small and may be neglected. At equilibrium, the condition $\Delta G = 0$ then leads to

$$\Delta G^0 = -RT \ln p^e_{CO_2}$$

where

$$\Delta G^0 = {}^{G}\overset{0}{C}_{aO} + {}^{G}\overset{0}{C}O_2 - {}^{G}\overset{0}{C}aCO_3 \qquad\qquad (10\text{-}42)$$

We can write

$$\Delta G^0 = -RT \ln K_p \qquad\qquad (10\text{-}43)$$

as usual, provided we define $K_p = p^e_{CO_2}$. If we now refer back to the chemical equation 10-41, we can deduce the rule for forming the partial pressure quotient, equal to K_p at equilibrium, in reactions involving gases, pure solids, and/or pure liquids: treat the gaseous partial pressures as usual (Eq. 10-23) but <u>omit</u> pure condensed phases from the quotient (because G for such a phase is virtually independent of pressure). However, it should be noted that the condensed phases are <u>not</u> omitted in ΔG^0, Eq. 10-42.

The temperature dependence of K_p is given by Eq. 10-33.

We shall return to this example in the next section.

Solubility of AgCl. The system we are interested in here is solid AgCl in contact with a very dilute aqueous solution containing Ag^+, Cl^-, and possibly other ions as well. This is a phase equilibrium (see p. 244) but we may also treat it as a chemical equilibrium:

$$AgCl(s) \rightleftharpoons Ag^+ + Cl^- \qquad (10\text{-}44)$$

Suppose we have an infinite amount of the above system. Then consider the constant p,T process

$$\text{one mole solid} \atop \text{AgCl at T} \quad \longrightarrow \quad {\text{one mole } Ag^+ \atop \text{at } c_{Ag^+}, T} \quad + \quad {\text{one mole } Cl^- \atop \text{at } c_{Cl^-}, T}$$

The pressure has an insignificant effect and can be omitted from the statement of the process. ΔG for this process is

$$\Delta G = \Delta G_{solid} + \Delta G_{soln}$$

$$= -G_{AgCl} + \frac{\partial G_{soln}}{\partial n_{Ag^+}} \Delta n_{Ag^+} + \frac{\partial G_{soln}}{\partial n_{Cl^-}} \Delta n_{Cl^-}$$

$$= -G^0_{AgCl} + \mu_{Ag^+} + \mu_{Cl^-}$$

where the μ's are of the type 10-38. At equilibrium, $\Delta G = 0$ and

$$G^*_{Ag^+} + G^*_{Cl^-} - G^0_{AgCl} = -RT \ln K_{sp} \qquad (10\text{-}45)$$

where K_{sp}, called the solubility product, is

$$K_{sp} = c^e_{Ag^+} c^e_{Cl^-} \qquad (10\text{-}46)$$

The rule for writing the equilibrium quotient for a reaction of type 10-44 is clear from this example: treat the concentrations of species in solution as usual (Eq. 10-27) but omit pure condensed phases from the quotient.

It is found experimentally that $K_{sp} = 1.6 \times 10^{-10}$ for AgCl at 25°C. Let us calculate the solubility of AgCl in pure water. If y = moles liter^{-1} of AgCl dissolved in the water, $c^e_{Ag^+} = c^e_{Cl^-} = y$. Then

$$1.6 \times 10^{-10} = y^2, \quad y = 1.3 \times 10^{-5} \text{ moles liter}^{-1}$$

10-4 CHEMICAL THERMODYNAMICS

OUR object in this final section is to illustrate the application of
thermal data to chemical equilibria. Some equilibrium constants can
be measured directly but use of thermal data provides another method
of obtaining these constants. In order to keep the discussion as simple as possible, we shall confine the examples very largely to one
temperature (25°C) and we shall not include reactions in solution.

Table 10-1 contains the basic data necessary for the analysis of
some chemical reactions between a few selected substances. All of
the data refer to 25°C and the standard state pressure 1 atm.

The standard molar entropy is given in the first column. The convention $S = 0$ at $0°K$, introduced in connection with the third law of

Table 10-1
Molar Thermodynamic Properties at 25°C and 1 atm

	S^0 (cal deg^{-1} mole^{-1})	ΔH_{fo}^{0} (kcal mole^{-1})	ΔG_{fo}^{0} (kcal mole^{-1})
Solids			
C (diamond)	0.583	0.453	0.685
C (graphite)	1.361	0	0
CaO	9.5	−151.9	−144.4
Ca	9.95	0	0
Na	12.2	0	0
$CaCO_3$	22.2	−288.4	−269.8
Liquids			
Hg	18.17	0	0
H_2O	16.72	−68.32	−56.69
Gases			
H	27.39	52.09	48.57
H_2	31.21	0	0
Ar	36.98	0	0
CH_4	44.50	−17.89	−12.14
H_2O	45.11	−57.80	−54.64
O_2	49.00	0	0
CO_2	51.06	−94.05	−94.26
C_2H_4	52.45	12.50	16.28
iso-C_4H_{10}	70.4	−31.45	−4.3
1-C_4H_8	73.48	0.28	17.09
n-C_4H_{10}	74.10	−29.81	−3.75

thermodynamics (p. 185), is employed here. The calorimetric method of obtaining the entries in the first column of the table is discussed on p. 172. However, some of these values may be found more accurately by combined spectroscopic and statistical mechanical procedures.

The entropy values in the table have considerable intrinsic interest as a measure of the extent of disorder in the various substances — especially because all the data refer to the same temperature and pressure. It is apparent that, generally speaking: (a) s^0(gas) $>$ s^0(liquid) $>$ s^0(solid); (b) more complicated molecules have a higher entropy than simple molecules; and (c) more rigid substances have a lower entropy than less rigid ones. In the latter category, for example, note that s^0 (diamond) $<$ s^0(graphite) $<$ s^0(sodium). A comparison of liquid Hg and liquid H_2O is interesting. One might expect water to have the higher entropy because H_2O is a more complicated molecule than Hg (rotational and internal vibrational motion are possible in H_2O), but on the other hand the molecules in liquid water are unusually restricted in their motions because of strong hydrogen bonds.

The second column in Table 10-1 gives the experimental heat of formation ΔH_{fo}^0 of one mole of the substance indicated, from its elements in their stable forms at 25°C and 1 atm. We use the subscript fo = formation to avoid confusion with f = fusion or freezing. For example, $\Delta H_{fo}^0 = -17.89$ kcal mole^{-1} for CH_4 is the value of $Q = \Delta H$ for the constant p, T process

$$C \text{ (graphite)} + 2H_2(G) \rightarrow CH_4(G) \tag{10-47}$$

(since graphite, not diamond, is the stable form of carbon at 25°C and 1 atm). With this definition of ΔH_{fo}^0, we of course have an entry $\Delta H_{fo}^0 = 0$ in the table for each element (stable form). Many of the ΔH_{fo}^0 values are negative because of the extra chemical bonds formed in the compound. Thus, in the reaction above, two moles of $H-H$ bonds are broken but four moles of $C-H$ bonds are formed. In fact, tables of approximate "bond energies" may be built up by an analysis of the ΔH_{fo}^0 values of an appropriate group of substances.

It was pointed out on pp. 131 that $H(T) - H(0)$ for any pure substance may be calculated from heat capacity and phase transition data [the same is true of $s(T) - s(0)$]. If we combine the values of $H - H(0)$ at 25°C and 1 atm for all substances in a "formation" reaction such as 10-47, we have

$$[H - H(0)]_{CH_4} - [H - H(0)]_C - 2[H - H(0)]_{H_2}$$

$$= \Delta H_{fo}^0 - \Delta H_{fo}^0(0) \tag{10-48}$$

We see from this equation that the availability of $H - H(0)$ for each

separate substance in a formation reaction is not sufficient by itself
to give the desired value of ΔH_{fo}^0 : the unknown quantity $\Delta H_{fo}^0(0)$ also
appears in the equation. We should expect this, of course, because
the quantities $H - H(0)$ contain no information having to do with the
making and breaking of chemical bonds. Therefore, to find ΔH_{fo}^0, it
is necessary either to measure $Q = \Delta H$ for the reaction 10-47, or to
obtain equivalent information through similar measurements on related reactions.

In the case of the entropy, for the same reaction,

$$[s - s(0)]_{CH_4} - [s - s(0)]_C - 2[s - s(0)]_{H_2}$$

$$= \Delta s_{fo}^0 - \Delta s_{fo}^0(0) \tag{10-49}$$

Here the situation is quite different because, according to the third
law of thermodynamics, $\Delta s_{fo}^0(0) = 0$. Therefore Δs_{fo}^0 values can be
deduced from the combined $s - s(0)$ values, and hence from heat
capacity and heat of transition data alone. However, instead of giving
Δs_{fo}^0 in Table 10-1, values of $s - s(0)$ are presented because these
latter numbers contain more information and easily yield Δs_{fo}^0. The
notation $s^0 = s - s(0)$ is used in the table because of the convention
$s(0) = 0$.

For example, Δs_{fo}^0 for the reaction 10-47 is

$$\Delta s_{fo}^0 = s_{CH_4}^0 - s_C^0 - 2s_{H_2}^0 = 44.50 - 1.36 - 2 \times 31.21$$

$$= -19.28 \text{ cal deg}^{-1} \text{ mole}^{-1}$$

The column in Table 10-1 labeled ΔG_{fo}^0 (free energy of formation)
contains no new information, but is included for convenience. ΔG_{fo}^0
for each substance may be calculated from

$$\Delta G_{fo}^0 = \Delta H_{fo}^0 - T\Delta s_{fo}^0 \tag{10-50}$$

Tables of the functions $H(T) - H(0)$ and $G(T) - H(0)$ for a number
of pure substances, at different temperatures, are available in more
advanced books. But we shall not include such tables here.

The remainder of this section is devoted to typical applications of
Table 10-1.

Dissociation of water vapor. Does water vapor dissociate appre-
ciably into H_2 and O_2 at 25°C ? Although we may suspect that the
answer is no, let us verify this by thermodynamic analysis. The
chemical reaction is

$$2H_2O(G) \rightleftharpoons 2H_2(G) + O_2(G) \tag{10-51}$$

This equation is the opposite of the formation reaction, and also has double the coefficients. Therefore, for the reaction 10-51,

$$\Delta G^0 = -2\Delta c_{fo}^0[H_2O(G)] = 109.28 \text{ kcal}$$

$$\Delta H^0 = -2\Delta H_{fo}^0[H_2O(G)] = 115.60 \text{ kcal}$$

The entropy can be found in two ways:

$$\Delta s^0 = 2s^0_{H_2} + s^0_{O_2} - 2s^0_{H_2O} = -2\Delta s_{fo}^0[H_2O(G)]$$

$$= \frac{\Delta H^0 - \Delta G^0}{T} = 21.20 \text{ cal deg}^{-1}$$

The fact that ΔG^0 is very large and positive means that, at equilibrium at 25°C, there will be virtually no dissociation.

The products H_2 and O_2 are favored by the entropy (Δs^0 is positive) mainly because two molecules have broken up into three molecules (which allows more freedom of atomic motion, on the whole), but this effect is far outweighed by the positive ΔH^0 which favors the water molecules. Four O—H bonds are a lot more stable (have a lower energy) than two H—H bonds and one O—O bond.

The equilibrium quotient is

$$K_p = \frac{\left(p^e_{H_2}\right)^2 p^e_{O_2}}{\left(p^e_{H_2O}\right)^2} \tag{10-52}$$

The numerical value of K_p is found from Eq. 10-24:

$$\log K_p = -\frac{\Delta G^0}{2.303 \, RT} = -\frac{109{,}280}{2.303 \times 1.987 \times 298.1} = -80.1$$

or

$$K_p = 10^{-80.1}$$

Thus K_p is zero (at 25°C) for all practical purposes. Such a small value of K_p could never be measured directly, through application of Eq. 10-52; but, as we have just seen, K_p is easy to calculate from the data in Table 10-1.

Vaporization of liquid water. Table 10-1 may be applied to phase transitions as well as to chemical reactions. Consider, for example, the equilibrium

$$H_2O \text{ (L)} \rightleftharpoons H_2O \text{ (G)} \tag{10-53}$$

at 25°C, where L = liquid. Since H_2O (L) and H_2O (G) contain the same elements, for the process 10-53 we have

$$\Delta G^0 = \Delta G_{fo}^0 [H_2O \text{ (G)}] - \Delta G_{fo}^0 [H_2O \text{ (L)}]$$

$$= -54.64 + 56.69 = 2.05 \text{ kcal}$$

$$\Delta H^0 = \Delta H_{fo}^0 [H_2O \text{ (G)}] - \Delta H_{fo}^0 [H_2O \text{ (L)}]$$

$$= -57.80 + 68.32 = 10.52 \text{ kcal}$$

$$\Delta S^0 = S^0 [H_2O \text{ (G)}] - S^0 [H_2O \text{ (L)}]$$

$$= \frac{\Delta H^0 - \Delta G^0}{T} = 28.39 \text{ cal deg}^{-1}$$

Since ΔG^0 is positive, H_2O (L) is more stable than H_2O (G) when both are at 25°C and 1 atm pressure—something we already know from the phase diagram for water (Fig. 1-3).

For this heterogeneous "reaction,"

$$\Delta G^0 = -RT \ln K_p = -RT \ln p_{H_2O}^e$$

where $p_{H_2O}^e$ is the pressure at which gas and liquid are in equilibrium— that is, $p_{H_2O}^e$ is the vapor pressure of liquid water at 25°C. We can calculate $p_{H_2O}^e$ from ΔG^0:

$$\log p_{H_2O}^e = -\frac{\Delta G^0}{2.303 \ RT} = -\frac{2050}{2.303 \times 1.987 \times 298.1} = -1.503$$

or

$$p_{H_2O}^e = 0.0314 \text{ atm} = 23.9 \text{ mm Hg}$$

Equation 10-33 becomes in this example

$$\frac{d \ln K_p}{dT} = \frac{d \ln p_{H_2O}^e}{dT} = \frac{\Delta H^0}{RT^2}$$

This is the same as the Clausius-Clapeyron equation, 8-35. Note that $\Delta H^0 = T\Delta S \ (p_{H_2O}^e)$, but $\Delta H^0 \neq T\Delta S^0$. Although the value of ΔH for the process 10-53 is practically independent of pressure, this is not true of ΔS because the entropy of the gas phase varies with pressure according to Eq. 8-29.

Isomerization of n-butane. Butane, an important constituent of natural gas, has two isomeric forms (p. 249). Let us study the equilibrium between these isomers:

$$\text{n-butane (G)} \rightleftharpoons \text{isobutane (G)} \qquad (10\text{-}54)$$

Though the rate of this reaction would be negligibly slow at 25°C, we can still investigate the equilibrium through Table 10-1. We find

$$\Delta G^0 = \Delta G^0_{fo}(\text{iso}) - \Delta G^0_{fo}(\text{n}) = -4.3 + 3.75 = -0.55\,\text{kcal}$$

$$\Delta H^0 = \Delta E^0 = \Delta H^0_{fo}(\text{iso}) - \Delta H^0_{fo}(\text{n})$$

$$= -31.45 + 29.81 = -1.64\,\text{kcal}$$

$$\Delta S^0 = S^0_{iso} - S^0_n$$

$$= \frac{\Delta H^0 - \Delta G^0}{T} = -3.7\,\text{cal deg}^{-1}$$

These results tell us that isobutane is a more stable molecule than n-butane at 25°C, in the gas phase. This stability is due to a lower energy in isobutane which more than compensates for the higher entropy of n-butane. Both molecules have the same numbers of C—H and H—H bonds. But there are usually small variations in the energies of bonds of the same type in different atomic environments. The higher entropy of n-butane arises from the flexibility of its carbon backbone. The carbon skeleton in isobutane is rigid (except for small vibrations). The equilibrium constant at 25°C is

$$\log K_p = -\frac{\Delta G^0}{2.303\,RT} = \frac{550}{2.303 \times 1.987 \times 298.1} = 0.403$$

$$K_p = 2.53 = \frac{p^e_{iso}}{p^e_n}$$

Hence the equilibrium composition is $x_{iso} = 0.72$, $x_n = 0.28$.

Let us use Eq. 10-34 to calculate the value of K_p at 50°C. We expect K_p to be smaller, i.e., more to the advantage of n-butane, at a higher temperature because n-butane has the larger entropy. Assuming ΔH^0 is constant,

$$\log \frac{K_p(T_2)}{K_p(T_1)} = -\frac{\Delta H^0}{2.303\ R}\left(\frac{1}{T_2} - \frac{1}{T_1}\right)$$

$$= \frac{1640}{2.303 \times 1.987}\left(\frac{1}{323.1} - \frac{1}{298.1}\right) = -0.0930$$

Hence

$$\frac{K_p(323.1)}{K_p(298.1)} = 0.807, \quad K_p(323.1) = 0.807 \times 2.53 = 2.04$$

The value of ΔG^0 at 50°C is then

$$\Delta G^0 = -1.987 \times 323.1 \times 2.303\ \log\ 2.04 = -0.42\ \text{kcal}$$

Dissociation of hydrogen gas. Let us verify that H_2 gas is un-dissociated at 25°C. The reaction of interest is

$$H_2\ (G) \rightleftharpoons 2\ H\ (G) \tag{10-55}$$

This is twice the formation reaction for H atoms. Therefore, from Table 10-1,

$$\Delta G^0 = 2\Delta G_{fo}^0(H) = 97.14\ \text{kcal}$$

$$\Delta H^0 = 2\Delta H_{fo}^0(H) = 104.18\ \text{kcal}$$

$$\Delta S^0 = 2s_H^0 - s_{H_2}^0$$

$$= \frac{\Delta H^0 - \Delta G^0}{T} = 23.57\ \text{cal deg}^{-1}$$

Also, from Eq. 10-35

$$\Delta E^0 = \Delta H^0 - RT$$

$$= 104.18 - 1.987 \times 298.1 \times 10^{-3} = 103.59\ \text{kcal}$$

Hydrogen molecules have a much lower energy than hydrogen atoms because of the H—H bond. The entropy favors dissociation into atoms, of course, but at this temperature the bond energy completely dominates the situation (notice that ΔG^0 is almost as large as ΔH^0).
We also have

$$K_p = \frac{(p_H^e)^2}{p_{H_2}^e}$$

and

$$\log K_p = -\frac{\Delta G^0}{2.303\ RT}, \quad K_p = 10^{-71.2}$$

Conclusion: H_2 gas is undissociated at 25°C. The reader should verify from the value of K_p that in H_2 gas at 1 atm and 25°C the average number of H atoms per liter is only 10^{-13} (not even one!).

Dissociation of solid $CaCO_3$. The reaction is

$$CaCO_3 \text{ (s)} \rightleftharpoons CaO \text{ (s)} + CO_2 \text{ (g)} \tag{10-56}$$

From Table 10-1,

$$\Delta G^0 = \Delta G_{fo}^0(CaO) + \Delta G_{fo}^0(CO_2) - \Delta G_{fo}^0(CaCO_3)$$

$$= -144.4 - 94.26 + 269.8 = 31.1 \text{ kcal}$$

$$\Delta H^0 = \Delta H_{fo}^0(CaO) + \Delta H_{fo}^0(CO_2) - \Delta H_{fo}^0(CaCO_3)$$

$$= -151.9 - 94.05 + 288.4 = 42.5 \text{ kcal}$$

$$\Delta S^0 = s^0(CaO) + s^0(CO_2) - s^0(CaCO_3)$$

$$= \frac{\Delta H^0 - \Delta G^0}{T} = 38.4 \text{ cal deg}^{-1}$$

The entropy favors dissociation (primarily because CO_2 is a gas) and the energy opposes it.

There is no dissociation at 25°C. Since $K_p = p_{CO_2}^e$, we have

$$\log p_{CO_2}^e = -\frac{\Delta G^0}{2.303\ RT}, \quad p_{CO_2}^e = 10^{-22.80} \text{ atm}$$

It is found experimentally that ΔH^0 is almost constant (it decreases slightly) up to 600°C. Therefore we can estimate $p_{CO_2}^e$ at 600°C from Eq. 10-34:

$$\log \frac{p_{CO_2}^e(873.1)}{p_{CO_2}^e(298.1)} = -\frac{42,500}{2.303 \times 1.987}\left(\frac{1}{873.1} - \frac{1}{298.1}\right)$$

Then

$$\frac{p^e_{CO_2}(873.1)}{p^e_{CO_2}(298.1)} = 10^{(20.52)}$$

and

$$p^e_{CO_2}(873.1) = 10^{20.52} \times 10^{-22.80}$$

$$= 10^{-2.28} = 5.25 \times 10^{-3} \text{ atm} = 4.0 \text{ mm Hg}$$

The measured value at 600°C is 1.84 mm Hg. The discrepancy is due to the small change of ΔH^0 with temperature, which we have ignored.

PROBLEMS

10-1. If K_p for the gaseous reaction $A + B \rightleftharpoons C$ at 25° C has the value $K_p = 10$ atm^{-1}, calculate ΔG for each of the following processes (all at 25° C):

   (a) one mole A (1 atm) + one mole B (1 atm) $\rightarrow$ one mole C (10 atm);

   (b) one mole A (1 atm) + one mole B (1 atm) $\rightarrow$ one mole C (1 atm);

   (c) one mole A (2 atm) + one mole B (10 atm) $\rightarrow$ one mole C (1 atm);

   (d) one mole C (1 atm) $\rightarrow$ one mole A ($\frac{1}{10}$ atm) + one mole B ($\frac{1}{10}$ atm)

10-2. At equilibrium, in the ideal gas reaction $2A \rightleftharpoons B$ at 27° C, $p_A = 1.42$ atm and $p_B = 0.81$ atm. (a) Calculate K_p in atm^{-1}. (b) Calculate ΔG^0 in cal. (c) What will be the two partial pressures at equilibrium if the total pressure is 1 atm?

10-3. Calculate the percentage dissociation in 10^{-2} M - HX (a weak acid), given that 10^{-4} M - HX is 0.1% dissociated at the same temperature.

10-4. ΔG^0 for the gaseous reaction $2I \rightleftharpoons I_2$ at 1000° K is -11.4 kcal. Calculate K_p in atm^{-1} and K_c in liters mole^{-1}.

10-5. The solubility product, K_{sp}, for CuS in water at 25° C is 8×10^{-37} moles^2 liter^{-2}. Calculate the number of Cu^{++} ions per cubic centimeter in a saturated solution of CuS.

10-6. Apply Eq. 8-61 in order to estimate the pressure at which diamond and graphite are in equilibrium at 25° C. Use Table 10-1, Table 5-4, and the densities 3.51 g cm^{-3} for diamond and 2.26 g cm^{-3} for graphite.

10-7. Estimate the temperature at which H_2 gas at 1 atm pressure is 1% dissociated into H atoms. As an approximation, assume ΔH^0 is constant.

10-8. Use Table 10-1 to discuss as fully as you can the gaseous equilibrium between 1-C_4H_8 and C_2H_4.

10-9. Let $c(0)$ be the concentration of an ideal gas at T and at the earth's surface ($h = 0$), and let $c(h)$ be the concentration of the same gas at T and at a height h in the earth's atmosphere. Equilibrium is assumed. Because of the extra potential energy at h, we have

$$G(0) = G(h)$$

$$G^*(T) + RT \ln c(0) = G^*(T) + Mgh + RT \ln c(h)$$

$$\frac{c(h)}{c(0)} = e^{-Mgh/RT}$$

If $p_{N_2} = 0.80$ atm at $h = 0$ at $25°C$, calculate p_{N_2} at $h = 10,000$ ft at $25°C$. Take $g = 980.7$ erg g^{-1} cm^{-1}.

PHYSICAL CONSTANTS, CONVERSION FACTORS, AND LOGARITHMS

PHYSICAL CONSTANTS

Avogadro's number, N_0	6.0226×10^{23} mole^{-1}
Charge on electron or proton	4.8029×10^{-10} esu
Planck's constant, h	6.6252×10^{-27} erg sec
Mass of "atom" of atomic weight = 1	1.6598×10^{-24} g
Boltzmann's constant, k	1.3805×10^{-16} erg deg^{-1}
Gas constant, R	0.08206 liter atm deg^{-1} mole^{-1}
	82.06 cm^3 atm deg^{-1} mole^{-1}
	1.9872 cal deg^{-1} mole^{-1}
Molar volume of ideal gas at STP, V_0	22.414 liters mole^{-1}

CONVERSION FACTORS

1 cal = 10^{-3} kcal = 4.184 joules = 4.184×10^7 ergs
1 (esu of charge)^2 cm^{-1} = 1 erg
1 atm = 1.0133×10^6 dynes cm^{-2} = 760 mm Hg

1 liter atm = 0.02422 kcal = 24.22 cal
1 cm = 10^8Å, 1 cm³ = 10^{24}Å³
0°C = 273.15°K

LOGARITHMS

If $y = 10^x$, then $\log_{10} y \equiv \log y = x$ (base 10).

Base of "natural" logarithms = e = $1 + \dfrac{1}{1!} + \dfrac{1}{2!} + \dfrac{1}{3!} + \cdots = 2.71828$.

If $y = e^x$, then $\log_e y \equiv \ln y = x$ (base e).

Since $10 = e^{2.3026}$, $\ln 10 = 2.3026$

If $y = 10^x = e^{2.3026x}$, then $\log y = x$ and $\ln y = 2.3026x$.

Therefore $\ln y = 2.3026 \log y$.

INTRODUCTION TO CALCULUS

THIS is a very elementary introduction to the notation and ideas of calculus. It is intended for the beginner but may be a useful review for others.

A2-1 THE DERIVATIVE

LET $f(x)$ be some function of x, for example, x^2, sin x, $x/2$, etc. Figure A2-1a represents a typical function plotted against x. The slope of the curve at some particular value of x is defined as $\tan \theta$, where θ is the angle shown in Fig. A2-1b.

Let us investigate the change in the value of $f(x)$ which results from a small change in the value of x. We start with particular values of x and $f(x)$ (Fig. A2-1c) and increase x by an amount Δx so that the new value is $x + \Delta x$. The new value of f is then $f(x + \Delta x)$. We denote the change in the value of f by Δf:

$$\Delta f = f(x + \Delta x) - f(x)$$

The rate of change of f with x, that is, the ratio of the change in f to that in x is

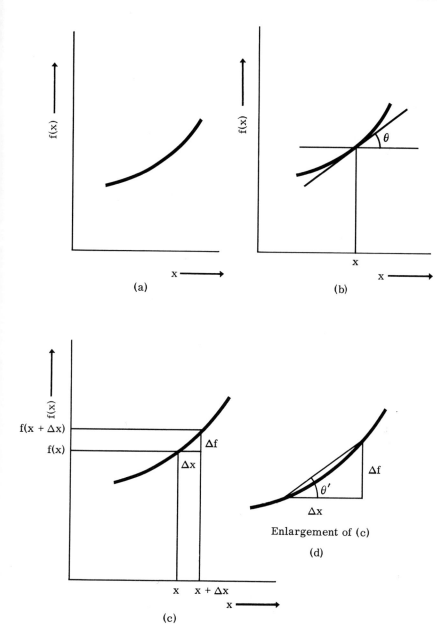

Figure A2-1
Derivative of f(x).

$$\frac{\Delta f}{\Delta x} = \frac{f(x + \Delta x) - f(x)}{\Delta x} \tag{A2-1}$$

As shown in Fig. A2-1d, this quantity is equal to $\tan \theta'$.

For a definite value of x, the value of the ratio in Eq. A2-1 is somewhat imprecise because it depends on the magnitude chosen for Δx. But we can eliminate this arbitrariness by taking smaller and smaller values of Δx, calculating the ratio $\Delta f/\Delta x$ for each of the successively smaller values of Δx, finally obtaining in this way the limiting ratio $\Delta f/\Delta x$ as $\Delta x \to 0$ (note that $\Delta f \to 0$ as $\Delta x \to 0$). This limiting ratio, the "instantaneous" rate of change of f with x at x (not over a finite range Δx as in Fig. A2-1c), is called the derivative of f with respect to x at x.

When $\Delta x \to 0$, that is, when Δx is arbitrarily small, it is called an infinitesimal and is denoted by dx. Similarly, when $\Delta f \to 0$, Δf is denoted by df. The notation for the derivative is then df/dx. Its mathematical definition is

$$\frac{df}{dx} = \lim_{\Delta x \to 0} \frac{\Delta f}{\Delta x} = \lim_{\Delta x \to 0} \frac{f(x + \Delta x) - f(x)}{\Delta x} \tag{A2-2}$$

where "lim" means limit.

It is clear from Figs. A2-1b and A2-1d that $\theta' \to \theta$ as $\Delta x \to 0$ so that $df/dx = \tan \theta$. Hence the geometrical interpretation of the derivative of f(x) at x is just that it is the slope of f(x) at x.

Equation A2-2 furnishes the necessary recipe for finding the derivative of any function f(x). To illustrate this, let us obtain the derivative of $f(x) = x^3$. First, we evaluate $f(x + \Delta x)$:

$$f(x + \Delta x) = (x + \Delta x)^3 = x^3 + 3x^2 \Delta x + 3x(\Delta x)^2 + (\Delta x)^3$$

Then we form the quotient $\Delta f/\Delta x$:

$$\frac{\Delta f}{\Delta x} = \frac{f(x + \Delta x) - f(x)}{\Delta x}$$

$$= \frac{3x^2 \Delta x + 3x(\Delta x)^2 + (\Delta x)^3}{\Delta x} = 3x^2 + 3x \Delta x + (\Delta x)^2$$

Finally, we take the limit $\Delta x \to 0$:

$$\frac{df}{dx} = \lim_{\Delta x \to 0} \frac{\Delta f}{\Delta x} = 3x^2$$

Thus the derivative of the function x^3 is $3x^2$.

The operation or procedure $f \to df/dx$ is called differentiation.

By application of the above procedure we can build up a table of derivatives. A few examples are given in Table A2-1. In this table, a is a constant, $e = 2.71828\cdots$ is the base of natural logarithms (see Appendix 1), ln x is the natural logarithm of x (base e), and u(x) and v(x) are arbitrary functions of x.

The derivative df/dx is itself a function of x. Its derivative is denoted by $d^2 f/dx^2$ (called the second derivative of f), etc.:

$$\frac{d^2 f}{dx^2} = \frac{d(df/dx)}{dx}$$

$$\frac{d^3 f}{dx^3} = \frac{d(d^2 f/dx^2)}{dx} \tag{A2-3}$$

Just as df/dx gives the slope of $f(x)$ at x, $d^2 f/dx^2$ gives the curvature (rate of change of slope). At a minimum in $f(x)$,

$$\frac{df}{dx} = 0 \quad \text{and} \quad \frac{d^2 f}{dx^2} > 0$$

At a maximum in $f(x)$,

$$\frac{df}{dx} = 0 \quad \text{and} \quad \frac{d^2 f}{dx^2} < 0$$

Table A2-1
Derivatives

$f(x)$	$\dfrac{df}{dx}$	$f(x)$	$\dfrac{df}{dx}$
a (const)	0	cos x	$-\sin x$
x	1	u(x) + a	$\dfrac{du}{dx}$
x^2	2x	au(x)	$a\dfrac{du}{dx}$
x^n	nx^{n-1}	u(x) + v(x)	$\dfrac{du}{dx} + \dfrac{dv}{dx}$
ln x	1/x	u(x) v(x)	$u\dfrac{dv}{dx} + v\dfrac{du}{dx}$
e^{ax}	ae^{ax}	$\dfrac{u(x)}{v(x)}$	$\dfrac{1}{v^2}\left(v\dfrac{du}{dx} - u\dfrac{dv}{dx}\right)$
sin x	cos x		

A2-2 THE INDEFINITE INTEGRAL

DIFFERENTIATION is a well-defined operation that converts one function, f(x), into another, df/dx; for example, $x^2 \to 2x$. The inverse operation, that is, finding a function whose derivative is given, is called integration. Thus the operation $2x \to x^2$ is an example of integration. The function x^2 is said to be the integral, or more precisely, the indefinite integral of 2x. The conventional notation used to indicate this is

$$\int 2x\ dx = x^2$$

$\int$ is the integral sign. The reason for this choice of notation will become apparent later in this appendix. In general, if G(x) is the function whose derivative is $g(x)\,[dG(x)/dx = g(x)]$, that is, if G(x) is the integral of g(x), we write

$$\int g(x)\ dx = G(x) \tag{A2-4}$$

We can emphasize the fact that differentiation and integration are inverse operations to each other as follows:

$$\int \frac{df}{dx}\ dx = f(x)$$

$$\frac{d \int g(x)\ dx}{dx} = g(x) \tag{A2-5}$$

Differentiation of f(x) followed by integration of the result gives f(x) back again; integration of g(x) followed by differentiation of the result gives g(x) back again.

Table A2-1, read backwards, is also a table of indefinite integrals. This allows the construction of a table of integrals, as illustrated in Table A2-2.

Table A2-2
Indefinite Integrals

g(x)	$\int g(x)\ dx$	g(x)	$\int g(x)\ dx$
0	arbitrary constant	e^{ax}	e^{ax}/a
1	x	cos x	sin x
x	$x^2/2$	sin x	$-\cos x$
x^n	$x^{n+1}/(n+1)$	au(x)	$a \int u(x)\ dx$
1/x	ln x	u(x) + v(x)	$\int u(x)\ dx + \int v(x)\ dx$

The operation of (indefinite) integration is always imprecise to the extent of an arbitrary additive constant. This can be seen as follows. Suppose $g(x)$ is the derivative of $G(x)$:

$$\frac{dG(x)}{dx} = g(x)$$

Then the derivative of $G(x) + c$ (any constant) is also $g(x)$:

$$\frac{d[G(x) + c]}{dx} = \frac{dG(x)}{dx} + \frac{dc}{dx} = g(x) + 0 = g(x)$$

That is, an additive constant does not affect the value of the derivative. Therefore, although the indefinite integral of $g(x)$ is $G(x)$, it is also $G(x) + c$:

$$\int g(x)\, dx = G(x) + c \tag{A2-6}$$

The most general way to write the indefinite integral is to include the arbitrary constant c. This constant is often omitted for convenience (as in Table A2-2), but it should always be understood.

A2-3 THE DEFINITE INTEGRAL

IN a sense the indefinite integral adds nothing basically new to the concept of the derivative because the former is simply the inverse of the latter. But the definite integral (introduced below) shows the practical value of integration.

We begin by asking a question: if we plot a function $g(x)$ against x, what is the area under the curve (Fig. A2-2) between two definite values of x, x_1 and x_2? Let us call this area $\mathcal{Q}$. We can approximate the desired area by dividing the interval $x_2 - x_1$ into n equal parts of width $\Delta x = (x_2 - x_1)/n$. The total area of the n rectangles shown in the figure, which we denote by $\mathcal{Q}_n$, is approximately equal to $\mathcal{Q}$. It is clear that if we take the limit $n \to \infty$, then $\Delta x \to 0$ and $\mathcal{Q}_n \to \mathcal{Q}$.

The explicit expression for $\mathcal{Q}_n$ is

$$\mathcal{Q}_n = g(x_1)\Delta x + g(x_1 + \Delta x)\Delta x + g(x_1 + 2\Delta x)\Delta x + \cdots$$

$$+ g(x_1 + (n-1)\Delta x)\Delta x$$

Then

$$\mathcal{Q} = \lim_{\substack{n \to \infty \\ \Delta x \to 0}} [g(x_1)\Delta x + g(x_1 + \Delta x)\Delta x + \cdots + g(x_1 + (n-1)\Delta x)\Delta x] \tag{A2-7}$$

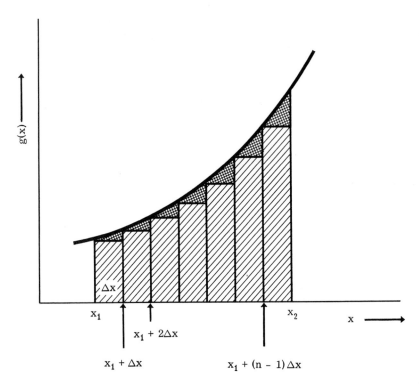

Figure A2-2
The area under a curve as a definite integral.

Now suppose $G(x)$ is the indefinite integral of $g(x)$. Whether we include an additive constant is immaterial because it would cancel out
below (see Eq. A2-9) in any case. Then $dG/dx = g(x)$. We can approximate $g(x_1)$ in Eq. A2-7 by

$$\frac{G(x_1 + \Delta x) - G(x_1)}{\Delta x}$$

as in Eq. A2-1. The error made in this approximation is of no consequence because the error vanishes when we take the indicated limit.
Similarly, we approximate $g(x_1 + \Delta x)$ by

$$\frac{G(x_1 + 2\Delta x) - G(x_1 + \Delta x)}{\Delta x}$$

etc., and finally we approximate $g(x_1 + (n - 1)\Delta x)$ by

$$\frac{G(x_1 + n\Delta x) - G(x_1 + (n - 1)\Delta x)}{\Delta x}$$

These approximations are all substituted in Eq. A2-7 to give

$$\alpha = \lim_{\substack{n \to \infty \\ \Delta x \to 0}} \{[G(x_1 + \Delta x) - G(x_1)] + [G(x_1 + 2\Delta x)$$

$$- G(x_1 + \Delta x)] + \cdots + [G(x_1 + n\Delta x)$$

$$- G(x_1 + (n-1)\Delta x)]\}$$

$$= \lim_{\substack{n \to \infty \\ \Delta x \to 0}} [G(x_1 + n\Delta x) - G(x_1)]$$

all terms except two having cancelled out in pairs. But $x_1 + n\Delta x = x_2$. Hence the final result[1] is simply

$$\alpha = G(x_2) - G(x_1). \tag{A2-8}$$

This states that the area under the curve $g(x)$, between x_1 and x_2, can be obtained directly from a knowledge of the indefinite integral of $g(x)$, $G(x)$.

As a simple example, let us calculate the area under the parabola $g(x) = x^2$ between $x_1 = -1$ and $x_2 = 2$. From Table A2-2, the indefinite integral of x^2 is $G(x) = x^3/3$. Therefore

$$\alpha = \frac{2^3}{3} - \frac{(-1)^3}{3} = \frac{8}{3} + \frac{1}{3} = 3$$

The conventional notation used for the area in Eq. A2-8 is

$$\alpha = \int_{x_1}^{x_2} g(x)\,dx = G(x)\Big|_{x_1}^{x_2} = G(x_2) - G(x_1) \tag{A2-9}$$

where

$$G(x) = \int g(x)\,dx$$

The integral in Eq. A2-9 is called a <u>definite</u> <u>integral</u>; x_1 is the <u>lower limit</u> and x_2 the <u>upper limit</u> of the integral. The notation makes sense if one refers to Eq. A2-7: the integral sign in Eq. A2-9 is an "S" which means sum the quantity $g(x)\,dx$ between x_1 and x_2. As can be seen from Eq. A2-9, $G(x)\Big|_{x_1}^{x_2}$ means evaluate $G(x)$ at x_2 and subtract from this the evaluation of $G(x)$ at x_1.

---

[1]This result (before the limit is taken) does not depend on n so we do not have to use the limit $n \to \infty$. This surprising absence of n dependence is due to an accidental cancellation of two errors: (1) the difference between α_n and α; and (2) the approximation $\Delta G/\Delta x$ employed following Eq. A2-7.

A2-4 PARTIAL DERIVATIVES

LET f be a function of two variables, x and y. We indicate this by
the notation f(x,y). Then we may be interested in the rate of change
of f with either x or y. If x is changed holding y constant, the instantaneous rate of change of f with x at x,y is called the partial derivative of f with respect to x. The mathematical definition, and the
notation used, is:

$$\left(\frac{\partial f}{\partial x}\right)_y = \lim_{\Delta x \to 0} \frac{(\Delta f)_y}{\Delta x} = \lim_{\Delta x \to 0} \frac{f(x + \Delta x, y) - f(x,y)}{\Delta x} \qquad (A2\text{-}10)$$

The subscript y means that y is held constant in the operation.
Similarly, the partial derivative of f with respect to y is

$$\left(\frac{\partial f}{\partial y}\right)_x = \lim_{\Delta y \to 0} \frac{(\Delta f)_x}{\Delta y} \lim_{\Delta y \to 0} \frac{f(x, y + \Delta y) - f(x,y)}{\Delta y} \qquad (A2\text{-}11)$$

As an example, suppose f(x,y) = ax³ + xy, where a is a constant.
Then, from Table A2-1,

$$\left(\frac{\partial f}{\partial x}\right)_y = 3ax^2 + y, \quad \left(\frac{\partial f}{\partial y}\right)_x = x$$

The notation used for higher partial derivatives is:

$$\frac{\partial^2 f}{\partial x^2} = \left[\frac{\partial}{\partial x}\left(\frac{\partial f}{\partial x}\right)_y\right]_y, \quad \frac{\partial^2 f}{\partial y^2} = \left[\frac{\partial}{\partial y}\left(\frac{\partial f}{\partial y}\right)_x\right]_x \qquad (A2\text{-}12)$$

$$\frac{\partial^2 f}{\partial y \partial x} = \left[\frac{\partial}{\partial y}\left(\frac{\partial f}{\partial x}\right)_y\right]_x, \quad \frac{\partial^2 f}{\partial x \partial y} = \left[\frac{\partial}{\partial x}\left(\frac{\partial f}{\partial y}\right)_x\right]_y \qquad (A2\text{-}13)$$

By applying the definition of partial derivative, the reader should
prove that

$$\frac{\partial^2 f}{\partial y \partial x} = \frac{\partial^2 f}{\partial x \partial y} \qquad (A2\text{-}14)$$

In the above example,

$$\frac{\partial^2 f}{\partial x^2} = 6ax, \quad \frac{\partial^2 f}{\partial y^2} = 0, \quad \frac{\partial^2 f}{\partial x \partial y} = \frac{\partial^2 f}{\partial y \partial x} = 1$$

If both x and y are varied or changed by infinitesimal amounts dx
and dy, respectively, what is the resulting change df in f(x,y)? This

question often arises. As usual, let us first consider changes Δx and Δy, then let Δx and Δy approach zero. The change in f is

$$\Delta f = f(x + \Delta x, y + \Delta y) - f(x,y).$$

We can break this up into two parts (first change x, then y):

$$\Delta f = [f(x + \Delta x, y) - f(x,y)]$$

$$+ [f(x + \Delta x, y + \Delta y) - f(x + \Delta x, y)]$$

$$= \left[\frac{f(x + \Delta x, y) - f(x,y)}{\Delta x}\right] \Delta x$$

$$+ \left[\frac{f(x + \Delta x, y + \Delta y) - f(x + \Delta x, y)}{\Delta y}\right] \Delta y$$

If we now take the limit $\Delta x \to 0$, $\Delta y \to 0$, we have the final result:

$$df = \left(\frac{\partial f}{\partial x}\right)_y dx + \left(\frac{\partial f}{\partial y}\right)_x dy \qquad\qquad (A2\text{-}15)$$

The last term follows because the derivative $\partial f/\partial y$ at $x + \Delta x$ approaches and becomes equal to $\partial f/\partial y$ at x in the limit $\Delta x \to 0$. Equation A2-15 shows that the contributions to df from the changes dx and dy are additive.

BOLTZMANN DISTRIBUTION LAW

CONSIDER a system of N independent molecules, all of the same type, in equilibrium with a heat bath at temperature T. From quantum theory we know that a molecule cannot have any arbitrary value of the energy (as it may in classical mechanics); only certain discrete values of the energy are possible. These are called the molecular energy levels, and we denote them (in increasing order) by ϵ_0, ϵ_1, ϵ_2, ... Each molecule in the system has the same set of energy levels available to it. The particular values of ϵ_0, ϵ_1, ϵ_2, . . . depend on the case under investigation.

The lowest level, ϵ_0, is called the ground state energy. The lowest possible energy E for the whole system is then $N\epsilon_0$ (all molecules in the ground state).

Perhaps the most frequently occurring theme in this book is that a thermodynamic system, such as the one we are now discussing, is subject to two primary tendencies in its approach toward equilibrium and in its selection of a final equilibrium state: first, the energy of the system tends to approach a minimum; and second, the disorder or randomness tends to approach a maximum. In the present system, the first tendency would be satisfied if all molecules were in the ground state ($E = N\epsilon_0$). But the system is more random or disordered the more the molecules are distributed haphazardly among the energy levels (Fig. A3-1). Of course a system with such a random distribution necessarily has a higher energy than $N\epsilon_0$. For example, in Fig. A3-1, the minimum energy is $5\epsilon_0$ while the energy of the system in the state shown is $\epsilon_0 + \epsilon_2 + \epsilon_3 + \epsilon_5 + \epsilon_6$.

The energy of a system increases as it absorbs heat and as its temperature T is increased. Also, of course, if T approaches its lowest possible value ($T \rightarrow 0$), the energy approaches its lowest possible value ($N\epsilon_0$ in the present case). This state not only has minimum energy; it also has maximum order or minimum disorder. At a very high temperature, the energy of the system will be large and hence the molecules can distribute themselves among the energy levels in a relatively random fashion and over a wide range of energy level values. At intermediate temperatures there will be a compromise between the two extremes above: most of the molecules will be in the lowest energy levels but there will be a certain amount of occupation of higher levels, the more so the higher the temperature.

The above discussion of the distribution of molecules among energy levels is based largely on intuition. Let us now turn to a very simple example which we shall work out exactly. We shall follow this by a statement, without proof, of the general law (the Boltzmann distribution law) that governs this kind of distribution. We omit a proof of the general law because the mathematics and physics required are

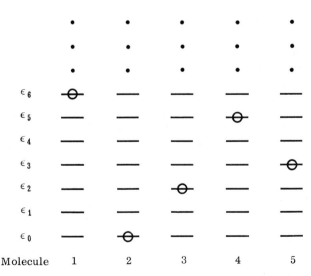

Figure A3-1
Distribution of molecules among energy levels.

a little too advanced. The interested reader should consult a text on physical chemistry or statistical mechanics.

The example is the following. The system consists of N molecules. The energy levels available to each molecule are equally spaced, with spacing a, and are infinite in number:

$$\epsilon_0 = 0, \quad \epsilon_1 = a, \quad \epsilon_2 = 2a, \quad \epsilon_3 = 3a, \quad \dots$$

Let us choose first a temperature such that the average energy per molecule is a. That is, $E = N\bar{\epsilon}$, $\bar{\epsilon} = a$. We shall investigate several values of N, but in each of these cases we take $\bar{\epsilon} = a$. Thermodynamic systems have huge values of N. But we take N small in order to be able to do the arithmetic easily and exactly. However, for comparison, we shall also give — without proof — the result for $N \to \infty$.

First, we take $N = 2$ and $E = 2a$. That is, we have two units or parcels or quanta of energy that can be distributed among two molecules. The only three possibilities are:

<u>N = 2</u>

	(1)	(2)	(3)
Energy of molecule 1:	0	2a	a
Energy of molecule 2:	2a	0	a

The system will make repeated transitions among these possibilities. What we want to know is the probability P_n, at equilibrium, that a particular molecule has an energy $\epsilon_n = na$. This is the same quantity as the mean fraction of molecules having an energy $\epsilon_n = na$ at equilibrium. In order to compute P_n for $n = 0,1,2$ (the only possible values of n in this case), we have to know what weights to give the three possibilities listed above. The rule on weights that we use is adopted without proof because it has the status of a postulate — the basic postulate — in statistical mechanics. The rule is: at equilibrium, give equal weight to each possibility. Although it is not at all apparent, this statistical mechanical postulate corresponds to the thermodynamic principle of minimum free energy at equilibrium in an isothermal system (Chapter 8).

Since, in the above chart for $N = 2$, the six entries are equally divided (two each) among 0, a, and 2a, and since we are to give equal weight to each entry, we have the result in this case that

$$P_0 = P_1 = P_2 = \tfrac{1}{3}.$$

Now consider the case $N = 3$ and $E = 3a$ (the average energy is still $\bar{\epsilon} = a$). There are ten possibilities:

$$\underline{N = 3}$$

	(1)	(2)	(3)	(4)	(5)	(6)	(7)	(8)	(9)	(10)
Energy of molecule 1:	0	0	3a	0	0	a	a	2a	2a	a
Energy of molecule 2:	0	3a	0	a	2a	0	2a	0	a	a
Energy of molecule 3:	3a	0	0	2a	a	2a	0	a	0	a

There are thirty entries, all to be given equal weight. The tally is:

Energy = 3a	Entries =	3	$P_3 = \frac{3}{30} = 0.100$
2a		6	$P_2 = \frac{6}{30} = 0.200$
a		9	$P_1 = \frac{9}{30} = 0.300$
0		$\dfrac{12}{30}$	$P_0 = \frac{12}{30} = \dfrac{0.400}{1.000}$

For $N = 4$, $E = 4a$. There are 35 possibilities of five types:

$$\underline{N = 4}$$

0	0	0	0	a
0	0	0	a	a
0	a	2a	a	a
4a	3a	2a	2a	a

The respective numbers of possibilities of each type are 4,12,6,12,1. The total number of entries is $4 \times 35 = 140$, and the tally turns out to be:

Energy = 4a	Entries =	4	$P_4 = 0.029$
3a		12	$P_3 = 0.086$
2a		24	$P_2 = 0.171$
a		40	$P_1 = 0.286$
0		$\dfrac{60}{140}$	$P_0 = \dfrac{0.429}{1.001}$

The reader can easily carry this further. In fact, we notice that if the entries 2,2,2; 3,6,9,12; etc., are divided by N, we get binomial coefficients:

N = 2	3	4
1		
1	1	
1	2	1
	3	3
	4	6
		10
		15

This allows easy extension of the above results. Table A3-1 collects some P_n values. For $N = \infty$, $P_n = (\frac{1}{2})^{n+1}$. The values for small N converge toward the values for $N = \infty$. The present case, $\bar{\epsilon} = a$, clearly corresponds to an intermediate temperature: the lower levels are more populated but there is an appreciable spread of the probability distribution into higher levels.

One can of course repeat the above calculations for other choices of $\bar{\epsilon}$. Table A3-2 compares $N = \infty$ values for $\bar{\epsilon} = a/2$, a (the case worked out above), and 2a. These average energies correspond to three different (increasing) temperatures, of course. For $\bar{\epsilon} = a/2$, $P_n = (\frac{2}{3})(\frac{1}{3})^n$; for $\bar{\epsilon} = 2a$, $P_n = (\frac{1}{3})(\frac{2}{3})^n$. Note how the distribution concentrates more into the lower levels as the temperature or average energy is lowered, and how it becomes more spread out (more random) at a higher temperature.

This is about as much progress as can be made by looking at a special case. A general treatment, based on the postulate given above, and applicable to systems with large N and an arbitrary set of energy levels (Fig. A3-1), gives the following simple result for P_n (in terms

Table A3-1
Energy Distribution for $E = Na$

N =	2	3	4	5	6	7	8	9	10	∞
P_9										0.001
P_8										0.002
P_7										0.004
P_6					0.002					0.008
P_5				0.008	0.011					0.016
P_4			0.029	0.032	0.032					0.031
P_3		0.100	0.086	0.079	0.076					0.062
P_2	0.333	0.200	0.171	0.159	0.152					0.125
P_1	0.333	0.300	0.286	0.278	0.273					0.250
P_0	0.333	0.400	0.429	0.444	0.455	0.462	0.467	0.471	0.474	0.500

Table A3-2
Energy Distributions for N = ∞

$\bar{\epsilon}$	a/2	a	2a
P_9		0.001	0.009
P_8		0.002	0.013
P_7		0.004	0.020
P_6	0.001	0.008	0.029
P_5	0.003	0.016	0.044
P_4	0.008	0.031	0.066
P_3	0.025	0.062	0.100
P_2	0.074	0.125	0.148
P_1	0.222	0.250	0.222
P_0	0.667	0.500	0.333

of T rather than $\bar{\epsilon}$): P_n is proportional to $e^{-\epsilon_n/kT}$, where k is the Boltzmann constant. This is the <u>Boltzmann distribution law</u>. The function $e^{-\epsilon_n/kT}$, called the Boltzmann factor, has the two important properties expected from the examples just considered: (1) for a given temperature, $e^{-\epsilon_n/kT}$ decreases as ϵ_n increases; and (2) the distribution is more spread out the larger the value of T.

According to the above statement of the Boltzmann distribution law,

$$P_n = \text{const} \times e^{-\epsilon_n/kT}$$

To evaluate the constant, we use the fact that the sum of probabilities must equal unity:

$$\sum_{n=0}^{\infty} P_n = 1 = \text{const} \times \sum_{n=0}^{\infty} e^{-\epsilon_n/kT}$$

Therefore

$$P_n = \frac{e^{-\epsilon_n/kT}}{\sum_{n=0}^{\infty} e^{-\epsilon_n/kT}} \qquad (A3\text{-}1)$$

As an illustration, let us go back to the special case of equally spaced energy levels: $\epsilon_n = na$. Then if, for convenience, we define $x \equiv e^{-a/kT}$,

$$P_n = \frac{x^n}{\Sigma_{n=0}^{\infty} x^n} = \frac{x^n}{1/(1-x)} = (1-x)x^n \qquad \text{(A3-2)}$$

We can now see the origin of the numbers in Table A3-2. The case $\bar{\epsilon} = a$ corresponds to a temperature (let us call it T_2) such that

$$x = e^{-a/kT_2} = \tfrac{1}{2}$$

$\bar{\epsilon} = a/2$ corresponds to a temperature T_1 such that

$$x = e^{-a/kT_1} = \tfrac{1}{3}$$

and $\bar{\epsilon} = 2a$ corresponds to a temperature T_3 such that

$$x = e^{-a/kT_3} = \tfrac{2}{3}$$

Therefore

$$\frac{1}{T_1} : \frac{1}{T_2} : \frac{1}{T_3} = \log 3 : \log 2 : \log 1.5$$

$$= 0.477 : 0.301 : 0.176$$

As a check, let us derive an equation for $\bar{\epsilon}$ in terms of x (this will establish the connection between $\bar{\epsilon}$ and T for this example):

$$\bar{\epsilon} = \sum_n \epsilon_n P_n = \sum_n na(1-x)x^n = a(1-x) \sum_n nx^n$$

$$= a(1-x)x \sum_n nx^{n-1} = a(1-x)x \frac{d}{dx} \sum_n x^n$$

$$= a(1-x)x \frac{d}{dx}\left(\frac{1}{1-x}\right) = \frac{ax}{1-x} \qquad \text{(A3-3)}$$

When we put $x = \tfrac{1}{3}, \tfrac{1}{2},$ and $\tfrac{2}{3}$ in this equation, we get $\bar{\epsilon} = a/2$, a, and 2a, respectively—as we should. Note that if $T \to 0$, $x \to 0$ and $\bar{\epsilon} \to 0$ (all molecules in ground state). Also, if $T \to \infty$, $x \to 1$ and $\bar{\epsilon} \to \infty$ (molecules spread over all energy levels).

For the harmonic oscillator problem of Eqs. 7-24 and 7-25, the levels are equally spaced with $a = h\nu$. In addition, the ground state energy $h\nu/2$ is added to each level:

$$\epsilon_n = h\nu n + \tfrac{1}{2}h\nu \qquad (n = 0,1,2, \ldots)$$

Therefore Eq. A3-3 becomes, in this case,

$$\bar{\epsilon} = \frac{h\nu e^{-h\nu/kT}}{1 - e^{-h\nu/dT}} + \tfrac{1}{2}h\nu$$

$$= \frac{h\nu}{e^{h\nu/kT} - 1} + \tfrac{1}{2}h\nu$$

KINETIC THEORY
OF GASES

WE shall be interested here in a monatomic ideal gas with molecules of mass m. We saw in Appendix 3 that in a system of independent molecules, such as the present one, at temperature T, the probability that any one molecule is in a molecular quantum state with energy ϵ_i is proportional to $e^{-\epsilon_i/kT}$ (the Boltzmann factor). Except for very light gases at very low temperatures, we can use classical (i.e., Newtonian) mechanics rather than quantum mechanics in studying the motion of molecules. The classical analogue of the above statement about $e^{-\epsilon_i/kT}$ is this: the probability that any molecule in an ideal monatomic gas at temperature T has velocity components v_x, v_y, v_z within the intervals dv_x, dv_y, dv_z, respectively, is proportional to

$$e^{-m(v_x^2 + v_y^2 + v_z^2)/2kT} \, dv_x \, dv_y \, dv_z \tag{A4-1}$$

This follows because the classical energy is

$$\epsilon = \tfrac{1}{2} m(v_x^2 + v_y^2 + v_z^2) = \tfrac{1}{2} m v^2 \tag{A4-2}$$

and the classical state (aside from the position of the molecule, which does not affect ϵ) is specified by the three quantities v_x, v_y, and v_z.

In Fig. A4-1, the state of the molecule is indicated by locating the element of volume $dv_x\, dv_y\, dv_z$ anywhere in the three dimensional v_x, v_y, v_z space. All possible states are represented if the element of volume is moved over the entire space. Alternatively, if we are interested just in v and not in the separate components v_x, v_y, v_z, we can cover the entire space by using the element of volume (spherical shell) $4\pi v^2\, dv$ instead of $dv_x\, dv_y\, dv_z$. Then the probability that any molecule has a velocity between v and $v + dv$ is proportional to

$$e^{-mv^2/2kT}\, 4\pi v^2\, dv \tag{A4-3}$$

In A4-3, let us call the proportionality constant C. Since the sum of the probabilities for all states must be unity, we can find C from

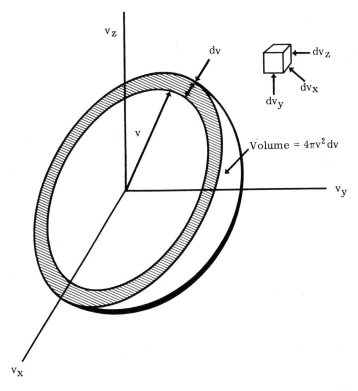

Figure A4-1
Volume element for integration over velocity.

$$\int_0^\infty C\, e^{-mv^2/2kT}\; 4\pi v^2\; dv \;=\; 1$$

On employing the definite integral

$$\int_0^\infty x^2 e^{-x^2}\, dx \;=\; \frac{\sqrt{\pi}}{4}$$

we find $C = (m/2\pi kT)^{3/2}$. Therefore the probability that any molecule has a velocity between v and $v + dv$ is

$$4\pi\left(\frac{m}{2\pi kT}\right)^{3/2} e^{-mv^2/2kT}\; v^2\; dv \tag{A4-4}$$

This is also the fraction of all molecules in the gas that have velocities between v and $v + dv$. The expression A4-4 is known as the Maxwell-Boltzmann distribution.

The average velocity $\bar{v}$ can now be deduced by multiplying the probability A4-4 by v and integrating over v from 0 to ∞. This requires use of the definite integral

$$\int_0^\infty x^3 e^{-x^2}\, dx \;=\; \tfrac{1}{2}$$

The result is

$$\bar{v} \;=\; \sqrt{\frac{8kT}{\pi m}} \tag{A4-5}$$

The most probable velocity v_m is found from

$$\frac{d}{dv}\left(e^{-mv^2/2kT}\, v^2\right) \;=\; 0$$

We obtain

$$v_m \;=\; \sqrt{\frac{2kT}{m}} \tag{A4-6}$$

The energy distribution follows directly from A4-4 if we eliminate v^2 and dv using

$$\epsilon \;=\; mv^2/2 \quad \text{and} \quad d\epsilon \;=\; mv\, dv$$

The probability that a molecule has an energy between ϵ and $\epsilon + d\epsilon$ is then

$$\frac{2\pi}{(\pi kT)^{3/2}} e^{-\epsilon/kT}\; \epsilon^{1/2}\; d\epsilon \tag{A4-7}$$

Multiplication by ϵ, followed by integration from 0 to ∞, gives

$$\bar{\epsilon} = \tfrac{3}{2}kT \tag{A4-8}$$

where we have employed the definite integral

$$\int_0^\infty x^{3/2}\, e^{-x}\, dx = \frac{3\sqrt{\pi}}{4}$$

We can now find $\overline{v^2}$ without doing additional work, because

$$\epsilon = \tfrac{1}{2}mv^2, \quad \bar{\epsilon} = \tfrac{1}{2}m\overline{v^2}$$

and

$$\overline{v^2} = \frac{2}{m}\bar{\epsilon} = \frac{3kT}{m} \tag{A4-9}$$

If we average Eq. A4-2 over a Boltzmann distribution, we have

$$\bar{\epsilon} = \tfrac{3}{2}kT = \tfrac{1}{2}m\left(\overline{v_x^2} + \overline{v_y^2} + \overline{v_z^2}\right) = \tfrac{1}{2}m\overline{v^2}$$

The three directions in space are equivalent so

$$\bar{\epsilon} = \tfrac{3}{2}kT = \tfrac{3}{2}m\overline{v_x^2} = \tfrac{3}{2}m\overline{v_y^2} = \tfrac{3}{2}m\overline{v_z^2} = \tfrac{1}{2}m\overline{v^2}$$

The average kinetic energy associated with the motion in any one direction is then

$$\tfrac{1}{2}m\overline{v_x^2} = \tfrac{1}{2}m\overline{v_y^2} = \tfrac{1}{2}m\overline{v_z^2} = \tfrac{1}{3}\bar{\epsilon} = \tfrac{1}{2}kT$$

The factor of three in Eq. A4-8 is thus the dimensionality of the space in which the molecules move.

The expression A4-1 can be written as the product of three factors,

$$\left(e^{-mv_x^2/2kT}\, dv_x\right)\left(e^{-mv_y^2/2kT}\, dv_y\right)\left(e^{-mv_z^2/2kT}\, dv_z\right)$$

where each factor involves only one variable (v_x, v_y, or v_z). This means that the three variables have independent probability distributions (as we should expect). Consequently the probability that a molecule has an x component of velocity between v_x and $v_x + dv_x$ (irrespective of the values of v_y and v_z) is proportional to

$$e^{-mv_x^2/2kT}\, dv_x$$

Call the proportionality constant C'. Then

$$\int_{-\infty}^{+\infty} C' e^{-mv_x^2/2kT} \, dv_x = 1$$

From

$$\int_{-\infty}^{+\infty} e^{-x^2} \, dx = \sqrt{\pi}$$

we find $C' = (m/2\pi kT)^{1/2}$. Therefore the probability that v_x is between v_x and $v_x + dv_x$ is

$$\left(\frac{m}{2\pi kT}\right)^{1/2} e^{-mv_x^2/2kT} \, dv_x \qquad\qquad (A4\text{-}10)$$

Pressure. The pressure is the normal (i.e., perpendicular) force per unit area exerted by the gas molecules on a wall. This is equal to the normal force per unit area exerted by a wall on the molecules (Newton's third law). The force on a molecule is equal to the time rate of change of the momentum of the molecule (Newton's second law). Therefore the pressure is equal to the normal momentum change of the molecules, arising from collisions with the wall, per unit time per unit area.

A molecule with x component of velocity v_x at collision has a normal momentum mv_x before collision and $-mv_x$ after collision. The normal momentum change for this one collision is then $2mv_x$.

Consider the molecules in a cylinder of cross-sectional area α (Fig. A4-2) and the collisions these molecules make with the wall in a short time period τ. In the time τ, molecules with x component of

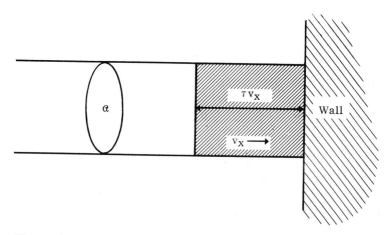

Figure A4-2
Calculation of pressure.

velocity between v_x and $v_x + dv_x$ will hit the wall provided they start within a distance τv_x from the wall. The number of molecules in the (shaded) volume $\mathfrak{a}\tau v_x$ with x component of velocity between v_x and $v_x + dv_x$ is (see Eq. A4-10)

$$\frac{N}{V} \cdot \mathfrak{a}\tau v_x \cdot \left(\frac{m}{2\pi kT}\right)^{1/2} e^{-mv_x^2/2kT} dv_x \qquad (A4\text{-}11)$$

Multiplication of A4-11 by $2mv_x$ gives the contribution of these molecules to the normal momentum change. The total normal momentum change, in the time τ, arising from all the molecules in the cylinder is then obtained by integrating over v_x from 0 to ∞. Finally, division by $\tau\mathfrak{a}$ gives the pressure:

$$p = \frac{1}{\tau\mathfrak{a}} \cdot 2m \cdot \frac{N}{V} \cdot \mathfrak{a}\tau\left(\frac{m}{2\pi kT}\right)^{1/2} \int_0^\infty v_x^2 e^{-mv_x^2/2kT} dv_x$$

$$= \frac{NkT}{V} \qquad (A4\text{-}12)$$

Of course, the molecules starting from inside the area $\mathfrak{a}$ will not all hit the wall while still within this same area. But those that do not will be just balanced by other molecules that start outside $\mathfrak{a}$ but hit the wall within $\mathfrak{a}$.

In this derivation we have passed over without comment several other complicating points that really require further consideration. It would be a good exercise for the reader to try to locate these points.

Number of collisions with wall. Next, we want to calculate the number of collisions gas molecules make with a wall per unit time and per unit area. This is an important property of a gas. We shall use it in Chapter 6.

The argument is almost the same as above, but a little simpler (we omit the momentum factor $2mv_x$). All we have to do is integrate A4-11 as it stands, and then divide by $\tau\mathfrak{a}$:

$$\frac{\text{Collision rate}}{\text{per unit area}} = \frac{1}{\tau\mathfrak{a}} \cdot \frac{N}{V} \cdot \mathfrak{a}\tau\left(\frac{m}{2\pi kT}\right)^{1/2} \int_0^\infty v_x e^{-mv_x^2/2kT} dv_x$$

$$= \frac{N}{V}\left(\frac{kT}{2\pi m}\right)^{1/2} = \frac{1}{4}\frac{N}{V}\bar{v} \qquad (A4\text{-}13)$$

where we have used

$$\int_0^\infty x e^{-x^2} dx = \tfrac{1}{2}$$

Since $pV = NkT$, an alternative expression is

$$\frac{\text{Collision rate}}{\text{per unit area}} = \frac{p}{(2\pi mkT)^{1/2}} \qquad (A4\text{-}14)$$

At STP, $N/4V$ is about 10^{19} molecules cm^{-3} (see p. 29) and $\bar{v}$ is about 10^5 cm sec^{-1} (see p. 28). Therefore, at STP, there are about 10^{24} collisions with the walls per sec per cm^2.

INDEX